Architectu
Anthropocene

Critical Climate Change

Series Editors: Tom Cohen and Claire Colebrook

The era of climate change involves the mutation of systems beyond 20th century anthropomorphic models and has stood, until recently, outside representation or address. Understood in a broad and critical sense, climate change concerns material agencies that impact on biomass and energy, erased borders and microbial invention, geological and nanographic time, and extinction events. The possibility of extinction has always been a latent figure in the textual production and archives; but the current sense of depletion, decay, mutation and exhaustion calls for new modes of address, new styles of publishing and authoring, and new formats and speeds of distribution. As the pressures and re-alignments of this re-arrangement occur, so must the critical languages and conceptual templates, political premises and definitions of 'life.' There is a particular need to publish in timely fashion experimental monographs that redefine the boundaries of disciplinary fields, rhetorical invasions, the interface of conceptual and scientific languages, and geomorphic and geopolitical interventions. Critical Climate Change is oriented, in this general manner, toward the epistemo-political mutations that correspond to the temporalities of terrestrial mutation.

Architecture in the Anthropocene

Encounters Among Design, Deep Time,
Science and Philosophy

Edited by Etienne Turpin

( )

OPEN HUMANITIES PRESS

An imprint of Michigan Publishing
University of Michigan Library, Ann Arbor

2013

First edition published by Open Humanities Press 2013
Freely available online at http://dx.doi.org/10.3998/ohp.12527215.0001.001

ISBN-978-1-60785-307-7

OPEN HUMANITIES PRESS is an international, scholar-led open access
publishing collective whose mission is to make leading works of contemporary
critical throught freely available worldwide. Books published under the OPEN
HUMANITIES PRESS imprint at Michigan Publishing are produced through
a unique partnership between OHP's editorial board and the University of
Michigan Library, which provides a library-based managing and production
support infrastructure to facilitate scholars to publish leading reearch in book
form.

MICHIGAN
PUBLISHING
www.publishing.umich.edu

OPEN HUMANITIES PRESS
www.openhumanitiespress.org

Contents

Acknowledgments

If a book can be said to begin in a place, this collection surely has its point of origin in the office of Professor Jane Wolff, then the Director of the University of Toronto's graduate programme in Landscape Architecture, who asked me, rather provocatively, why I had not yet considered the trajectory of my recent doctoral research in relation to the Anthropocene thesis. Prompted by her insistence that I more carefully investigate this relationship, I can say without any doubt that most of my philosophical, design-based, and activist work has, since that crystalizing conversation, been an attempt to more fully comprehend the implications of our planetary geological reformation. In early 2011, with the financial support of both the Walter B. Sanders Fellowship at the Taubman College of Architecture and Urban Planning, and a grant from the Institute for the Humanities, I curated a symposium at the University of Michigan titled *The Geologic Turn: Architecture's New Alliance*. While the title was at first intended to be more suggestive than scientific, the lecture presentations and panel conversations left little doubt that if the geological and stratigraphic sciences were themselves becoming more speculative by way of their consideration of the Anthropocene thesis, then design could also benefit from a similar turn toward a much broader but no less urgent paradigm for contemporary practice. During this symposium, the support of my students in the Master of Science in Design Research programme—a post-professional degree programme the College sadly decided to eliminate, despite its tremendous success—helped execute the event without a hitch through their concerted, convivial participation. I owe a debt of gratitude to all the students and faculty who supported and attended this event, as well as everyone who participated, especially those whose work appears in this book, as well as Edward Eigen, D. Graham Burnett, Jamie Kruse and Elizabeth Ellsworth of smudge Studio, and Peter Galison, all of whom enlivened our discussion and imparted insights that have carried over into this collection. A thanks also to my colleagues from the College who facilitated the panel discussions, including Rania Ghosn, Meredith Miller, and Rosalyne Shieh, all of whom shared their expertise while opening the discussion toward new directions and concerns. During my two years at the University of Michigan, while this collection was beginning to take shape, I was incredibly fortunate to both teach and learn alongside a group of generous, challenging, and thoughtful colleagues, including Robert Adams, McLain Clutter, Robert Fishman, Andrew Herscher, Perry Kulper, Kathy Velikov, Jason Young, and Claire Zimmerman. As I was moving from Michigan to Jakarta, I also incurred a significant debt of gratitude to my colleagues at the Haus der Kulturen der Welt in Berlin, both for their organization of the *Synapse: International Curators' Network* workshop, and for their ongoing support and interest in my research. This workshop was incredibly transformative, and every presentation challenged and encouraged me in unique ways. I would like to thank curators Xiaoyu Weng, Vincent Normand, Nabil Ahmed, and Anna-Sophie Springer for their continued friendship, conversation, and advice as this book project came to fruition. To our *Synapse* special guest, Richard Pell, I would also like to extend my gratitude for sharing insights, strategies, and support. To Scott Sørli, who has both curated my artistic work on the Anthropocene, and taught together with me as a co-instructor for our graduate seminar on landscapes of extraction—a critical test for much of this project—I am especially grateful for mentorship and provocation. Farid Rakun, my fixer who quickly became a dear friend, and without whom I would have not made it a single day in Jakarta, is owed a special thanks for his ongoing patience and direction. I would also like to thank my new mentors at the University of Wollongong, especially Dr. Pascal Perez, Research Director of the SMART Infrastructure Facility, and Dr. Ian Buchanan, Director of the Institute for Social Transformation Research, both of whom have encouraged my scholarship and pushed me to develop my work on the Anthropocene through new practices and protocols of research. At SMART, I am also grateful to all my colleagues, especially Research Fellows Dr. Tomas Holderness and Dr. Rohan Wickramasuriya, who, as part of our Urban Resilience Research Group, have inspired me to develop new tools and techniques adequate for addressing the urban condition of the Anthropocene. This book would not exist if not for the advice of John Paul Ricco, my advisor, mentor, and friend, who suggested that the Critical Climate Change series was the proper vehicle for disseminating this collection of research on the Anthropocene. I am also deeply indebted to my friend and colleague Heather Davis, who was essential in both conceptualizing and conducting many of the conversations in this book, and with whom I have already begun co-editing a second volume, *Art in the Anthropocene: Encounters Among Aesthetics, Politics, Epistemologies and Environments*, which we hope will further extend and intensify the concepts and concerns of the present collection. To each and every contributor whose work inspired this collection, I owe you all more than any edited volume could ever deliver for what you have shared with and inspired in me. To my copy editors, Lucas A.J. Freeman and Jeffrey Malecki, I owe a debt for their precision, patience, and superhuman attention. As series editors, Claire Colebrook and Tom Cohen have been fundamental in seeing this project through with their generous advice and encouragement; Sigi Jottkandt and David Ottina of Open Humanities Press have likewise been thoughtful and tireless advocates. Because this book departs significantly from previous OHP projects in terms of its demanding graphic design, I would like to extend my sincere gratitude to Sara Dean, whose prolific skill as a graphic designer allowed this project to be realized, and whose patience and support have been unflinching from start to finish. This collection would not have been possible without the stalwart support of my friends and family who, as generous as always, tolerated my often frustrating commitment to solitary research while encouraging me with care, love, and important reminders to sleep. Finally, as a gesture of deep, enduring gratitude, I would like to dedicate this book to my mentor, Jane Wolff, who taught me—and no doubt many others—to see the landscape as made, not given.

Introduction

by Etienne Turpin

Who Does the Earth Think It Is, Now?

> *What amazed them more than anything was that earth, as an element,*
> *does not exist.*

—Flaubert, *Bouvard and Pécuchet* (1881)

While the Anthropocene thesis has recently received significant attention in both the news media and academic scholarship—certainly drifting well beyond its original loci of consideration within the meetings of the International Commission on Stratigraphy and the International Union of Geological Sciences—there remains a fundamental ambivalence about the value of the concept from the point of view of both cultural theory and design practice. Is the Anthropocene not just another assertion, typical of European society, of the ascendancy of man over nature? Is the Anthropocene, when read through the lens of cultural criticism, not just another appropriation of a properly scientific nomenclature for the purposes of provoking aesthetic or moral shock? Is the Anthropocene not an apolitical, even fatalistic idea, given that it implicates all humanity equally in the production of a geophysical stratigraphy that is, and has been—since the "beginning" of the era, which is also a matter of debate—asymmetrically produced according to divisions of class, race, gender and ability? Is there really any role for the theoretical humanities after the division between nature and culture is erased by a geological reformation?

The present collection of essays, conversations, and design projects and proposals responds to these questions by problematizing the very terms of their address. While each of the contributions in this volume operates on the Anthropocene thesis through the specificity of its own particular considerations and concerns, several important premises might first be summarized here. Regardless of the eventual conclusion arrived at by the geo-scientific community of experts considering the merit of this new era, the concept of the Anthropocene affords contemporary scholars, activists, and designers a unique opportunity to reevaluate the terms of theory and practice which have been inherited from modernity. Not least among these inheritances is the assumption of an ontological distinction between human culture and nature. The Anthropocene thesis not only challenges this inherited assumption, but demands of it a fatal conceit: with the arrival of the Anthropocene, this division is *de-ontologized*; as such, the separation between nature and culture appears instead as a epistemological product mistakenly presumed as a given fact of being. If the will to knowledge characteristic of modernity provided the assurance that the fault line between human culture and nature was indeed factual, the production of the Anthropocene counter-factually relieves our contemporaneity the burden of perpetuating this epistemic illusion.

A second inheritance worthy of reconsideration in light of the Anthropocene thesis is the climate of the Earth System. The overwhelming and irrefutable evidence of planetary climate change has, so far, cast only the faintest shadow on planning and policy, this despite the notable increase in devastating weather events whose unprecedented intensity has become well known over the last decade. Climate is an outcome, not a given; it is the result of a vast co-production of forces, both human and nonhuman, which produce, through a complex series of interactions, the patterns we call weather. The predictability of these patterns, and the anticipation of regularized changes in their intensity, allows for the production of seasonal agriculture and attendant practices upon which the vast human population relies for survival. The aggressive and irreversible destabilization of these patterns—climate change—guarantees the disproportionate increase of exposure to weather extremes and their attendant risks for the planet's most economically and geographically vulnerable communities. Whether the response to this exacerbated vulnerability will be greater hostility, conflict, and violence, or more radical forms of political solidarity and mutual aid, the record of our planetary reaction to climate change is presently being written into the geological archive of the Anthropocene.

Not unlike climate, human societies also tend to inherit from previous generations any number of tools and techniques for the management, modification, and assumed emendation of their proximate natural environments. In this respect, architecture is a well-regarded tradition usually tasked with the organization of spatial adjacencies—inside and outside, sacred and profane, sick and healthy, natural and cultural. These organizational patterns can be leveraged to either reify distinctions and separations, or to complicate the divisive categories used to manage the assemblages of habit and settlement that we call societies. The establishment of distinction was thus a common concern for both philosophical modernism and its shorter-lived architectural double. But, as a practice just as capable of complicating divisions as securing them, architecture has tended to challenge ways of working, thinking, and relating in a given society with the help of historical, geographical, and speculative strategies: Have things always been done, thought, or produced this way? Are things done, thought, or produced this way differently in other places? And, can we imagine other ways in which things could be done, thought, or produced in the future? Such simple questions—whether posed by design or scholarship—can begin to undermine the assumed givenness of inherited situations and their intolerable circumstances. The Anthropocene thesis offers contemporary architects, theorists, and historians an occasion to encounter the urgency of these modes of inquiry and unfold their consequences with the effort and attention required by struggles for greater social-environmental justice.

With the scale of the planet as the spherical horizon for such activities, it is not surprising that problem-formations are, within the condition of the Anthropocene, necessarily multi-disciplinary. How might architecture encounter this multi-disciplinary, multi-scalar, and multi-centered reality? This question is the core concern of this book. It is my conviction that by discovering affinities and alliances with both the sciences and the theoretical humanities, architecture as a practice can begin to reassess its privilege, priorities, and capacities for inscription within the archive of deep time. In what remains of the introduction, I explain the editorial organization of the contributions to this volume and very briefly describe their content. I then conclude these introductory remarks by considering how strategies of *problematisation* used to approach the Anthropocene thesis enlist philosophy, politics, science, and architecture to engender an ecology of practices adequate to the contemporaneity of deep time.

Encounters

This collection is arranged according to a rhythm of interaction among the three types of contributions which comprise it—essays, conversations, and design projects and proposals—each of which produce distinct encounters through their specific concerns and their textual adjacencies. The essays, which help produce new ways of navigating the interconnected trajectories of deep time and design, as well as the history and theory of architecture, offer a range of concerns, narrative strategies, and politics positions, each of which attends to a particular perspective elicited by the Anthropocene thesis. The essays begin with "Three Holes: In the Geological Present," a text by Seth Denizen, which endeavors to provoke the pragmatic and speculative questions of geological contemporaneity. By asking how the soil of the earth becomes evidence—both of other processes and, eventually, of itself as a process—Denizen invites the reader to travel with the question of contemporaneity as a political and epistemological problem accessed through the manifold technologies of vision and taxonomic classification. Following these considerations, Adam Bobbette's essay "Episodes from a History of Scalelessness: William Jerome Harrison and Geological Photography," offers a reading of the singular history of the geological photograph, noting how the forces of photographic production suggest a minor repetition of cosmic forces which are inscribed throughout the solar economy into the archive of deep time. In her contribution to the volume, "Architecture's Lapidarium: On the Lives of Geological Specimens," Amy Catania Kulper considers the role of the geological specimen within the history of the architectural imaginary. According to Kulper, this collection of specimens affords us a glimpse into the entangled history of architecture and vitalism—strangely operative on even the most static objects—that also connects to biographical and philosophical conceptions of "a life." In "Erratic Imaginaries: Thinking Landscape as Evidence," Jane Hutton analyzes the political landscape of contingency, mapping the diverse modes of appropriation that have produced the theory of glaciation and its attendant social effects. What we encounter here is the peculiar refrain of geological time which marks its place, however obliquely, within practices of leisure and science. Mark Dorrian's essay, "Utopia on Ice: The Climate as Commodity Form," offers another approach to the leisurely landscape and its architectural ambitions by examining the history of climate modification as a manifestation of utopian design. The current commodification of the climate, in Dorrian's estimation, is thus suggestive of a longer history of architectural projections which imagined social emancipation to be inherently tied to the emendation of the natural environment. The distinction between the human and non-/in- human is then taken up by Eleanor Kaufman in her essay "The Mineralogy of Being," which argues for a revaluation of the philosophical lineage that refused to admit any continuity between the registers of the animate and inanimate. Kaufman here contends that this denial of continuity may actually be *more* attentive to the obdurate inertia of inanimate objects than contemporary theoretical trends promoting their continuity, whether as thing-power or object oriented-ontology. The social and cultural valences of metal—that peculiar "thing" which obeys its own rules of transformation—is taken up in Guy Zimmerman's essay, "In the Furnace of Disorientation: Tragic Drama and the Liturgical Force of Metal." Zimmerman considers the theatricality of material transformation, which he examines through the historical emergence of the deities of the stage whose role was that of mediating the radical revelation of the inner life of metal revealed by ancient smelters. Finally, in his essay on the history of cultivation and conflict in Amazonia, Paulo Tavares contributes a series of remarkable insights on the politics and violence which have produced the Anthropocene. His essay, "The Geological Imperative: Notes on the Political-Ecology of Amazonia's Deep History," is a provocation to rethink the terms with which nature is constructed as well as the policies and planning that manifest the ideology of political regimes, because, as he contends, "nature is not natural."

These eight essays are organized in relation to another series of conversations and a series of design projects and proposals which clarify, extend, and intensify each other. "What is the use of a book, thought Alice, without pictures or conversations?" In the conversations gathered together for this collection, architects and theorists offer insights into how their practices have encountered the Anthropocene thesis, and, more importantly, how this encounter affords architects, activists, and theorists the opportunity to transform, through design, narration, and interference, the trajectory of the Anthropocene. The multiplicity of these matters of discussion are intended to signal a certain intensive variability among architecture practices; between matters of fact and matters of concern, we are exposed to a heterogeneous meso-sphere where strategy and speculation become complimentary modes of inquiry. In conversation with John Palmesino and Ann-Sofi Rönnskog of Territorial Agency, we are encouraged to consider the practice of architecture with a more precise, historical specificity; in so doing, we discover that architecture does not require an expanded field or a new imperialism, since, "The object of research and practice is architecture, and the means is architecture." In the subsequent conversation with Eyal Weizman—"Matters of Calculation: The Evidence of the Anthropocene"—Heather Davis and I take up the question of architecture research in relation to calculative violence and the production of evidence. Understanding more precisely how these asymmetrical co-productions operate can help us avoid the philosophical and political pitfalls of both actor-network theory and object-oriented ontology; where the former approach valorizes the connectivity of the network, and the latter position emphasizes the irreducibility of nodes as the primary constituents of the network, a more coherent and politically operative analysis requires a multi-scalar and multi-centered approach, where agency is negotiated as a co-production among vertical pressures (from both above and below) and heterogeneous lateral affinities. In this discussion, we discover new approaches to the urgent problems of multilateral violence as it is modulated by international humanitarian law, environmental law, and non-human rights. These approaches are, of course, inevitably marked by the fundamental philosophical problem of temporality. In conversation with Elizabeth Grosz—"Time Matters: On Temporality in the Anthropocene"—Davis and I attempt to further interrogate the *chronotope* of the Anthropocene by engaging the question of evolutionary time. Throughout this discussion, Grosz offers a series of insights that compel our reconsideration of the emergence, futurity, and precarious duration of the human species. The precarity of the human species is likewise at stake in our conversation with Isabelle Stengers. In "Matters of Cosmopolitics: On the Provocations of Gaïa," Davis and I question the role of the human in relation to Gaïa as a force, which, for Stengers, both suggests a way out of the "reign of man" and "intrudes upon the use of the Anthropocene in trendy and rather apolitical dissertations." How then to fabulate the narratives capable of carrying the human species beyond the limited horizon of reactionary architecture culture? In "Matters of Fabulation: On the Construction of Realities in the Anthropocene," I discuss this question with François Roche of New-Territories, R&Sie(n), and [eIf/bʌt/c], who suggests that architects should not attempt to work directly with concepts; instead, architects can benefit from a dosage of vulgarity, deception, nostalgia, and the forbidden, all of which allow for expressions of human pathology and emotion that have been largely excluded from architecture in recent decades.

In addition to these conversations, the book includes a series of design projects and proposals which attempt, as Aby Warburg suggested, to "abolish *de facto* the distinction between accumulation of knowledge and aesthetic production, between research and performance."[1] These projects and proposals respond to and extend the content of the essays and discussions, suggesting productive adjacencies and disjunctions. In Michael C.C. Lin's exhibition project *AnthroPark*, we are invited to imagine a menagerie of primate visions that question the hierarchical ordering of nature as a linear line of (evolutionary) progress. Likewise, in Lisa Hirmer's photo essay *Fortune Head Geologies*, we encounter the park as a planetary condition, where stratifications of meaning are extracted from the heaps of refuse and debris that accompany our human will to progress. Yet, such stratigraphic mixtures are not only of the earth; they are also atmospheric, as the projects by Nabil Ahmed and Emily Cheng make especially clear. In Ahmed's video installation, *Radical Meteorology*, we are beckoned to consider the politics

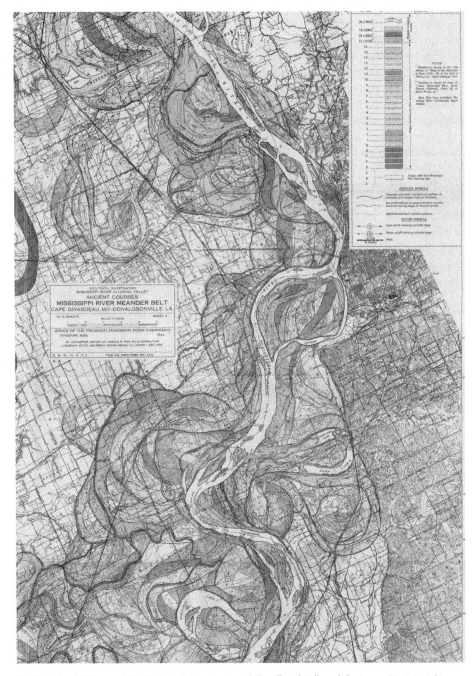

Fig. 01   Harold Norman Fisk, *Geological Investigation of the Alluvial Valley of the Lower Mississippi River* (Vicksburg, Miss.: 1945), M.R.C. print. Plate 22-5.

of a tropical cyclone that struck the Bay of Bengal, connecting it forever to the "genocide and war of national liberation for present-day Bangladesh." In Cheng's mixed media work, *Inquiries and Interpretations Concerning the Observations and Findings from Atmosphere-Investigating, Landscape-Exploring, Universe-Tracking Instruments, Their Experiments, Studies, Etc.*, drawings and models suggest how the hygienic, anesthetized architecture of the weather station might be appropriated and inverted to produce sensual, embodied rituals for physio-knowledge production. The production of knowledge is then also examined from the perspective of landscape literacy. In her illustrated field guide to San Francisco's shoreline, *Bay Lexicon*, a project developed in collaboration with the Exploratorium of San Francisco, Jane Wolff creates "a nuanced, place-based vocabulary that makes the hybrid circumstances of San Francisco Bay apparent and legible" to a range of audiences concerned with the future of this postnatural landscape. Similarly, in her speculative mixed media design proposal, *Amplitude Modulation*, Meghan Archer imagines how design interventions could offer other narratives to the southern coal towns of Appalachia, where the industrial and geological scales have already become indelibly intermixed. Finally, projects by Chester Rennie and Amy Norris and Clinton Langevin of Captains of Industry both suggest, through a kind of speculative pragmatism, modes of adaptive reuse that challenge the hierarchies of traditional redevelopment. By focusing on a derelict iron mine long abandoned by its former owners, Rennie suggests—with rhetoric reminiscent of the later land art proposals of Robert Smithson—that by *Swimming in It*, a leisurely reappropriation of the site would also afford a space of aesthetic meditation on the violent legacies of our industrial heritage. For Norris and Langevin, their proposal for a *Tar Creek Supergrid* is supported by extensive research on landscapes disturbed by human industry, which carry with them the latent potential for new patterns of human settlement and innovation.

Among the three series of inquiries—scholarly essays, contemporary conversations, and design proposals and projects—the potential of the Anthropocene thesis as both a discourse to embolden design and theory, and as a condition within which these practices must struggle for social-environmental justice, begins to emerge. While the work collected here does not exhaust the many new vectors of research animated by concerns regarding climate change, environmental crises, political ecology or land use interpretation, it is nevertheless exemplary of how the Anthropocene thesis encourages a mode of *problematisation* that is especially valuable for design practice in our all-too-human era.

Problematisation

A philosophy is never a house; it is a construction site.

—Georges Bataille

If the Anthropocene can be understood as a *chronotope* specific to the moment when the human species begins to recognize its impact not only on spaces of settlement and habitation, but also on the scale of geological time, then we might conclude these introductory remarks by speculating on how the strategies of *problematisation* used to approach the Anthropocene thesis can generate collaborations among philosophy, politics, science, and architecture. In his essay "On the Earth-Object," Paulo Tavares remarks: "'Global nature' is therefore and above all a space defined by a new socio-geological order in which the divisions that separated humanity and the environment, culture and nature, the anthropological and the geological have been blurred."[2] The *problematisation* made possible by this blurred reality is one that undoes the givenness of our inherited assumptions about the earth as an object of knowledge; that is, the confusion created by the act of *de-ontologizing* the separation between humans and nature allows contemporary theorists, activists and designers to develop problem-formations adequate to the politics of hyper-complexity that accompany our postnatural inhabitations of the earth. In nearly every book he wrote, including those he co-authored with Félix Guattari and Claire Parnet, Gilles Deleuze managed, in one way or another, to integrate his favored refrain: *problems get the solutions they deserve according to the terms by which they are created as problems.* The varied repetition of this notion is certainly not meant as a slogan; for Deleuze, the work of producing problems, that is, of problem-formation, is a fundamental task of philosophy. With the provocation of the Anthropocene thesis, philosophy can produce new constructions that transform trajectories of thought; by developing affinities and collaborations through multi-disciplinary, multi-scalar, and multi-centered approaches, architecture too can discover its unique capacity to transform the present and future condition of the Earth System. In the Anthropocene, designers, activists, and philosophers will all have the earth they deserve; we hope this collection contributes to the conversation about how it might be constructed.

Notes

1   Philippe-Alain Michaud, *Aby Warburg and the Image in Motion* (New York: Zone Books, 2004), 229-230.

2   Paulo Tavares, "On the Earth-Object," in *Savage Objects*, edited by Godofredo Pereira (Guinarães, Imprensa Nacional-Casa da Moeda, 2012), 219.

AnthroPark (2012)

Michael CC Lin

Mixed Media Installation

AnthroPark is an entertainment and educational facility dedicated to the advancement of knowledge and public appreciation of the Middle Anthropocene, the third epoch of the Quartenary Period, following the Holocene and Pleistocene, or the eighth epoch of the Cenozoic Era.

"For a time they calmly drink a cup of tea..."

The Anthropocene is a yet-to-be formalized term designating an epoch in which human impact is considered to be significant enough to constitute a new geological era for its lithosphere. For instance, chlorine from atomic weapons testing has been found in ice core samples, as have mercury traces from coal plants. The beginning of this epoch can be linked to the industrial revolution, after which it developed rapidly through the trinity of efficiency, consumption, and enjoyment, which together suggest a machinic *modus operandi of the epoch.*

Meanwhile, individuals in late capitalist society are estranged from social relationships as we respond to incessant injunctions to "Enjoy!"—we can say "no man is an island," except in enjoyment. Such an injunction both distracts and distances human beings from each other, creating a network of islands that co-produce contemporary reality.

But the island is an illusion. In our inexorable interconnection, each action on each island has both direct and indirect consequences; as such, each is implicated in producing or dissolving our veils of isolation. Through *telemorphosis*, all distances begin to collapse as separations entangle to form a twisted knot of the contemporary.[1] Progress and atrocity, excess and lack, even culture and nature begin to appear as merely two sides of the same coin of modernity. Just as inevitably, false dichotomies beget false projects

"...All of a sudden, they'll go apeshit and start to smash everything up
because they can't stand the boredom, the absence of incident."
—The Primate Tea Party

for synthesis. Where lines are drawn, we reveal difference, perspective, and the multiplicity of realities.

AnthroPark is a theme park for line-drawing. The park form offers an immersive experience and moves seamlessly from utilitarian to symbolic moments, intensifying both corporeal and psychological perturbations. The *AnthroPark* experience is co-produced by a collection of by-products from Anthropocenic enjoyment, which, as they aggregate, become even more entangled in the participatory *jouissance* that reveals the tragicomedy of past and present enjoyments.

Like an institutional chimera, *AnthroPark* brings together a mosaic of disparate objects to form a specialized repository of attractions suited for an epoch of telemorphic implications. The dynamic forces of managed life are celebrated among the collection of interactive assemblages that provide curious visitors with an unusual, hands-on experience of the Anthropocene.

In its original sense, the term "amusement park" referred to a garden open to the public for pleasure and recreation, often containing attractions beyond the plantings and landscape. Likewise, the particular form of the "menagerie," a pleasure garden containing a collection of common and exotic animals, is housed in some architectural structure. These historical

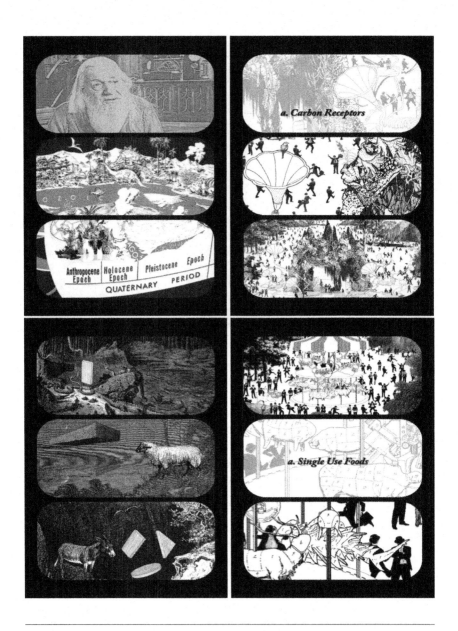

products can be read as precedents for the *AnthroPark* and its contemporary ambition to provoke both zoological and political responses to the Anthropocene.

Notes

1 See Tom Cohen, ed., *Telemorphosis: Theory in the Era of Climate Change, Volume 1* (Ann Arbor: Open Humanities Press/MPublishing, 2012).

Matters of Observation

John Palmesino and Ann-Sofi Rönnskog in Conversation
with Etienne Turpin

On Architecture in the Anthropocene

Territorial Agency is an independent organization that promotes innovative and sustainable territorial transformations. It is engaged in strengthening the capacity of local and international communities with regards to comprehensive spatial transformation management. Territorial Agency's projects channel available spatial resources towards the development of their full potential, and work to establish instruments and methods for ensuring higher architectural and urban quality in contemporary territories. This work builds on wide stakeholder networks, combining analysis, advocacy and action. The activities of Territorial Agency are grounded in extensive territorial analysis, which focuses on complex representations of the transformations of physical structures in inhabited territories, and lead to comprehensive projects aimed at strengthening regional performance through seminars and public events as a process of building capacity to innovate.1

During their visit in April 2013 to the SYNAPSE: International Curators' Network workshop at the Haus der Kulturen der Welt (HKW) in Berlin, John Palmesino and Ann-Sofi Rönnskog gave our group of curators a tour of the Anthropocene Observatory, a project they developed (as Territorial Agency) with Armin Linke and Anselm Franke. Following this tour of the Observatory, I spoke with John and Ann-Sofi about their ambition for the project and its relation to the discipline of architecture in the era of the Anthropocene; part way through our conversation, we were joined by the curator, artist, and writer Nabil Ahmed, whose work is included later in this volume; what follows is an edited transcript of our conversation.

Etienne Turpin I am trying to understand why so much architecture today is ultimately afraid of the world. We can see this through reactionary commitments to the building-scale as the "proper" index of the discipline. I am interested in how the Anthropocene thesis might challenge this reactionary tendency. Without making any argument for an "expanded field" for architecture—many others have already done so, with greater or lesser degrees of imperialist ambition—do you think that the Anthropocene occasions a rethinking, or reconceptualization, of the field of architecture? How does Territorial Agency see the relation between the Anthropocene thesis and the discipline today?

John Palmesino I think it might be an issue of viewpoint and perspective. In the sense that there is a possibility of thinking that if architecture is setting up the perspective, then it can easily fall into the conceptual trap of conceptualizing itself as being on the outside, and as looking at an object; from this view, the object is the point of reference and it is what architecture tries to shape. Yet, in structuring a perspectival space, both the point of view and the object are established at the same time: there is no outside. So I don't think there is a need for re-conceptualizing anything, but there is a need to be a little bit more clear about what we are talking about when we talk about architecture.

The conceptual misunderstanding that architecture is an "object"—that it is sitting within the perspective drawing, rather than creating the perspective drawing itself—I think this might be the problem you are referring to. At least since the fourteenth century, architecture has produced the possibility of understanding horizons, vanishing points, and of setting views and view heights. So it's not necessary to re-conceptualize architecture. Architecture is not buildings; buildings are mainly stuff. Architecture is an active connection, a practice which activates a relation between material spaces and their inhabitation; and, it structures that relation, it structures what we call the relation between space and polity, as well as the construction of polities themselves.

This is a problem with many levels; it relates to sets that are in movement relative to one another, as well as to spaces being modified by shifting infrastructural procedures, political decisions, and social dynamics. Modifications of space and material configurations all eventually reshape (and possibly hinder) many of our spaces of cohabitation. Conceptually, I don't think we need to do much more than that. The question is, then: from whose perspective does this occur? Whose point of view? What we are working on, as Territorial Agency, is a project that is both about the territory of agency and the agency of territories. We are trying to understand how to engage with this condition, or situation, which is apparently a conundrum of points of view, different territories, different agencies, etc. In this sense, the work that we are putting forward for discussion, evaluation, and possible testing is that of re-tracing different territories according to different polities, and trying to understand how those re-tracings, and the reorganization of points of view, can activate paths toward the re-appropriation of resources, the reorganization of action, and so on. The point for us is to start with a horizon and multiply that horizon; it is not about fields or about reconceptualization because I think, somehow, it is very important for us as architects and urbanists to insist that this project is not about making something more about architecture; this *is* architecture. There is no reconceptualization needed. The object of research and practice is architecture, and the means is architecture.

ET Does the Anthropocene thesis pressurize that claim, or perhaps give it more leverage? Does it allow us to insist on architecture as a practice more precisely? Like architecture, the Anthropocene can be read through everything, but it is not just anything, as you have said.

JP I really want to resist any pressure of urgency. We are really not interested in claiming that there is a new land that might allow us to go on and do new work and be more and more contemporary about it. That is exactly the paucity of the discipline; we have something happening outside the discipline, let's go and conquer it! This reveals how precariously the practice is in its current conceptualization. It also outlines architecture's condition of imperialism and with it the greed to occupy more and more space for the sake, I guess, of many academic careers. We must resist any conceptualization of a new land to be claimed. Contrary to geographical expansion, what we are actually seeing is a shift in intensity.

Ann-Sofi Rönnskog Through this approach, what we are trying to do with many of our current projects is to look at the management of projects themselves. In the last few decades, the architect has been the one who gets instructions at the end of a particular decision chain. The architect is told to address given parameters, meet certain requirements, etc. What we are trying to do is to look through the territory and determine where the architect can intervene earlier, before being given the object to design. Instead, we are considering how we can also work to design the overall perspective, that is to set up the instruction of design and briefs, to structure relations from the very outset of a project.

ET I would like to ask about the figure of Gilles Deleuze and the role of his philosophy in your practice. Much of Deleuze's work was drawn into a very formal architectural language and ended in so many dead ends. Could you say more about the role of Deleuze's philosophy in shaping your practice and what you try to develop through your engagement with his work?

JP It is happening on many levels. There is usually, as we know, a distinction between theory and practice. What we are interested in is how to see theory as a practice, and a very specific kind of practice in the sense that it does not outline the framework, the reference, or the margins within which you can operate and to which you have to refer in order to make sense; I think what it does, instead, is unhinge the reference points. Theory, as Irit Rogoff would say, undoes. What is a theorist? One who undoes.

I think that the possibility of thinking of architecture as a practice of the project has, on one hand, enabled it to claim a central position as the master of the arts, and of the organization of transformation; on the other, this has put it in a deadlock situation in the sense that architecture is never really the master. Such a position does not allow other practices to configure themselves in relation to architecture, even though it claims to be open to this negotiation. Architecture operates among other practices, and we are interested in this as a disorienting condition. Somehow we can take the discipline away from the central condition it imagines and have it negotiate with other practices. In that sense maybe, it is important to understand that a negotiation is a situation which ends up in a transformation.

ET   Transformation on both sides...

JP   In order to negotiate, you have to be able to give up something and you have to be willing to change what your claims are. It is not a game of who will win, a competition; rather, it's a transformative relation. In that sense, for us, the role of making so many projects in collaboration with schools, or within schools, and with different schools, is not because we want to be teaching, but because we are learning.

You mentioned Gilles Deleuze, and I think our position is approximating the wild condition, the wild creation of concepts, the possibility of a feral condition for architecture that tries many ways to come to grips with the world; it is about trying to make a claim for a central position without having to occupy this central position in stability. To use an expression that we like a lot, it is to be *inter-alia*, among things, out there among radically different practices that all claim a certain form of centrality. Anthropology, sociology, politics—all of these claim centrality. Architecture, meanwhile, has had this enormous energy in recent years, all dedicated to defining the discipline, and not one of these definitions or demarcations actually looks at the other disciplines also claiming the same centrality. There is no real conceptualization of a multi-centred organization for the transformation of space, or a multi-centred transformation of the social. This is remarkable! It is a situation that is symptomatic, at least on one side, since it becomes the visible element of the underlying tension in the discipline; on the other side, it is interesting because I think it indicates a complete circularity and internalization of architecture. If there is no other possible way of organizing the discipline of architecture as architecture, why even bother to practice it? It starts to sound a lot like Don Quixote fighting against the windmills, or breaking through open doors. To understand what architecture does, we do not need to accept this stable definition of the discipline.

ET   We often try to bring in people for our studio reviews who are outside of the discipline for precisely this reason—we don't want to waste all the time in the review talking about "Architecture" and spoil the conversation. But it is still difficult to explain why there is just so much empty talk about the discipline in nearly every review in the United States and Europe.

JP   Architecture has recently become more self-referential, and through this process has oriented itself toward a sectorial condition. It has become a sector, separated and inserted only in clearly outlined possibilities of knowledge production, diversion, mixture, departure, and even closure. It is mainly producing discourses of similarity and closure. It reasserts models of authority that quite clearly have a centralizing position; this is not something that interests us.

ET   How was the Observatory conceptualized in relation to your practice and the project on the Anthropocene thesis at the HKW?

JP The Observatory is a collaborative project with the filmmaker and photographer Armin Linke and curator Anselm Franke. We are trying to make a project with someone who, by insisting so much on the production of images, might be mistaken as the observer. But, what we are interested in is exactly that thing—putting forward a little space, in the HKW—that observes the making, unfolding, and transformation of practices, including image-production and architecture, as they are variously charged by the thesis of the Anthropocene. It that sense, we conceptualize the observatory as part of the institution of the HKW. It is not just a project hosted by them; it is a part of the HKW, and it operates as both a sensor and a producer of background images. We are interested in the behind-the-scenes, in the procedures, complex machines, and "vast machinery," to quote Paul Edwards, of this very beautiful and word: the Anthropocene.[2] It is a word that puts so many people in an uneasy situation because it completely reconfigures the distinction between humans and nonhumans; it also calls into question the project of the humanities, which is also why so many people feel uncomfortable with it. How to conceptualize the distinction between the sciences and the humanities? Suddenly, this invitation by science offers a way of creating and taking apart boundaries, borders, fractures and an array of evidence. This is what we are trying to trace and chart with the Observatory. At the same time, we are trying to intervene in the making and unmaking of those boundaries.

ET This is really important. For you, it is not just a matter of reflecting on, but also a question of intervening into, this situation, in relation to these reflections.

JP For instance, we are interested in understanding what are the images that architecture can produce of the Anthropocene? What does it look like? Where is it? Is this building [the HKW] part of the Anthropocene, or is it just before the Anthropocene? Which part of the building? Perhaps the railing, because it was added after 1951? This year is now being considered as demarcating the Anthropocene.

ET Is the year 1951 related to the sought-after Golden Spike?[3]

JP I am talking about the time. There is the possibility of the Golden Spike in a place; that discussion is about whether or not it will be in a lake in Ontario, Canada.[4] That is just one example. The Observatory is in the early stages, but this is what we are aiming for. To somehow show that the relationship is not one of documentation, of things that are happening outside; instead, it is a relationship of interference. Margaret Mead, for example, in the first installment of the Observatory, epitomizes this figure of interference. You have to negotiate; you have to relate to other groups and people you are working with.

ET Do you see the relationship between the Anthropocene thesis and the discipline of architecture as productively undoing some of the reactionary aspects of the discipline?

JP On many levels I am afraid that it does not. I am afraid that the Anthropocene thesis, on the contrary, is reasserting certain conditions within architectural di course, as if we are the ones changing the surface of the earth—as if it is about architecture.

ET That architects read the Anthropocene as a valorization of architecture?

JP That suddenly it is a new time for architecture. It reminds me a lot of 1930s and 1940s discourses on the "manmade landscape." The signs we are seeing within architecture discourse, with the exception of a very few cases, go in that direction. At the same time—and this is a very interesting thing—other explorations in architecture are wild, and are taking completely unexpected turns, completely unexpected conditions, and hypotheses with radical transformations that are rethinking what a practice can be and how to organize a practice. That is the interesting thing—you don't have a middle ground—you either have a very conservative take that says this has always been the case and remains reactionary, or you have people who are very excited about the Anthropocene and producing new concepts and practices. But, there is very little gradient in between these two positions.

But another interesting element of the conservative understanding of the Anthropocene thesis for architecture is the question of scale. Scalarity, but especially multi-scalarity, is now what is at stake. I think the possibilities are very close, in that sense, to thinking multi-scalarity and the multiplication of relations to what the practices of organizational theory and management theory have been working on for the last ten or fifteen years with respect to "integrated approaches." It is quite interesting that the integrated assessment report is the practice of large institutions like the Intergovernmental Panel on Climate Change. The integration, the possibility of bringing everything together within one overarching system and ordering capacity, is what fascinates the most conservative people in architecture. Suddenly, through the Anthropocene, there is a framework which allows us to think at the largest scale possible, allowing us to think of levels of agency that go from one to the other and somehow trace the entire supply chain of possibilities and mediations.

ET But this tends to remain entirely representational.

JP It doesn't work, that's the problem, the entire take on architecture as representation; as opposed to interference, constructive practice, and making things up. It is quite interesting because it is reestablishing and locking in a lot of the recent discourse in a conservative way. Take, for instance, the entire problem of ecological architecture. On many levels, it asserts the claim: "Look, we told you so! You have to be green." This is interesting as a completely circular take on what architecture can do. Again, environmentalism as conservatism.

ET This is also where we see so much work that is just aestheticizing data and creating fantasies of ecological infrastructure that become the "wish-images" of architecture's agency. There are so many examples, which we know, but these projects do not interfere—they are architecture as a wish-image, in Walter Benjamin's sense of the term.

Nabil Ahmed Except that some of these projects are also redrawing the lines of conflict; these are very real politics implicating states of war.

JP What is interesting in this claim of reshaping the chessboard of politics is that there is also a growing incapacity for negation, or of having something to negate. We have been a part of many of these kinds of projects that try to re-imagine how conflictual conditions are represented and made in the conflict. What we have seen is the difficulty, almost an incapacity, of acting. There is no consequence in that there is no moment when the consequences are immediately traceable. What is interesting, of course, is that at the same time as you start to see this incapacity to articulate consequences, there is a theorization of multi-causality. Somehow we hear the claims, "Look, this is it! We found the perfect solution. We will claim complete agency over the entire world, but without consequences for our actions because the world goes on by itself." This is the strange dream of self-organization that Anselm Franke and Diedrich Diederichsen highlight in the in Whole Earth exhibition.[5] We can think of self-organization as the ultimate vanishing point of contemporary architecture. It will organize itself, and we will be a part of that self-organization through our institutions, through our representations, through our architecture, through our political stances. It is really interesting, but I am bothered by this because I don't think that one can keep the circle open without some kind of negation.

ET You have suggested that the paradox is now quite clear—at the moment where we can recognize the maximum human impact on the world, we also discover a minimum human agency that would be able to do anything about it.

JP This is Bruno Latour's position on the Anthropocene: "Suddenly, agency and historicity are in the glacier!"

ET But, you also look at institutions, or the various relations between architecture and institutions. What is the impetus for this line of inquiry with respect to the Anthropocene thesis?

JP It is not so formalized. I think that the simultaneous positioning of the Observatory as a space where the telescope is turned both toward the intensified ground of the Anthropocene and toward the theatre of this experiment is important. One of the main aims of the project is to create a theatre of experimentation. From this perspective, it becomes really difficult to think of the Anthropocene, and of the architecture of the Anthropocene, as possibilities that are given. The institutions of the Anthropocene are not given; the publics and the audiences of the Anthropocene are in the making. They are being shaped, carved, and molded as the discourse is unfolding. We are interested in this process, in seeing how the background is reshaping the frame of polities. For instance, we were recently in a discussion about how to organize multi-lateral policies in relation to logistics in a large metropolitan area of Europe. Typically, the background, as conceived by architects, is both geological and institutional space; these spaces, for most architects, are just given. Mountains and institutions are given; these are what you cannot touch.

ET Architects only put the figure, as object, in front of this backformation?

JP Yes, exactly. In a way, following Le Corbusier and Modernism, you have the construction of the window that will build a new view. For architecture, this act of framing is the maximum engagement with the background. The construction of the history of the context indicates that it is a project; but architecture is not the only variable, while the context is merely a given. What I think is elucidated in the initial work on the Anthropocene is that institutions, like geology, are not given. They have agency—multiple and conflicting forms of agency. They create different territories, which can be mobilized and reconnected, but also blocked, as agencies. But not in the sense of Gaia as a self-regulating system; on the contrary, there is no clear object. We gave the first installation of the Anthropocene Observatory the title "Plan the Planet."[6] Today it is no longer possible to plan the planet; it was a dream, an aspiration that was meant to enable the mid-twentieth century. I don't think we are in that situation any longer.

NA This period also witnessed the formulation of our planetary institutions as well, such as the United Nations.

ET It is also the time when architects still accepted the brief from the client without questioning the condition, instead assuming that it was given.

AS We understand that this is a new process, where architects accepting those givens form the dominant culture. Bruno Latour, in his Gifford lectures, says something that relates to scale for the architect quite nicely when he explains that we have been understanding the world as something that expands, out there for humans to go and colonize, but that now, in the Anthropocene, this has to do instead with intensities.[7] It is a big challenge for architects to remove this extensive distance; it is a completely new configuration, and that is one of the interesting aspects of Anthropocene thesis.

JP It might be similar to an aesthetic shift like that of thinking of the world as a conservation of energy. Latour mentions in the Edinburgh lectures that we might be back in the sixteenth century; but we might be back in the late nineteenth century on this level as well, in the sense that thermodynamics was such a major shift. We are no longer in a situation where we can see things like Galileo, who could point at the slope and indicate that the two spheres were falling at the same rate of acceleration; the thermodynamic shift, from the point of view of aesthetics, means that there is nothing to point at, there is no object. Instead, it is about how you look at things. The Anthropocene is a similar situation in the sense that there is no object—there are only intensities. This is very difficult for architects to think because intensities cannot be measured against other things; you cannot measure temperature against external measurements; you can only measure temperature against a transition point of water, when it solidifies or when it melts, but this is not a measure of temperature, it is a measure of transformation. That is the interesting thing for us—intensity is a necessary concept of the Anthropocene because you can only understand it through transformation. That is a constructive practice, and it is something architecture is good at.

ET One curiosity I have about the role of the Observatory is that when we try to return to the question of politics, even a politics of intensity, we encounter the difficulty of negation, or the vanishing horizon of the negative as a requirement of politics, which, at least historically, requires some form of assertion through negation as one of its constitutive components. How does politics appear in this cartography of intensity, given that when we talk about climate modeling, the conflict is already included in the model and there is no way outside of it?

JP It is completely within the model itself. The Schmittian enemy is what stabilizes an ecological move; it is an engagement of information between irreconcilable conditions. This is an ecological model. But, for the politics of non-action, of not acting, we have a model for that as well. It has a name, which is neutrality—not to act, not to take a position, not to engage with conflicts, not to partake in territorial conditions and the reorganization of factions and parties. We hope that we are offering this space of the Observatory for looking on, inquiring into the making of the thing, but also hopefully holding back claims for the larger implications, actually allowing a discourse to take place, but in a neutral space. Similar to the space of the high seas, where the claims of sovereignty and territoriality are open. We hope the Anthropocene Observatory will give due respect to the Anthropocene thesis; it is only a small thing, really, but the point is that we have to take into consideration what it means to hold back on claims about the Whole Earth. When is it that we can claim the earth? Who can claim the whole earth as their perspective? Let's build a space for the discussion about this. This is the difficult task of architecture today— where can this discussion happen? In which space? In which architecture? Who will be involved?

AS But let's not try to rush it...

JP Yes, we cannot rush it. There is time, we have to give it time—geological time.

Notes

1   Excerpted from the Territorial Agency mission statement, http://www.territorialagency.com/, accessed 1 May, 2013.

2   Paul Edwards, *A Vast Machine: Computer Models, Climate Data, and the Politics of Global Warming* (Cambridge, Mass.: MIT Press, 2010).

3   A "golden spike" refers to a specific, distinct marker—typically a consistent chemical, magnetic, climatic or fossil trace—that distinguishes a geological period globally; in this case, the golden spike would separate the geological period of the Holocene from the Anthropocene.

4   Gordon W. Holtgrieve et. al., "A Coherent Signature of Anthropogenic Nitrogen Deposition to Remote Watersheds of the Northern Hemisphere," *Science* 334, no. 6062 (16 December 2011): 1545–1548. For a poetic reading of the golden spike in relation to the Anthropocene, see Don Mackay, "Ediacaran and Anthropocene: Poetry as a Reader of Deep Time," *Prairie Fire* 29, no. 4 (Winter 2008-9); see also Lisa Hirmer's "Fortune Head Geologies" in this volume.

5   The Whole Earth: California and the Disappearance of the Outside, curated by Diedrich Diederichsen and Anselm Franke, Haus der Kulturen der Welt, Berlin, Germany, 26 April – 1 July, 2013.

6   John Palmesino and Ann-Sofi Rönnskog, "Plan the Planet," in *The Whole Earth: California and the Disappearance of the Outside* (Second Edition), ed. Diedrich Diederichsen and Anselm Franke (Berlin: Sternberg Press, 2013), 82–90.

7   Bruno Latour, *Facing Gaia: Six Lectures on the Political Theology of Nature*, 2013 Gifford Lectures on Natural Religion, http://www.bruno-latour.fr/node/486.

Radical Meteorology (2013)

Nabil Ahmed

Video. 5'53", 3'46" and 4'12"

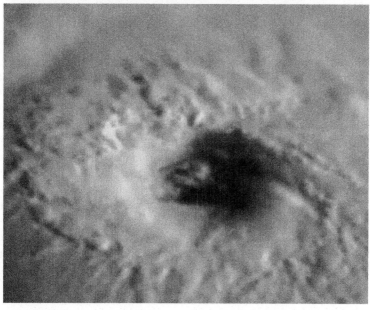

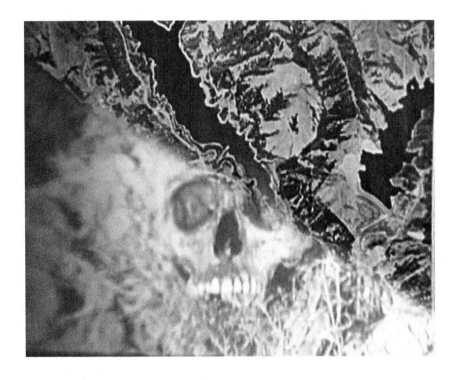

Solar energy raises the temperature of the tropical ocean to 26 degrees Celsius. Heat passes into the air above through conduction. Warm, moist rising air creates a centre of depression intensifying the trade winds that blow diagonally towards the equator from the northeast and southeast. Portuguese explorers had unlocked the trade winds and planetary currents in the tropics as far back as the fifteenth century. Like a conveyor belt, they made possible the fast movement of ships from Europe to Africa and Asia, a colonial technology which for hundreds of years enabled the exploitation of resources, as well as the enslavement and slaughter of local populations. Released from the evaporated warm water of the tropical seas, massive amounts of energy are stored in water vapour, which transforms into terrifying columns of clouds and rain as it condenses. Warm air caused by the release of heat energy further decreases the pressure; more warm water from the sea is drawn up, creating a positive feedback loop—a heat engine always moving clockwise in the Southern hemisphere.

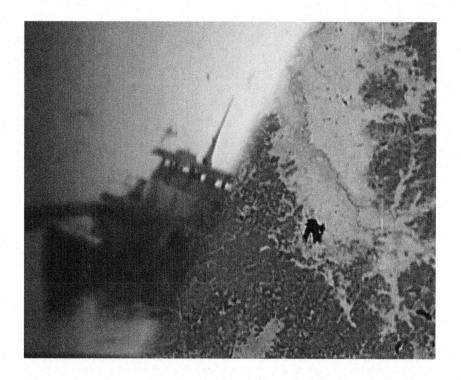

A tropical cyclone in the Indian Ocean was captured in the iconic "Blue Marble" image of the Earth. The unnamed storm struck the city of Cuddalore on the coast of the Bay of Bengal the same week of the launch of the Apollo mission in December 1972. Chennai, almost 200 kilometres away, was also flooded. Combined in the cyclone are the violence of the wind, sun, and the spinning of the earth, their continual variation captured in a single, striated image and calculated in the coldness of space. Icy, deep water summoned from phantom depths, spellbound, foaming, murderous wind and sea. The cyclone in this image is from the same tropical storm system that produced Bhola, which devastated the coast of East Pakistan in November 1970. In its aftermath followed a genocide and war of national liberation for present-day Bangladesh. After Bhola, looking at a cyclone will never be the same; the potential for political violence and an ever-circling wind are united as one.

Changes in the weather, changes in temperature, those of us that are trained CPP volunteers we are able to sense it.

Radical Meteorology takes as a point of departure the cyclone captured in the "Blue Marble" image to emphasize the entanglement between natural and political violence in Bangladesh in 1970-71. In the following year the US launched its Landsat program, which first used satellite images to map earth's resources. It technically facilitated the Green Revolution, a form of neo-colonial system of agriculture imposed on the planet's hungry and poor, including a war-ravaged Bangladesh. The agricultural and hydraulic interventions in agrarian ecology dramatically increased the fledgling state's rice production and population. It also provided laboratory conditions for the ushering in of neoliberal policies and practices of international development and debt finance. Several decades on, Bangladesh, along with other southern states of the megadelta, is a frontier zone facing the hostile effects of climate change in the Anthropocene. In 2012, I interviewed two members of the Cyclone Preparedness Program (CPP) in the coastal Cox's Bazaar region, who warn the most vulnerable populations of incoming storms and bring them to the safety of cyclone shelters. In the interview one of the volunteers, Hossain M., told me how he senses depressions in the Bay of Bengal through his body. The cyclone returns as affect.

Three Holes

by Seth Denizen

In the Geological Present

En construcción (*Under Construction*), directed by José Luis Guerín (2001)   Fig. 01

> *Derived from the Latin forensis, the word "forensics" refers at root to "forum."*
> *Forensics is thus the art of the forum—the practice and skill of presenting an*
> *argument before a professional, political, or legal gathering. Forensics is in this*
> *sense part of rhetoric, which concerns speech. However, it includes not only*
> *human speech but also that of things.*
>
> — Eyal Weizman, *Forensic Architecture*[1]

The talent the geological sciences have for placing humans on unfathomable time lines—in which human history appears as little more than a gracious footnote to forces too powerful to measure and too slow to watch—seems to be exercised less and less as images of melting glaciers and exponential curves produce a very different kind of feeling. The image of the city, in particular, as a thing that is made *of* geology or *on* geology, increasingly has to contend with the idea of the city as a thing that *makes* geology, in the forms of nuclear fuel, dammed rivers, atmospheric carbon, and other metabolic products of urbanization whose impacts will stretch into future epochs.[2] The geological sciences—atmospheric and ocean chemistry,

Fig. 02   Hiroshi Sugimoto, *Ordovician Period Photo* (1994). Photo 81 x 71 cm

soil science, geophysics, physical geography and geology—seem to be more often summoned to review evidence at the scene of a crime than to record the annals of a former world. In this sense, there has been a convergence between the forensic science of war crimes tribunals as described by Eyal Weizman's Forensic Architecture project and the geological sciences as they are confronted for the first time by an urgent futurity in their work. In the testimony of scientists, the expertise that is called upon is the epistemological power to make matter speak. What do the rocks say? What do the bones tell us? At the moment geology is asked to testify on behalf of its materials, regarding issues that concern the unfolding of ecological catastrophes, it becomes a forensic science in the legal sense. However, unlike the materials of forensic science, the geological materials that are brought to trial have not stopped speaking. Even the nature of the crime is in question. In short, geologists are increasingly being asked to answer the question *what's going on?* rather than *what happened?*

In this way, the geological sciences are not only called on to reconstruct the past, but also participate in the construction of the present. Recent calls for the establishment of a geological epoch known as the Anthropocene are, in fact, calls for the production of what cultural critic Laurent Berlant has named a "genre of the present," in which a geological catastrophe too slow to watch could be rendered present and, perhaps, intelligible.[3] For Berlant, the present is something that has a history because it is produced. Crucially, "we understand nothing about impasses of the political without having an account of the production of the present."[4] One might see the political impasse of current climate change debates as hinging precisely on

Hiroshi Sugimoto, *Earliest Human Relatives* (1994). Photo 81 x 71 cm   Fig. 03

this problem: how to produce the geological present. The production of geological materials as *things* also requires the concomitant production of unexpected geological relations, such as those between aerosol cans and the ozone layer, which come to participate in the production of the present as a time of perpetual crisis.

What seems clear is that the ways in which a geologist becomes contemporaneous with her materials—insofar as the geological relations that bring them into being are still changing—will require new methodologies. The ways these methodologies participate in the production of the present also beckons careful examination. To say this in another way, the dioramas in natural history museums are serious business. In the dioramas of Ordovician sea life or the "Earliest Human Relatives," photographed by Hiroshi Sugimoto, the geological past is a place of tension and drama that is filled at every moment with the differences that make it distinct from our own time. [Figs. 02, 03] Its actors strike a pose in their tableau that suggests where we are, now, in relation to those differences; in this way, the diorama produces an image of the geological present. Certainly, these speculative engagements with empirical objects are always fully animated by contemporary concerns. In speculating on what a methodology for the production of the geological present would look like today, this essay pursues an intimate relation with the venerable tradition of the diorama. What follows is an attempt to work in this genre by taking three geological holes, and their attendant stratifications, as the empirical objects to be animated or re-animated for the production of the geological present.

Hole #1: The Forum

"There's no need to get upset. That's all we are, with all our obsessions. Look at what we are."
"Yeah..."
"So much irritation in life."
"We all fit in the same hole."
"All of us."
"Everyone, both rich and poor. There's no difference."
"Yes, there is no distinction. Luckily, or it would be too much."
"What a thing, we live directly over bodies and don't even know it."

José Luis Guerín's documentary film *En construcción* [*Under Construction*] begins with conversations among residents of Barcelona's District V, also known as "El Raval," about a hole in their neighbourhood. [Fig. 01] Literally, the demolition of a housing block to make way for an urban renewal project has left a large hole in the ground. While first imagined as a temporary inconvenience, the discovery of medieval ruins at the base of the excavation has halted construction, affording the hole an improbable permanence. In a strange reversal, the demolition that promised a break with the neighbourhood's past (as Barcelona's red light district) has instead produced an archeological site. Rather than looking up at the construction of the future city, Guerín documents the moment in which the residents of El Raval find themselves looking down at the bones and buildings of the former city. Everyone in Guerín's film has a different explanation of what they see:

"To me, it's Arabian."
"That? Arabian?"
"On TV they said it's Roman. But who knows?"
"They used to die on the street. I remember, here in this area, during the war, they'd die right on the street."

In these conversations, the hole bears witness to an astonishing diversity of evidence, which overlaps and proliferates among the chance encounters of passersby. It is a vestige of the Arabian occupation of Barcelona in the eighth century, a burial site for the "crimes committed by Spain" in the twentieth century, a Roman ruin from the sixth century, a legal entity under religious law, a scientific discovery to be analyzed, a burial site for kings, a former factory, a psychic shadow of the civil war.

What Guerín is documenting is clearly not the hole as it appears in the street. Aside from a few short images of skulls and stone roofs, Guerín never actually films the hole. Instead, he places the hole between his camera and the residents of El Raval, always just out of sight. Through this documentary technique, what we see instead is the hole in its capacity to produce the present. In this sense, what Guerín presents us with is the moment of the hole's formation—the moment at which a hole becomes *this* hole, rather than just another ephemeral moment blurred by the rapid pace of urban renewal. The hole becomes *this* hole by taking on a duration in time that has suddenly become capable of forensic speech through its relation to human bones.[5]

The process by which the contours of a hole are discerned will always bear this hallmark moment of recognition—what could be called its "forensic recognition"—that is, the passage from something that was not presumed to have its own unique duration in time to something that suddenly does. At this moment the recognition is not only that there is a hole, but also that it was already there; that there was a hole all along: "We live directly over bodies and don't even know it."

Hole #2: Forensic Rhetoric

Guerín's film gives us a clear image of the production of the "forum" in "forensics," in which the production of the present through the speech of things is brought about by a proliferation of forensic science on the streets of Barcelona. This hole has as its empirical analogue the largest hole to have ever appeared in the twentieth century, the ozone hole, which also came into being as a hole through the discovery of its unique duration and the human artifacts that caused it—its forensic recognition.[6] [Fig. 04]

A brief account of this history is instructive. The ozone hole was discovered in 1985 by three scientists from the British Antarctic Survey (BAS) who were just as surprised as the general public by the existence of a hole currently the size of North America.[7] At the time of this discovery, they were in Antarctica to find ways to improve theories of weather forecasting. The ozone data that the team recorded, even once it was plotted, still did not appear as a hole: it was scattered, showing no definite trend. Jonathan Shanklin, who was on the team that discovered the ozone hole, recalls first presenting the same data that later led to its discovery as evidence that the hole was not there:

Ozone hole measured 5 September, 2012. Fig. 04
Ozone Hole Watch, National Aeronautics and Space Administration, Goddard Space Flight Center. http://ozonewatch.gsfc.nasa.gov/

> The popular press was reporting at the time on studies suggesting that aerosol spray cans and exhaust gases from Concorde flights could destroy the ozone layer. Models showed, however, that the expected loss of ozone thus far was only a few per cent. I wanted to reassure the public by showing that our ozone data from that year were no different from 20 years earlier. The graph we presented to the public showed that no significant change in ozone had been detected over the years, which was true overall—but it seemed that the springtime values did look lower from one year to the next.[8]

The springtime values Shanklin refers to are now called "the ozone hole."[9] The contours of this hole only began to take shape when the members of the team looked at these springtime values specifically, ignoring what happened in the ozone layer for the rest of the year: the hole turned out to be seasonal. What the data showed was a steady decrease in the springtime ozone levels, year by year, at a rate that was rapid enough to suggest the existence of a strong causal relationship. Since the work identifying chlorofluorocarbons (CFCs) as a catalyst for ozone depletion had already been done, the team decided to publish an overlay of the two trends in a very unorthodox way, so as to make the image of the hole appear to the rest of the world.[10] To do this, they plotted the springtime ozone values between 1954 and 1984 on a scale that *decreased* from top to bottom on the graph, and then overlaid this with the CFC concentration in the atmosphere on a scale that *increased* from top to bottom.[11] [Fig. 05] The combination of the two different scales, in two different orientations, produced a graph that looked for the first time like a hole and contained within it the human artifacts that gave it duration: CFCs. Even from the beginning, Shanklin seems to have been aware of the power of their forensic rhetoric: "In retrospect, that was a really good thing to call it, because an ozone hole must be bad. Almost automatically, it meant that people wanted something to be done about it. The hole had to be filled in."[12]

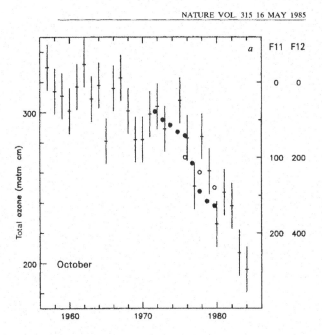

NATURE VOL. 315 16 MAY 1985

Fig. 05   J. C. Farman, B. G. Gardiner and J. D. Shanklin, "Large Losses of Total Ozone in Antarctica Reveal Seasonal ClO_x/NO_x Interaction," *Nature* 315 (May 1985): 207–210.

But why does a hole have to be filled in? It seems clear that there is something reversible about a hole. Since a hole is made, it can be unmade. This property of holes distinguishes them from gaps: in a gap something is merely missing. Without the CFCs, the ozone hole would just be a gap, a seasonal thinning of the ozone, in the same way that without a cemetery the hole in El Raval would just be *en construcción*. It is precisely this reversibility of holes that the American minimalist sculptor Carl Andre was describing in his famous claim: "A thing is a hole in a thing it is not." The distinction Andre draws between things and holes should not be understood simply as a relation between absence and presence, as this would be the spatial relation that defines gaps. Rather, holes are always produced as "things" through a process of individuation in which a skull, or chlorofluorocarbon, suddenly produces the distinct duration that defines it as a "not" in Andre's axiom. In other words, duration in a hole is not produced from an absence, but from a thing that does the digging.

From the history of the production of the ozone hole, it becomes clear that the "forum" in *forensis* is just as much a place of rhetoric in the empirical sciences as it is on the streets of Barcelona. What also becomes clear through the work of Carl Andre is that the relation defined by a hole and its contents is simply a general description of matter itself, and in this sense, the production of the material as a "thing" is the first act of rhetorical speech in the forum of forensics.

Hole #3: A New Look at Hole #1

The hole in El Raval seems to keep getting deeper: each time the bottom would appear to be in sight, another hole opens up. But, to understand this hole, we have to reconsider the fact that the soil itself did not enjoy the status of a "thing" until it was empirically produced in the late nineteenth century. The history of its production also happens to be a history of the very question that is being asked in relation to El Raval—what do the bones really reveal about the hole? Is it a human image that is discovered in the geological material of the hole, or is it a geological image that is discovered in human bones? And, what do these trajectories of meaning reveal about the present? The third hole, which we will now examine for its power to produce the present through an anthropogenic geology, will be the same hole as the first, but in this iteration the forensic lens will be focused on the soil itself.

Before soil was produced empirically as a thing, it was conceptually identical to rock. In geological descriptions of rocks, the internal heterogeneity of all the elements and mineral formations is consolidated into a single term—for instance, "granite"—and that term then stands in for the heterogeneity of the mixture. In the stratigraphic sections of geological profiles, these heterogeneous mixtures are represented as homogenous bodies so that the "strata" which characterize the profile can be differentiated.

The earliest texts on soil science apply this geological method directly to soil, with the understanding that soil comes from rock. An 1820 geological survey of Albany County, New York, elevates this understanding to the philosophical standard of common sense: "That all the earthy part of soil consists of minute fragments of rock does not require argument, or need proof, but inspection merely to determine it. We have only to place specimens under the magnifier and their rocky origin will become manifest."[13] Giving form to this understanding of soil, John Morton's 1843 treatise *The Nature and Property of Soils* deploys a series of drawings to compliment the manuscript.[14] [Fig. 06] In these drawings, the soil is depicted at the scale of geological sections, in which it appears as a thin, homogenous layer at the surface of a section hundreds of feet deep. Morton's intention was to show a genetic relationship between this soil layer and the geology underneath.

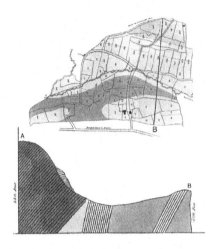

In contrast, F. A. Fallou's later work, from 1862, elevates soil to the status of geology itself; the soil is not simply a sub-category of its underlying rock, but is instead given the same kind of existence in time, and stratographic complexity, as rock sections. [Fig. 07] Here, the alternating layers and wavy lenses that flow through the soil profile have the capacity to be in nonconformity with adjacent soil layers, which appear to have been offset from one another as if by some tectonic shift. In giving soil the status of rocks, however, Fallou denies soil its own duration distinct from rocks; soil has yet to be produced as a thing.

Fig. 06 From John Morton, *The Nature and Property of Soils*, 4th ed. (London, 1843), in Alfred E. Hartemink, "The Depiction of Soil Profiles since the Late 1700s," *Catena* 79 (2009): 113–127.

Nevertheless, for Fallou, nothing escapes the tooth of time: "Soil is considered to be the product of weathering, formed as the tooth of time incessantly grinds the solid covering of our planet and gradually decomposes and destroys its solid mass."[15] This image of soil as a kind of plaque on the tooth of time, or terminal residue of the geological destruction of the earth, derives from the uniformitarian geology of the nineteenth century, which saw the process of erosion as a plausible theory for long-term changes in the appearance of the Earth. In the uniformitarian narrative, the life of soil appears as the death of rock. As rocks are given a date of birth corresponding to the historical moment they are constituted as a body, the dissolution of this body— the production of soil—constitutes its empirical death. This dissolution becomes responsible for explaining the formation of soils, which is achieved through an analysis of the many differences in the rock's material durations. Whereas Henri Bergson's well-known sugar cube consisted of a single duration, rocks generally consist of multiple durations. The sodium, potassium, and magnesium found in the feldspars and micas of granite are dissolved at different rates while in contact with the climate, whereas the iron and quartz remain relatively insoluble. The tooth of time may grind incessantly, but the solid mass it chews is not uniformly affected; soil is thus the product of difference which time encounters in the mastication of the Earth's crust.

The modern, or post-mastication, theory of soils begins with the idea that soil is not the residue of a process, but rather a process in itself, in which a system of layers

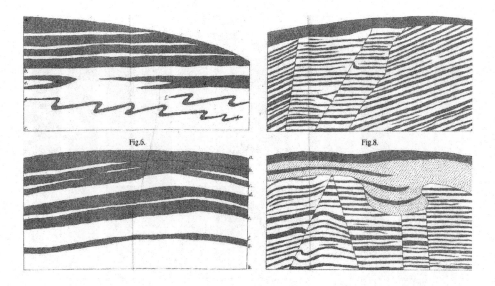

Fig.6.

Fig.8.

From F. A. Fallou, *Pedologie oder Allgemeine und besondere Bodenkunde* (Dresden: Schöenfeld, 1862), in Alfred E. Hartemink, "The Depiction of Soil Profiles since the Late 1700s," *Catena* 79 (2009): 113–127.

Fig. 07

critical to life on Earth grows out of fine rock particles. The Russian geologist Vasily Dokuchaev is given credit for producing the earliest comprehensive description of these layers, which he termed the soil "body."[16] What Dokuchaev's work describes is the soil as a thing, in Andre's sense, rather than a residue, which can only be studied as a postscript to some other process. That is, Dokuchaev's soil is a thing with its own process, composed of many different parts, and its consistency as a body comes from its capacity to be recognized by a system of resemblances that repeat, and whose repetition is produced by soil's specific duration in time and space.

This concept of soil formation begins its story where Fallou left off. The granite that met its sad end as soil in nineteenth-century uniformitarian geology suddenly springs to life again. The tiny weathered particles of feldspar take on a new geological identity as the clay mineral kaolin. Over the course of 50 to 100 years, the resistant quartz sand and weathered kaolin will form kind of clay loam, and the untransformed iron in the original granite will give the soil a reddish hue. During this time it becomes a refuge for bacteria, fungi, and a diversity of soil fauna, from amoebae to arthropods. These organisms fundamentally affect the structure of soil, causing the clay to form larger aggregates that have a greater capacity to resist wind erosion and retain moisture. Over time this process creates distinct layers in the soil, produced by differences in the way the soil is weathered, as well as by the work of organisms. When this process does not occur the soil is called young, and is homogenous like a sand dune.[17] When it does occur, it produces a pattern of layers, and these are the essential repetition required for the production of a system of resemblances known as soil taxonomy.

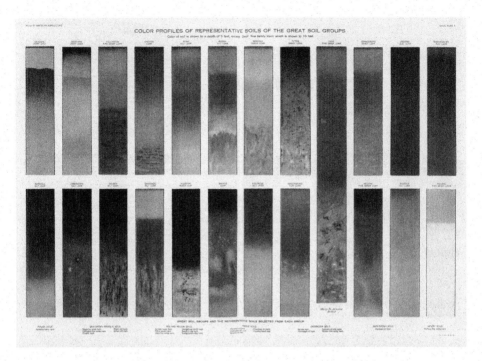

Fig. 08   Curtis F. Marbut, "Color Profiles of Representative Soils of the Great Soil Groups," in *Atlas of American Agriculture: Physical Basis including Land Relief, Climate, Soils, and Natural Vegetation of the United States*, ed. Oliver E. Baker, Plate 3 (Washington DC: United States Government Printing Office, 1936), www.davidrumsey.com.

The complete transformation of a material from something that was simply the leftover detritus of rocks to something that is itself a body, complete with organs, something that grows and develops and is capable of being young or elderly, is a kind of alchemical transformation in the empirical understanding of soils that undoubtedly merits a historical marker. The difference in the understanding of soil before and after this turn can be clearly discerned by comparing the images of soil in Morton and Fallou [Figs. 06 & 07], with those of Curtis F. Marbut [Fig. 08], who worked as the Director of the Soil Survey Division at the United States Department of Agriculture from 1910 until his death in 1935. Marbut published these paintings as a part his landmark soil taxonomy, which classified all soils of the United States into 13 "Great Groups." Each painting is a "typical" or general-ized soil profile, which not only shows the set of layers and layer thicknesses that characterize that soil, but also the processes that produce the layers over time. For instance, in the painting of the Grundy Silt Loam Great Group [Fig. 08], the vertical striations and blotchy light and dark brown colours depict a soil process known as "mottling," which is produced by a rising and falling water table. In this painting, the lower limit of the uppermost soil layer is not shown as a clean and distinct line separating the brownish red from the black, as in the layers of the Kalkaska or Sassafras Great Groups, for example, but is rather an indistinct gradient of asymmetrical intensities. The blotchy colours and vertical striations in the lower layer are meant to evoke the anaerobic chemistry produced by periodic inundation.

In order to make this taxonomy visible, Marbut produced paintings, rather than mechanically representing the surface of the soil profiles through photography; the paintings attempt to reproduce an image of the latent diagnostic criteria of messy geological processes, such as periodic inundation, in the quantifiable colours of the Munsell system.[19] The paintings that Marbut produced for his taxonomy are an attempt to represent the new durations specific to soil, and distinct from rock that had become so important to soil classification. Marbut's taxonomy had incorporated the insights of Dokuchaev and the Russian school by organizing all soil knowledge into the new form of the soil profile.[18] Soil in this taxonomy was no longer something that could be picked up in a handful; it was something that could only be known as a system of layers between six and ten feet deep, created by the forces of climate, parent material, relief, organisms, and time. For Marbut, and every other soil scientist at the time, messy geological processes—as they exist in relation to the production of recognizable forms in the soil profile—mark the proper duration of soil, necessarily distinct from the duration of rock.

At this point in the history of soil, we find a structure analogous to that of the ozone hole in its production as a thing. Just as CFCs established a geological relation internal to the structure of the ozone hole (it gets bigger seasonally with CFC emissions), the production of the soil profile established the geological relation internal to the structure of soil (it grows layers over time). However, just as in the previous two holes, the production of a material as a thing and its investment with forensic speech are processes that emerge through the many voices of the forum, and as such are rhetorical and cosmopolitical, rather than immutable.[20]

According to soil scientist Roy Simonson, Marbut's Sassafras Great Group would be broken up into more than 50 different soils through subsequent revisions of the USDA taxonomy.[21] While each of these revisions changed the things that were said by the forensic speech of the soil, there was no fundamental revision of the way in which soil was capable of forensic speech. Such a fundamental revision to the concept of soil would remain unthinkable for almost a century, and would only come about through a reconsideration of the human relation to geological production.

In 1995, a committee within the USDA's National Resource Conservation Service was created to investigate the relation between human-made soils and soils produced solely by geological and biological conditions. Until this time, there was no way to classify the layers in urban soil, and by 1995 the hole this left in the soil survey was large enough to merit some attention. In every soil map the USDA had ever made, the city limit defined the perimeter of this hole, where soil suddenly ceased to have layers—and as such also ceased to have duration.[22] It had taken almost a century to systematically organize the complex durations of soil into a taxonomy that was capable of taking into consideration the diverse effects of climate,

Fig. 09   Venezia 2003, Societa Italiana di Geologia Ambientale. Scale = 1:50,000.

plant and animal life, the slope of the ground, geologic parent material, and the scales of time relevant to each element in the soil body. As the world has become increasingly urbanized since the 1860s, this body became contingent on a new set of processes. Things like trash, construction debris, coal ash, dredged sediments, petroleum contamination, green lawns, decomposing bodies, and rock ballast not only alter the formation of soil but themselves form soil bodies, and in this respect are taxonomically indistinguishable from soil. Thus the third hole in the anthropogenic geology of the present is also every hole in the soil survey that takes the shape and size of the city. [Fig. 09]

To illustrate the problem of inserting human bodies into the taxonomy of soil bodies more clearly, one could simply ask a more direct question: what kind of soil does a cemetery make?[23] In the case of a cemetery, a layer of commodities of various durations is deposited with a dense mass of organic material below the level in the soil profile at which aerobic decomposition can take place. [Fig. 10] In the United States, this amounts to roughly 30 million board feet of hardwood caskets, 104,272 tons of steel caskets, 2,700 tons of copper and bronze, and 1.8 million bodies per year.[24] These bodies contain approximately 827,060 gallons of formaldehyde and 11,905 pounds of mercury, primarily from tooth fillings.[25] The layer structure of the soil above this deposition is mixed into homogeneity by gravediggers or backhoes, and effectively returned to a state of youth whereby the process of differential weathering is reset. In roughly 20 years, the only organic material remaining will be bone, and in 30 to 40 years, a wooden coffin will also break down, leaving a thin and distinct layer of organic material and commodities in the profile. The formaldehyde will break down in the first few years of decomposition, but the average amount of mercury in a human body will remain in the soil for around 2,600 years. In other words, the layer structure that forms the profile of cemetery soil has a set of complex material durations that change and, as is evident from El Raval, will be clearly diagnostic of a recognizable soil structure for thousands of years.

Among the most common soils to repeat throughout the city are soils that form in construction debris. [Fig. 11] The basic metabolic functions of construction and demolition in urban areas produce a huge amount of waste material in the form of concrete, asphalt, brick, masonry blocks, drywall, steel, rebar, ceramic, etc. This material is expensive to remove, so it is typically mixed with fill or simply buried. Like the soil sediment deposited by rivers, the building materials mixed into the soil create a clear geographical and even architectural specificity to the soil. In at least this sense, the soil and the city are mirror images of each other, not only in the negative image of extraction, as has often been pointed out, but also in the positive image of deposition. The current forensic muteness of soils in urban areas—a large hole in the USDA soil taxonomy—is all the more strange given that the richness of the material relations such soils could speak of comes directly from a geologic reciprocity with the city. The reason for this muteness is clear enough, however, as present day descriptions of soil date to the original geological relations used to define soil against rock. It also comes from the lack of interest in these urban processes, as the usefulness of soil knowledge has historically been defined by its relation to agricultural production.

Recently, in an effort to understand the useful properties of its soil in relation to the real soil horizons produced by urban processes, the City of New York has taken a different approach. This involved digging a series of holes and describing the varying, and at times especially bizarre, results. For example, a USDA survey team in the city discovered that "Fishkill" soil, which "has formed in a thick mantle of industrial 'fly ash' mixed with demolished construction debris," is "good" for use as a wildlife habitat for freshwater wetland plants.[26] The "typical soil profile" for Freshkills Landfill, also now included on the map, consists of 30 to 80 inches of "extremely cobbly sandy loam" which is "20% cobble-size biodegradable artifacts, 45% cobble-sized non-biodegradable artifacts, and 5% cobbles." Its Soil Taxonomy classification is "Coarse-loamy, mixed, active, hyperthermic Typic Dystrudepts." Classifying Freshkills Landfill in the Great Group "Dystrudept" means that it is dystrophic (infertile for agriculture), udic (regarding its moisture regime), and of the order Inceptisol (meaning it has poorly developed subsurface horizons). These subsurface horizons are up to 75% trash, but classifying Freshkills Landfill as Inceptisol has led the USDA to the curious conclusion that this soil has much in common with forests on the steep slopes of North Carolina's Appalachian Mountains.

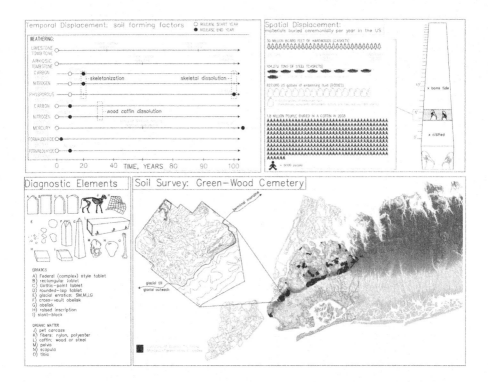

Fig. 10   Seth Denizen, "Adams Family Series," *Eighth Approximation: Urban Soil in the Anthropocene*
(MLA Thesis: University of Virginia, 2012).

What better diorama of the emerging geology of the present could be
produced? The convergence of mountains of trash and Piedmont Mountains
in the USDA's taxonomy is a convergence of resemblances in which the
geological relation of newness, with respect to processes of soil formation,
is privileged over the difference between human trash and naturally formed
mountains. Each of these soils is subject to very rapid and powerful forces
of deposition and removal which result in a young soil (Inceptisol) that is
infertile. In this description, there is both an understanding of soil as a system of
layers, and as a useful thing produced by an analysis of geologic relations, rather
than anthropocentric descriptions of geological origins. This focus on geological
relations assumes that all matter is geological, insofar as it has a duration in time,
and that this duration is produced in another forum of forensics: taxonomy.

The practical necessity of mapping the surface geology of cities has encouraged a
deeper understanding of the stratigraphic relations between human beings and the
geological present. Understanding the extent to which patterns of urbanization,
domesticity, burial, recreation, architecture, horticulture, and warfare are factors
of soil formation has produced a new set of possibilities for the production of the
geological present. As both an historical archive and a living body, soil exists at

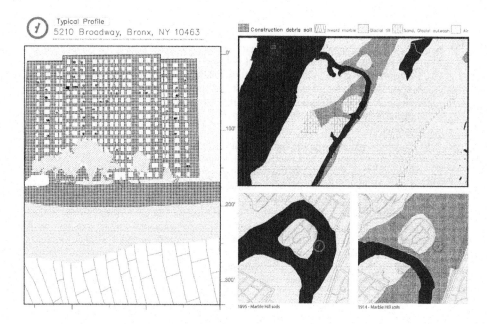

Seth Denizen, "Robert Moses Series," *Eighth Approximation: Urban Soil in the Anthropocene*
(MLA Thesis: University of Virginia, 2012).

Fig. 11

precisely that interval between the geological past and future that is bracketed by the term "Anthropocene." And as a material in direct reciprocal relation to all the material processes that define daily life, soil constitutes an immense forum, and an immense hole, around which a lot of things could be said about the present—if only in passing.

Notes

1 Eyal Weizman, *Forensic Architecture: Notes from Fields and Forums*, 100 Notes, 100 Thoughts No. 062 (Ostfildern: Hatje Cantz, 2012).

2 The damming of rivers has produced a measurable alteration of the speed of the rotation of the Earth. For an excellent primer on the city as a geologic force, see Smudge Studio's *Geologic City: A Field Guide to the GeoArchitecture of New York* (2011).

3 The term "Anthropocene" was coined by atmospheric chemist Paul Crutzen and ecologist Eugene Stoermer (independently) to refer to the present—since 1800 CE—as geologically distinct from everything that has happened since the end of the last ice age 11,700 years ago. This geological distinction comes from the global scale of human alteration of the environment, from things like dams, agricultural erosion, ocean acidification, urbanization, and atmospheric change. The formalization of this term by the International Commission on Stratigraphy (ICS) would mean the end of the current geological epoch, the Holocene. The current target date for this decision is 2016.

4 For Berlant, "emergency is another genre of the present." See *Cruel Optimism* (Durham: Duke University Press, 2011), 294, note 14. For an account of the construction of the historical present, see Chapter 2, "Intuitionists."

5 The use of the term "duration" as a property attributable to things comes from the French philosopher Henri Bergson. In Bergson's 1907 book *Creative Evolution*, he observes that the only thing that distinguishes "sugar" from other forms of matter in the universe is that it makes him wait. That is, his idea of sugar doesn't come from its shape or the space it takes up as a volume, but rather from the unalterable duration of time it takes for the sugar to dissolve in his glass, which he must live, and in this case, experience as impatience. Sugar is a duration that he has to mix with the duration of his own finite life. The usage of the term duration in this text will refer to the property of a thing having such an existence in time.

6 Ozone is what atmospheric chemists call "odd oxygen," or O_3. When odd oxygen loses its third oxygen atom to become O_2, it is no longer ozone, and ceases to perform the functions associated with ozone, like protecting the Earth from ultraviolet radiation. Chlorine, known for being among the most reactive elements on the periodic table, is a powerful catalyst for the reaction that breaks O_3 down into $O + O_2$. The result of this process is not only the breakdown of O_3, but also the liberation of the same chlorine atom that initiated the reaction. This leaves it free to begin the reaction again with another ozone molecule, and as such, creates a chain reaction in the stratosphere in which a single element of chlorine can convert huge amounts of ozone. The set of equations that explain this earned Paul Crutzen, Mario Molina, and F. Sherwood Rowland the 1995 Nobel Prize in Chemistry, but oddly enough, didn't lead to the discovery of the ozone hole. The problem was understanding how it is even possible for an element as highly reactive as chlorine to ever reach the stratosphere, after passing through more than 20 kilometers of atmosphere from the surface of the earth. This anthropogenic chemistry turned out to involve some extremely beautiful and very rare high altitude clouds, called nacreous or polar stratospheric clouds, whose icy surface provides a site for chemical reactions. This was not understood until after the ozone hole's discovery.

7 The 2011 ozone hole recorded average between 7 September and 13 October was 24.7 million square kilometres. Source: NASA Ozone Watch, Ozone Hole Watch, National Aeronautics and Space Administration Goddard Space Flight Center, 7 September 2011, http://ozonewatch.gsfc.nasa.gov.

8 Jonathan Shanklin, "Reflections on the Ozone Hole," *Nature* 465 (May 2010): 34–35.

9 Spring in the southern hemisphere is from September to November.

10 Crutzen, the inventor of the term "Anthropocene," shared the Nobel Prize for this work in 1995. See Paul Crutzen, *Nobel Lecture: My Life with O_3, NO_x and Other YZO_xs*, http://www.nobelprize.org/nobel_prizes/chemistry/laureates/1995/crutzen-lecture.html.

11 J. C. Farman, B. G. Gardiner and J. D. Shanklin, "Large Losses of Total Ozone in Antarctica Reveal Seasonal ClO_x/NO_x interaction," *Nature* 315 (May 1985): 207–210.

12 Jonathan Shanklin, interview from documentary, *The Antarctic Ozone Hole: From Discovery to Recovery, a Scientific Journey*, United Nations Environment Programme (UNEP) Division of Technology Industry and Economics (DTIE), 2011. The film was produced as part of the UNEP's work program under the Multilateral Fund for the Implementation of the Montreal Protocol, www.unep.org/ozonaction.

13 A. Eaton and T. R. Beck, *A Geological Survey of the County of Albany* (Albany: Agricultural Society of Albany County, NY, 1820).

14 John Morton, *The Nature and Property of Soils, 4th ed.* (London: 1843).

15 F. A. Fallou, *Pedologie oder Allgemeine und besondere Bodenkunde* (Dresden: Schöenfeld Buchhandlung, 1862).

16 There is some dispute as to what precisely to credit Dokuchaev with. Tandarich et. al. (see below) argue that that Orth's 1875 manuscript *Die geognostisch-agronomische Kartirung* contained the soil profile concept in the term "boden-profil." In Dokuchaev's 1879 publication, he used the terms "zaleganiya chernozem," (stratification of the chernozem) and "stroenie chernozem" (structure of the chernozem) to describe the soil profile. His descriptions of the soil as a body do not appear until his major work *Russian Chernozem* (1883), in which he cites both Orth and Fallou as having influenced his own thinking. However, it was in this work that Dokuchaev published his famous ABC system for soil profile layers, which is still in use today. The biologist and evolutionary theorist Charles Darwin also published an ABC system of soil layers in his book on earthworms in 1881, which contained detailed drawings of the soil layers. See: Charles Darwin, *Earthworms and Vegetable Mould* (London, 1881); Vasily, Dokuchaev, *Tchernozeme (terre noire) de la Russie D'Europe*, Societe Imperiale Libre Economique (Moscow: Imprimeric Trenke & Fusnot, 1879); A. Orth, *Die geognostisch-agronomische Kartirung* (Berlin: Verlag von Ernst & Korn, 1875); and John P. Tandarich, Robert G. Darmody, Leon R. Follmer and Donald L. Johnson, "Historical Development of Soil and Weathering Profile Concepts from Europe to the United States of America," *Soil Science Society of America* 66, no. 2 (March-April 2002): 335–346.

17 This is known as the "pedological age" of soil, which refers to the amount of weathering, and therefore layer formation that the soil has undergone. Weathering is most rapid where there is an abundance of water and heat. Soils in the tropical rainforest therefore tend to be pedologically old, whereas soils in the arctic are forever young. Sand dunes are also among the youngest soils.

18 Marbut was a keen reader of Russian soil science, and considered it to be far more advanced than American soil research at the time. He was particularly influenced by Dokuchaev's student Konstantin Glinka, whom he translated into English.

19 The Munsell system is a taxonomy for the classification of colours that was adopted by the USDA under Marbut for the specification of soil colour. It's taxonomic criteria are hue, value, and chroma, which form the axes of a three-dimensional colouration space that can be used to locate colours perceptible to the human eye. For example, 2.5YR 4/3 would specify a reddish brown.

20 Isabelle Stengers develops the idea of cosmopolitics in a three-volume work by that title. For Stengers, atomic particles like the neutrino participate in the production of the present through the cosmological commons they create. Just as soil is brought into being by a consensus that it is different from rock, the neutrino is brought into being by a consensus that it is different from the atom. These cosmological commons are precisely the forum of forensics referred to by Weizman. For Stengers, the consensus about what a material says—its forensic speech—constitutes a community of believers, who then live by the social and political implications of this cosmos: "The neutrino is not, therefore, the 'normal' intersection between a rational activity and a phenomenal world. The neutrino and its peers, starting with Newton's scandalous force of attraction, bind together the mutual involvement of two realities undergoing correlated expansions: that of the dense network of our practices and their histories, and that of the components and modes of interaction that populate what is referred to as the 'physical world.' In short, the neutrino exists simultaneously and inseparably 'in itself' and 'for us,' becoming even more 'in itself,' a participant in countless events in which we seek the principles of matter, as it comes into existence 'for us,' an ingredient of increasingly numerous practices, devices, and possibles." That is: "If something is to be celebrated or must force others to think, it is not the neutrino but the coproduction of a community and a reality of which, from now on, from the point of view of the community, the neutrino is an integral part." See Isabelle Stengers, *Cosmopolitics I*, trans. Robert Bononno (Minneapolis: Minnesota Press, 2010), 26.

21 Roy Simonson, "Concept of Soil," in *Advances in Agronomy*, Vol. 20, ed. A. G. Norman (Waltham, Mass.: Academic Press, 1968), 1-47.

22 There have been four soil surveys in the history of the USDA which attempt to map a city: *Soil Survey Report of Washington, DC* (Smith 1976), *Soil Survey Report of St. Louis County*

(Benham, 1982), *Soil Survey Report of Montgomery County* (Brown and Dyer, 1985), and *Soil Survey Report of the City of Baltimore* (Levine and Griffin, 1998). In each of these surveys, the soil is described in very broad terms such as "urban land," "human-made," or "disturbed," without any reference to the soil profile of these urban soils. Without the soil profile, soil is effectively returned to its origin as geology.

23 For an excellent paper on the soil a cemetery makes, see: Przemysław Charzyński, Renata Bednarek and Beata Solnowska, "Characteristics of the Soils of Toruń cemeteries," (paper presented at the Nineteenth "World Congress of Soil Science, Soil Solutions for a Changing World," Brisbane, Australia, 2010).

24 All figures from Alexandra Harker, "Landscapes of the Dead: An Argument for Conservation Burial," *Berkeley Planning Journal* 25, no. 1 (2012): 150–159.

25 Mercury figures from A. Hart and S. Casper, "Potential Groundwater Pollutants from Cemeteries," *Science Report*, (December 2004): 29–35.

26 All soil descriptions from New York City Soil Survey Staff, *New York City Reconnaissance Soil Survey*, Soil Survey, Staten Island, NY (United States Department of Agriculture Natural Resources Conservation Service, 2005).

Episodes from a History of Scalelessness

by Adam Bobbette

William Jerome Harrison and Geological Photography

H.T. Hildage, "Mining Operations in New York City and Vicinity," in *Transactions of the American Institute of Mining Engineers* (New York: Institute of Mining Engineers, 1908), 392, Fig. 18.

Fig. 01

> *If we now put the question, how we are to explain the riddle that by means of such illogical, indeed senseless concepts, correct results are to be obtained, the answer lies in what we found to be the general law of fictions, namely in the correction of the errors that have been committed.*

—Han Vaihinger, *The Philosophy of 'As If'* (1924)

The ponderance of temporal scale is foundational for any consideration of the Anthropocene thesis. As we know, this thesis would demarcate our epoch on that imprecise though pervasively referenced scale called "geological time," which renders sensible an earthly duration from the outer limits of the conceivable. This essay pursues such limits by considering several of the technical and poetic practices by which they were explored in the late nineteenth and early twentieth centuries.

These practices have, to borrow Latour's term, "translated" the vast temporality of the geologic, typically by way of a spatial translation into the hardness of stone or, for instance, the gradations of erosion.[1] However, as with any translation, remainders persist. The literary apparatus will provide our first brief encounter with this remainder.

Fig. 02 G. Bingley, *Baldersby Park, near Thirsk. Large Boulder of Carboniferous Grit*, 1891. Courtesy of the British Geological Survey

In Lewis Carroll's 1876 nonsense poem *The Hunting of the Snark (An Agony in 8 Fits)* we are told of a nautical crew in search of an inconceivable creature. At sea, the Bellman, provides the crew with the following directions: a blank map. It is the ocean, he claims. "And the crew were much pleased when they found it to be / A map they could all understand / What's the good of Mercator's North Poles and Equators / Tropics, Zones, and Meridian Lines?" / So the Bellman would cry: and the crew would reply / "They are merely conventional signs!" As a map, it is a "perfect and absolute blank," the form most appropriate for translating the ocean's content as a vast undoing of direction, position, and scale.[2]

What the Bellman does to the ocean, Virginia Woolf applies to the body: "We are edged with mist. We make an unsubstantial territory," she writes.[3] The first chapter of *The Waves* (1931) depicts a morning as the frenzied, excessive minutiae of the world begin wiggling together into a whir. A faucet begins to run; "Mrs. Constable pulls up her thick black stockings"; a door unlocks; the church bell rings, once at first, then again; a sauce pan crackles with oil. Louis, one of the characters, is left suddenly alone in the garden and his scale begins to transform. He stands looking at the grass under his feet becoming an ocean of green. He holds and then becomes the stem of a flower, but longer and deeper. He presses into the earth, passing mines of lead and silver. "I am all fibre. All tremors shake me, and the weight of the earth is pressed to my ribs. Up here my eyes are green leaves, unseeing." But, "down there my eyes are the lidless eyes of a stone figure in a desert by the Nile. I see women passing with red pitchers to the river; I see camels swaying and men in turbans. I hear trampling's, trembling's, stirrings round me." A parental yell from the house causes him to return to his recognizable form.[4]

And, again, in 1931: "Où est l'homme qui n'a pas exploré en esprit la nature abyssale?" ["Where is the man who has not explored the abyssal nature of the mind?"][5] Paul Valéry's *Cahiers* incessantly return to the territory of the insubstantial to which he often arrives through this particular scene: the telescoping of the world's detail as the body moves through space. Each thing we see is a one-sided surface hiding an infinity of details that expands and contracts according to our changing positions and their relations to each other. Valery's paintings and drawings dwell on this very schema through an endless unravelling of the same objects. For instance, in one painting an island is pictured as a lump, in another, the same island becomes a geology of crisp, defined perimeters.[6] Scale snaps the world in and out of focus, while the insubstantial is at the edge, on the backside, and in the recesses of every scene.

Fifty years later, we return to the Bellman's boat. In *A Thousand Plateaus*, Gilles Deleuze and Félix Guattari adapt Carroll's image of the sea as "the archetype of smooth space."[7] Deleuze and Guattari devote this plateau to describing the smooth space of the sea and the various iterations it has afforded science, mathematics, art, and philosophy—each encounter either proliferating or evading its menacing qualities. In one memorable example, they offer an explication of the image of Wacław Sierpiński's puzzling sponge: a cube precisely hollowed out by smaller cubes. Each cube is surrounded by eight cubes a third the size of the larger one; each smaller cube is similarly surrounded in turn by a constellation of eight other smaller cubes. "It is plain to see," they suggest, "that this cube is in the end infinitely hollow. It's total volume approaches zero, while the total lateral surface of the hollowings infinitely grows."[8] The authors included an image of this cube. It is an impossible image in that it attempts to represent all that it is not. It is an infinite, scaleless object; it is an arresting of the object unfolding across countless scales. The image appears through, departs from, and returns to its own scalelessness like an infinite circuit.

These four episodes, spanning a century of curiosity about the inexorable problem of scale, might be productively aggregated to initiate a fictional history of scalelessness. What can we find in common among them? From even this cursory collection, two important characteristics are evidently given: the unconventionality of direction and the withering of boundaries that could determine a location. Spatial coordinates disappear into an unfathomable depth in Carroll; the body expands beyond its corporeal limits in Woolf; discrete objects lose their definition in Valéry; surface and depth become hollow in Deleuze and Guattari. In each, time and space are manifestly and corporeally infinite. That is, for each of these poetic concretions, the infinite becomes materialized and actual. Could there be other qualities of scalelessness constructed by different literatures? Can we see, at particular historical moments, more or less of a concern with this perplexing experience of scale? Is the confusion of scale intertwined with some particular historical phenomena, a reaction to something off stage? No less problematic than such queries are the definitional limitations when considering such a fictional history. How does scalelessness relate to concepts of void, the negative, or nothingness? Are these concepts each a way of describing the same experience of the irresolvable within their particular metaphysical configuration? In what follows, I attempt to open this history, engage some of these troubling questions, and trace some of the contours

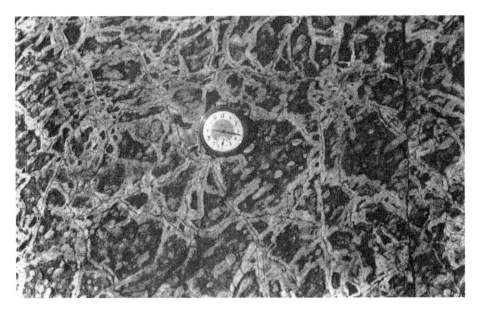

of scalelessness by examining a single case study comprised of a series of photographs. My approach is neither exhaustive nor definitive; instead, it is an attempt to open up a history of poetic vexation through a focused analysis of the image of scale itself.

The photographs were taken in 1886 by the geologist and photographer William Jerome Harrison, admittedly a minor figure in the history of geology, and an even less significant contributor to the history of photography. But these particular, unstudied photographs—all taken on the same day by this doubly minor character—are of interest because they appear to be the first specimens of a new type of image: photographs of everyday objects and rocks. No humans appear in these images, only manufactured objects and rocks: pocket knives, watches, hammers, basalt, granite, flint. If the manufactured objects had not appeared in the photographs, the rocks would appear without scale, the rocks could be read by observers just as easily as images of mountains or pebbles. This type of photograph would proliferate in the twentieth century as geologists began to regularly incorporate photography into their practice. But long before this trend emerged, Harrison's photographs stand out as the first series of compositions to remove humans from the frame of the image and replace them with objects. Through this act, as the camera moves toward the technological destiny of the "close-up," a quality of scalelessness is both subtly produced and carefully negotiated. This nimble encounter is what we can now examine in detail.

Nineteenth-century geology is an especially intriguing moment of investigation when cultivating a history of scalelessness. Its practitioners were deeply concerned with the nature of temporal and spatial scales and the possibility of experiencing the eventualities of deep time that verged on infinity. Geologists, including Harrison, were eager to account for how processes distributed over vast distances could be made legible by singular, localized marks and signs. The absolutely "scaleless" is a limit which their science must constantly negotiate; it is likewise a limit that Harrison's work, both photographic and geological, necessarily occupies and navigates. However, these images are worthy of consideration for an additional reason. For Harrison, both photography and geology are constituted by similar processes. The technical and the geological are entangled with one another, and the human artifacts that populate his photographs are similarly imbricated in these processes as well. To be entangled is not to come away from a relation unaffected but contaminated. What Harrison thus contributes to the history of scalelessness is the use of scale itself as a medium to create improbable and unexpected entanglements among technical, geological, and human registers.

Not surprisingly, the history of scale is more easily assembled than that of the scaleless. For instance, the architectural linear scale bar, which is related to the linear scale on maps, is a technology that locks objects into a fixed spatial relation so that they can be translated from two to three-dimensional space. It appears at the intersection of the history of metric systems (and more broadly, systems of divisible numbers) and the production of precision instruments. While there are numerous examples of different types of rods and staffs used by builders, cartographers, and sailors to determine base units and translate size accurately across scales, it is not until the eighteenth century that the dramatic increase in the production of precision instruments for determining scale finally occurs. According to Pyenson and Sheets-Pyenson, this technological trajectory was driven by the new desire for accuracy that determined both the production of scientific instruments, the machines that made them, and how these instruments read the world. They write, "With Jesse Ramsden's [...] dividing engine at the close of the eighteenth century, unusually precise scales could be turned out in great quantities. These were the scientific equivalent of mass-produced metal pots and pans at the dawn of the First Industrial Revolution."[9] The metric system of calculation, through which mutually agreed upon base units assure a smooth transition across scales in powers of ten, was adopted throughout France in 1799 and became the standard grammar of measurement for engineering and architecture, which spoke its exactitude through manipulations in both landscape and building architecture.

William Jerome Harrison's photographic and geological work is heavily influenced by this history of accuracy; it can be seen in his use of the instruments and conventions of precision, such as the scaled map, and through his advocacy for the visual accuracy of photography. However, his work also exceeds such a narrow preoccupation with accuracy. He was a nineteenth-century polymath who spent much of his life in Leicester and Birmingham, travelling extensively within the region to document its geology. He taught and developed the science curriculum at the Birmingham school board and, in 1877, published *A Sketch of the Geology of Leicestershire and Rutland*.[10] In 1888, he published the *History of Photography*. Both photography and geology were still relatively new inventions at the time, and Harrison was one of the earliest to integrate the two, as well as consider the implications of both practices upon one another; for him, they were two distinct but fundamentally related trajectories.

In *History of Photography*, Harrison characterizes the protagonists of the art form as apprentices of impressions. According to his assessment, "impressioning" is a process as ancient as the tanning of human skin under the sun, or the bleaching of wax by the sun. In each case, the sun has created an impression on a body. For Harrison, this was the earliest and most basic form of photography. Such a logic would also extend to Fabricius' observations in the seventeenth century that mined silver and chlorine compounds would turn black when left in the sun, and necessarily include Charles' 1780 anecdote suggesting he "obtained profiles of the heads of his students by placing them so that the required shadow of the features was cast by a strong beam of sunlight upon a sheet of paper coated with chloride of silver."[11] However, this fine art of impressions enters its most crucial historical period, according to Harrison, with the emergence of the *camera obscura*. Developed by John Baptista Porta in the middle of the sixteenth century, the *camera obscura* was a darkened room with a single "window shutter" through which an inverted image from outside was projected by sunlight onto a white wall. Porta later added double convex glass lenses to the aperture and fixed a mirror outside to brighten and sharpen the image.[12]

When the *camera obscura* was combined with the chemical experiments of Nicéphore Niépce, the enclosure allowed for a greater control of sunlight's contact with impressive media. Niépce, the under-celebrated collaborator of Daguerre, discovered the "bitumen process in photography in 1825."[13] For Harrison, Niépce's experiments entangle the geological enterprise with the combined architectural history of the *camera obscura* and the use and control of lighting conditions. Niépce studied lithographic forms of image reproduction, the geological implications of which are evident: *litho* is Greek for stone, and *lithography* is the process of imprinting an image onto a stone. In the eighteenth and nineteenth centuries, it was common to use limestone as the substance best suited for receiving such impressions. Niépce considered, radically, that light could be substituted for human labour as the agent for copying images into stone. To transfer an image from a sheet of paper to a limestone surface, he first covered the limestone in a layer of bitumen, then laid the image on top and exposed it to sunlight. When exposed to light, the bitumen hardens, creating a positive imprint of the image on the surface of the stone. Niépce moved on from limestone to working with metals such as tin, and later integrated the *camera obscura* in the process, placing metal sheets covered in bitumen in the interior of his small *camera obscura*: "When exposed to the action of the light forming the picture within a camera, the bitumen became insoluble in proportion to the intensity of the light by which the various parts of the image were produced, an effect which we now know to be due to the oxidation, and consequent hardening of this resinous substance."[14] The solubility of the bitumen on the surface created a new kind of physical landscape on the surface of the metal by fusing a stratum of bitumen to the metal. This process was named heliography—literally, "sun writing." The only one of Niépce's heliographs still in existence is a landscape portrait.

Harrison reads photography according to the residues of deep time contained within it; while the photograph may appear as a new technical entity, it is in reality an intensification of very old physical processes. His materialist disposition led him to tell the history of photography as a natural history rather than a history of signification or representation, as one might encounter in aesthetic or technical accounts. For Harrison, the contemporary photograph is a long accumulated history of the entanglements between techniques and material relations. The photographer is an apprentice to impressions enabled by the technical-material apparatus of the camera, plate, chemicals and light. This conception of impressions remarkably approximates another natural process, namely, that of fossilization. If fossilization is the impression of softer organisms onto harder geological forms, then photography is its modern, mediated extension. It is the impression of gradations of light and shadow onto stone, metallic, or glass surfaces—themselves the elder products of geologicial forces. This new technology is written back into the earth's deep history. Yet such a reading is not, for Harrison, a way of naturalizing photography by wiping away its embeddedness in social relations or remove it from history by making it immemorial; it is instead a means to place the photograph deep within the history of the earth, and conversely, to treat the earth as a source of invention through the entanglements of form and matter.

Harrison's estimation of geology is made remarkably clear in his *Geology of the Counties of England and of North and South Wales* (1882). It was published only a few years before his history of photography and declares many of his speculative interests. In addition to his history of photography as the art of impressions, his reading of geological time as it appears in the *Geology* lays the conceptual groundwork for his photographs of objects and rocks. The *Geology* is first and foremost an encyclopedic compendium of existing geological knowledge; it does not claim to be a presentation of new research. Its comprehensive scope is aimed at a mixed audience of both novices and experts, and it seems as though Harrison imagined a copy of the book in every British household as a way to anchor the specificity of their place within a broader narrative of geological time and transformation. In over 400 pages, the *Geology* accounts for every county of England and Wales in its topographical uniqueness and its deepest physical recesses. It covers the changes and re-arrangements of the ground from its distant past to its arrival in the present. The landscape becomes the physical inscription of deep time, both the result of and generator of change. It is the unthinkable immensity of time made legible and inhabitable. For Harrison, "it is certain that our earth is of exceeding antiquity," and, in fact, "we believe in its great age because the evidence given by the rocks reveals changes, for whose accomplishment periods of time would be required, which we may attempt to estimate in figures, but whose real significance the human mind can scarcely appreciate."[15] Even with such a caveat, Harrison remains convinced that reading, and thus appreciating, the landscape should not be restricted to specialists. In fact, while much of his research, he admits, freely builds upon and extends the work of the National Geological Survey—which was still in progress across the country at the time of the publication of *Geology*—it is his unique vocation to gather the results of this work and make them available to a non-specialist audience.

Harrison's conception of the landscape presented in the *Geology* is the impression of a temporal and spatial scalelessness. While Harrison tends to assume a distinction between the fossil and the ground or landscape that contains it, his theory of impression simultaneously begins to undo such a distinction. When he cites Charles Lyell's well-known definition of a fossil as "any body, or the traces of the existence of any body, whether animal or vegetable, which has been buried in the earth by natural causes," there is an assumption that a rock or a mineral cannot, as such, be such a body.[16] However, there is evidence in both Lyell and Harrison that they understand mineralization and the formation of rocks to be made of vegetable masses, or the deep compressions of gasses, liquids, and solids under the surface of the earth. The fossil is no longer an object contained in a rock; within this logic, it becomes the entirety of the earth itself—the fossil is necessarily that which we inhabit and that which we read. The landscape crosses over to the order of the photograph, and vice versa; each an impression, each a fossil. But where light creates the impression that constitutes the form of the photograph, the form of the landscape is co-produced by the infinity of temporal and spatial scales impressed into the crevices, holes, uplifts, and protrusions over which we pass and climb, and through which we burrow.

Fig. 04   William Jerome Harrison, *Sheringham Beach. Paramoudra in Chalk*, 1886. Courtesy of the British Geological Survey

Fig. 05   William Jerome Harrison, *Beeston Beach. Paramoudra*, 1886. Courtesy of the British Geological Survey

The archives of the British Geological Survey contain a series of thirteen photographs, dated 1 January 1886, which Harrison took at Sheringham Beach, Norfolk. This is the series that signals the emergence of a new form of geological photography: it includes the appearance of everyday, banal objects as scale devices. Prior to this series, human beings had been ghostly inhabitants of geological photographs, their bodies providing a scale device. However, here the close-ups of the camera capture geologic impressions at a scale too detailed for the presence of a human figure. Within geological photography this type of image does not become commonplace until some years later, largely due to the delayed uptake of the practice by field geologists. Cameras were often too cumbersome to carry on expeditions, and exposure time too lengthy to be practical. In the late nineteenth century, geological photography largely followed the conventions of landscape painting, and was mostly practiced by colonial explorers only partially familiar or interested in the emerging field of geology. By the early twentieth century, however, this type of photograph could be considered a common place in geological photography and a minor genre within photographic history; humans were replaced with a plethora of different objects in, on, or around rocks: small handbags, hammers, pocket watches, knives, picks, etc. Geologists on the hunt for resources, for instance, would photograph a small sachet, likely holding samples, or money, sitting on the shaft wall. Other photos were taken from a pit in the earth's surface, where a small pickaxe leans on clumps of dirt. What is uncertain in these photographs is their subject: is it the object or the rocks? Rarely appearing as a mere background, the objects are given an equal compositional treatment to the geology. For instance, a small bag or a watch sit on top of a pile of rocks, a hammer shares the middle ground with the rock it leans on. Nothing in the image signifies a hierarchy of subjects. This hierarchy could only emerge through the invocation of the scale as parerga, a device subservient (and self-effacing) to guaranteeing the realism of the image, just as a scale bar on a map is only partially part implicated in the image, without sharing the status of the map itself.[17] While this tradition asserts a strong conviction, a closer investigation of Harrison's photos reveals a strong sense that the sacks, hammers, and umbrellas in his photographs are lousy at effacement. They persist as productive remainders.

From the January 1st series, two photographs stand out. They are both of peculiar, taurus-shaped flint formations called Paramoudras. [Figs. 04 & 05] Quoting Lyell again in the *Geology*, Harrison describes the Paramoudra as "often hollow, and [they] seem to have been formed by the accumulation of flint around gigantic decaying sponges."[18] How the flint could have gained its form is only imprecisely described. The photographs show the smooth surfaces of the Paramoudras bulged and cracking. In one photo, a small hammer leans against a well-formed Paramoudra set within a field of cracked bits and pieces of other Paramadouras. It is clear that it is on the threshold of a shoreline: on the left is an accumulation of rounder stones leading towards land, while to the right the ground is more advanced in its erosion and moist from the tide. The split surface of the Paramadoura reveals a darkened, thick interior. The fore-grounded Taurus stands out from the others as a more complete formation in a field of pieces that blend into the distance of the dark, wet beach stones and sand. The threshold between beach and ocean that creates the central axis of the photo is a threshold between relative rates of erosion. It suggests the gradual deformation of the rounded stones into the mud and sand that the ocean carries away, stirs up, and deposits. It is "in this way," he says later on, that "the whole coast is receding." The sea, he notes, "by dashing

Fig. 06   William Jerome Harrison, *W. of Sheringham. Pinnacle of Chalk, embedded in drift,* 1886. Courtesy of the British Geological Survey

against the base of the cliffs, using as missiles the fallen stones, rapidly undermines them, when the upper part falls and is swept away by the waves: the spring slowing along the junction of pervious beds (sands) with impervious ones (clays) loosens the adhesion of the beds and the upper part slides down on to the beach."[19] The erosion of the landscape from the coast—by rain and wind—both impresses the land into its shape while simultaneously exposing the layers of geological strata which could identify the history of its making. Naturally, the very same process that gives shape also deforms. In its deformation, the coastal landscape reveals layers of sea shells, uncovers ancient tools, and exposes settlements of communities whose organization and culture Harrison and others would speculate on. It reveals ancient water courses and the plants and animals that fed on them. Erosion both impresses and loosens, or more correctly, impresses in its loosening. Foregrounded by this deep temporality of impressioning is the paramoudra: Is it too a fossil? Lyell suggests that massive, ancient sponges gave them their form; from his perspective, and as difficult as it is to imagine, they are the negative of a mysterious, missing animal. Additionally, the photograph of the Paramoudra is an impression on a glass plate, a higher order of impression than the sponge's impression in the Paramoudra, but fundamentally related. This is a photograph of fossils nested within fossils.

The hammer touching the right side of the Paramoudra connects it to the ground, and the ground to it, while the hammer itself is the connection between its metal head and wooden handle. There is nothing in the photo to suggest the usefulness of the hammer in the scene, no wood or nails, no construction, only shattered pieces of Paramoudra. It could be that the background has been broken as a comparative specimen to the foreground. We can also understand that the hammer, too, is a fossil, poised beside other fossils, found among the debris of the shore. Undoubtedly, it is placed in an uncertain relation with them, neither better or worse, nor more or less advanced, just touching, bridging two materialities in different states of the same process of erosion and exposure. As a fossil, the hammer is the impression of the machinic processes that formed both the wood and metal head, just as it is the impression of the person (perhaps Harrison) who placed it in the picture. Rather than a scale which would allow us to translate the accurate size of the objects in the scene, the hammer is an object poised in relation to the story of impressions and fossilization found on the beach and in the act of taking a photograph.

Another photograph from the same day shows three different exposed geological layers in a cross section. [Fig. 06] The cross section is one of the most preferred projections for stratified layers, according to the common way rock layers become exposed to the surface—either through geological forces such as uplift, or engineered exposures such as road or rail cutting. Roughly in the centre of this sectional photograph is an upright, closed umbrella leaning against a small patch of withered, scraggly grass. The different layers of rock are noticeable both through the different scales of their aggregates and their consistency. The top and bottom layers are the finer and more fragile, while the central layer contains denser, and what appear to be different, materials, slowly exposed by the erosion of the cliffs. Like the hammer, the umbrella connects different conditions within the geological strata while signaling the human. Also, like the hammer, nothing tells us that this umbrella was not also found by Harrison. Nor is the umbrella simply standing in for scale; it becomes part of the portrait. It does not disappear like a linear scale, but instead insists on becoming part of the photographic assemblage. Here we can detect the logic of material entanglements in the Anthropocene: semi-autonomous trajectories, which, at particular junctures, interfere with each other, and through their affective interference, co-produce events and their extended realities. The human artifact of the umbrella, like the hammer, is captured by the logic of the fossil, no longer set apart but instead entangled in the geological scene. The process of fossilization, as a process of impressioning, thus becomes a way of conceiving relations among the human object, the photographic apparatus, and geology. The umbrella that appears without its human figure, and like the dark, linear band in the centre of the image, becomes another geological strata.

There is in Harrison's series a photograph which at first sight has no object or identifying feature that could indicate the proper scale of the rocks. Three layers of strata are identified, although the image appears scaleless. It is difficult to tell if one is looking at a large landscape from above or at something the size of a human hand. It is equally possible to imagine cities nestled into the crevices of the rock, or a footprint crossing it. Yet, even if Harrison had placed an object in the frame of the image, it would still not resolve the scale. Rather, it would entangle another scale, further complicating the relations among scales. It would not produce accuracy, but enfold the object within the logic of the actualization of scaleless time and scaleless space produced by Harrison's geology and photography. As such, the scalelessness pursued in Harrison's work is not defined by an absolute dissolution of boundaries and direction, but follows a different course. It is an accumulation of fossilized impressions expanding in space and time.

Notes

1 Bruno Latour, *Reassembling the Social: An Introduction to Actor-Network-Theory* (Oxford: Oxford University Press, 2005).

2 Lewis Carroll, *The Hunting of the Snark: An Agony in Eight Fits* (London: Methuen, 2000), 45.

3 Virginia Woolf, *Jacobs's Room and The Waves* (New York: Harvest Books, 1967), 9.

4 Ibid., 7–9.

5 Paul Valéry, "Pièces sur l'art," *Oeuvres, Vol. II* (Paris: Gallimard, 1960), 1336. See also Paul Ryan, "Paul Valéry: Visual Perception and an Aesthetics of Landscape Space," *Australian Journal of French Studies* 45, no. 1 (Jan/Apr 2008): 43–58.

6 Paul Veléry, *Notebooks*, ed. Brian Stimpson, (Frankfurt am Main: Peter Lang, 2000). See in particular vols. X, XIX, XX, and C.

7 Gilles Deleuze and Félix Guattari, *A Thousand Plateaus*, trans. Brian Massumi (Minnesota: University of Minnesota Press, 1987), 474–499.

8 Ibid., 487.

9 Lewis Pyenson and Susan Sheets-Pyenson, *Servants of Nature: A History of Scientific Institutions, Enterprises, and Sensibilities* (New York: W.W. Norton, 1999), 186.

10 Bill Jay, "William Jerome Harrison 1845-1909: Brief Notes on One of the Earliest Photographic Historians," *The British Journal of Photography* (9 January 1987).

11 William Jerome Harrison, *A History of Photography Written as a Practical Guide and Introduction to its Latest Developments* (London: Trubner & Co., 1888), 7–12.

12 Ibid., 13–20.

13 Ibid., 21–27.

14 Ibid., 17.

15 William Jerome Harrison, *Geology of the Counties of England and of North and South Wales* (London: Kelly & Co., 1882), v.

16 Ibid., xiii.

17 Jacques Derrida, *The Truth in Painting*, trans. Geoff Bennington and Ian McLeod (Chicago: University of Chicago Press, 1987).

18 William Jerome Harrison, *Geology of the Counties of England and of North and South Wales* (London: Kelly & Co., 1882), 188.

19 Ibid., 191.

Inquiries and Interpretations Concerning the Observations and Findings from Atmosphere-Investigating, Landscape-Exploring, Universe-Tracking Instruments, Their Experiments, Studies, etc.[1] (2012)

Emily Cheng

Mixed Media

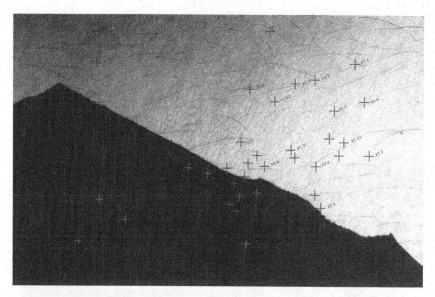

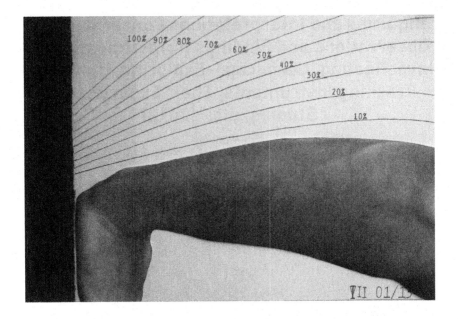

Originally constructed in 1905, the Dominion Observatory in Ottawa was Canada's primary reference for time measurement. By tracking the movements of the Sun relative to the Earth, a construction of time was determined and dictated to the country. The observatory closed in 1974 when its duties were succeeded by the more precise atomic clock. The shift from astronomical observations to the atomic clock meant a shift from an ontologically continuous experience to an analogical one. The observatory was abandoned because its technological functions were no longer needed. However, as Siegfried Gideon and Lewis Mumford have both noted, with the demands of pure functionality comes the risk of only *operating* technology, rather than also experiencing it. The distinction between pure functionality and the pleasure of experience recalls architecture's enduring goal of balancing utilitarian and hedonistic human tendencies. Meanwhile, the distinction between a model of nature and nature itself brings to mind the discipline's ongoing attempt to build reality from representation. The proposal for the observatory is a reformulation of the relationship between experience and abstraction; its instruments operate by registering the physicality of nature and demonstrating this process as a scientific abstraction. Through their operations, these instruments permit different interpretations of the architecture of the observatory and its consequences.

Notes

1   This title pays homage, through appropriation, to the artist Leah Beeferman.

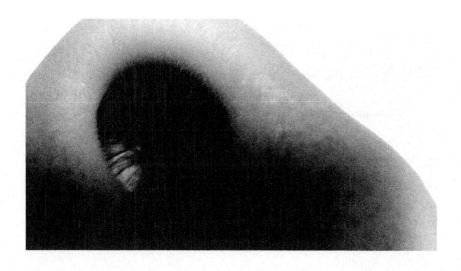

Wind Rose De-Abstractuator

The observatory is notorious for being in one of the windiest areas in Ottawa. Monthly wind rose diagrams for the area are translated into a 12-storey staircase, each step aligned with a cardinal direction in plan. Fine leather lashings are hung from the metal grating of the steps and translate the wind directly onto the skin of the user.

Magnetic Meridian Fluctuator

The Canadian Prime Meridian is made tangible with a row of magnetic benches that can be pivoted to momentarily break the longitudinal line. The benches oscillate between true north and magnetic north.

Inverted Telescopic Solar Magnifier & Tracker

The disused observatory telescope is inverted to magnify the solar rays back into the building to melt the installed wax surfaces. The result is an accumulation of effects that render solar movements sensuous and inhabitable.

Zone of Intermittent Saturation Registrator

The copper dome of the former photo-equatorial building is inverted to funnel rain into a cellulose sponge that stretches down into the water table. Users circulate through the sponge's cavities, which shrink and expand in response to the surrounding saturation levels.

Micro-seismic / Micro-tremor Periscoping Amplifier

Micro-seisms and micro-tremors, normally imperceptible to humans, are registered by geophones and amplified through an eight-sided periscopic enclosure with spring-mounted mirrors that visually vibrate the surrounding buildings.

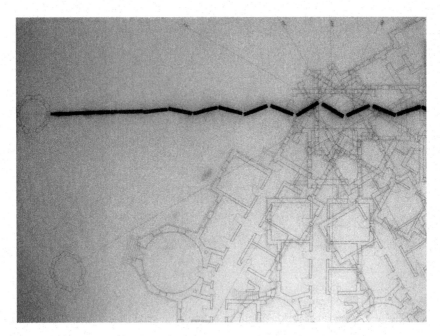

Matters of Calculation

Eyal Weizman in Conversation with Heather Davis and Etienne Turpin[1]

The Evidence of the Anthropocene

The *Guardian* recently reported that the US has set up a predator drone base just outside of Niamey, Niger, extending its surveillance regime while providing another base for extra-judicial killings and internationalized terror.[2] Meanwhile, US Secretary of State John Kerry is trying to reinvigorate peace talks between Israel and Palestine amidst rumours of a new intifada and renewed rocket fire from Gaza. To confront these and similar realities without accepting their terms as given, Eyal Weizman's work as an architect, professor, theorist, and activist addresses the use of systems of surveillance, mapping, NGOs, and international human rights law. His ongoing work and collaborations with artists, architects, and theorists in Forensic Architecture (FA), the Decolonizing Architecture Art Residency (DAAR), and the Centre for Research Architecture (CRA), navigate current political economic realities through a direct engagement with, and elaboration of, incommensurable positions. Weizman's concept of forensic architecture analyzes the contradictory role of critical thought within international humanitarian law, using the tools of journalistic investigation and conceptual theorization that remain, perpetually, co-constitutive of his practice. In both his writing and ongoing architecture projects, Weizman demonstrates that the division between amelioration and revolution is false; instead, his practice shows that we must learn to negotiate intense and radical contradictions in order to restructure our political reality. He insists on a political strategy that names specific individuals for their culpability in the deaths of others in ongoing colonial and frontier wars, while at the same time articulating the ways in which force, materials, and nonhuman actors diffuse and exacerbate these differential conditions. Weizman and his wide network of collaborators use counter-surveillance methods and the figure-ground relation as the beginning of a new topological articulation, linking cracks in architecture to geological fissures, within the field of immanent power.

Heather Davis & Etienne Turpin Perhaps a good place to begin is with your agile reading of the sequence of disasters that constitute the itinerary of Voltaire's *Candide* (1759). From our position in the humanities, we know that the epoch of the European Enlightenment was not universally celebrated; in fact, Voltaire's ridicule of Liebniz's theological optimism—wherein the best of all possible worlds was guaranteed by a divine calculus that permitted forms of destructive evil in order to optimize the invisible and mysterious good occurring elsewhere—is a key to understanding the violence of this period. Although less subject to ridicule, but certainly no less pernicious, is the contemporary condition wherein the optimal forms of destruction called for by new standards of international humanitarian law shield criminal perpetrators whose precise violence increases alongside the suffering of those oppressed by calculated violence, coercion, and collective punishments. What led you to return to Voltaire's critique of Leibniz? And how does this metaphysical disposition persist in what you call the "humanitarian present"?

Eyal Weizman It might be interesting to start this conversation with a little thought experiment. How would we, if we could, intervene in the "debate" between Leibniz, Rousseau, and Voltaire, about the meaning of the 1755 Lisbon earthquake (which is alluded to in the best-known part of *Candide*) from the point of view of the Anthropocene? Leibniz's theodicy was of course used (he was already dead when the earthquake struck) to explain this disaster as the result of a divine calculus that forever generates an optimal/optimist "best of all possible worlds." Voltaire mocked him and this concept, arguing instead that natural phenomena—which are never benign—could be better explained by rational science. Writing in a rather cheeky tone in reaction to Voltaire's response to his poem on Lisbon, the young Rousseau came to the defense of nature, using the earthquake to rehearse his argument against cities—he particularly faulted Lisbon's density—as part of his quest for a "return to nature." So, if we were to intervene rather gently in the controversy, we could start by giving some support to Rousseau: we know now that after the earthquake a tidal wave was created that broke through the embankments that fortified, and therefore made less porous, the edges of the Rio Tejo. It is this aspect of the earthquake that brought devastation to the dense dockyards and buildings that had proliferated in direct proportion to increased colonial wars and trade based in the port. When these waterways and buildings collapsed, fire broke out in several districts, multiplying the death toll. However, rather than aggravating the divide between a corrupt humanity and a benevolent nature, as Rousseau tried to do, we can see the Lisbon event as perhaps the first message from the Anthropocene, occurring, in fact, a quarter century before Paul Crutzen's date of origin.[3] In this conception, human action and what insurance companies still call "acts of god" are entangled on a planetary-scale construction site.

But we could also intervene in qualified support for Leibniz. Yes, our world is also described and thought to be controlled by an endless calculus, but this calculation is not undertaken by God alone; rather, it is aided by an increasingly complex bureaucracy of calculations that include sensors in the subsoil, terrain, air, and sea, all processed by algorithms and their attendant models. This reality might necessitate a different ethico-political response, as well as a different conception of universality not built on leveling the difference between cultures and people, but one that would also include the ocean. And, just to follow the circuit of polite discussions—we are among the pantheon of the Enlightenment after all—we could say something in support of Voltaire. Don't forget that, as a repost to Pangloss's Leibnizian mantra of all the best in the best of all possible worlds, Voltaire concluded *Candide* with "we must cultivate our garden." Now the garden is the size of the planet.

So, to answer your question more seriously now, what led me to return to Voltaire, and Lisbon, is the relation between calculus and disaster. It is a relation of crisis that we can see in so many fields now, from a humanitarianism that seeks to calculate the least of all possible evils (as war-making is reduced to acting on calculations of immanent risk) to financial speculation. In these fields and many others, instruments designed to reduce risk—derivatives, targeted killings, humanitarian aid—end up amplifying it exponentially.

HD&ET How has your thinking and approach to the neocolonial occupation of Palestine by Israel changed over time? We are particularly interested in the movement of your thought from *Hollow Land* (2007) and its elaboration of "political plastic" to your more recent development of forensic architecture in *The Least of All Possible Evils* (2011), *Forensic Architecture* (2012), and *Mengele's Skull* (2012), where the subject as witness is being replaced and surpassed by an emergent forensic sensibility, an object-oriented juridical culture. How much of this movement is influenced by the changing situation itself?

EW I think the latter works are to a certain extent a set of methodological reflections on *Hollow Land*. I had to find the language to understand—and it took some time and effort—in what ways materiality and territoriality participate in shaping conflict, rather than simply being shaped by it. *Hollow Land* was already structured around various material things at different scales, so the logic of a kind of forensic investigation was already present there. I guess I was personally attracted to the investigative intensity in forensics, less to the legal context in which its findings are presented, which are oftentimes quite skewed, especially in an international legal context, as I showed in the latest books. As well, the shift from *Hollow Land* to *The Least of All Possible Evils* also marks a shift in my attention from the West Bank to Gaza. This has obviously been shaped by events. In Gaza, one can notice a system of rule based on humanitarian violence, a form of control that operates through the calculation and modulation of life-sustaining supplies, the application of standards of the humanitarian minimum, and the seeming conduct of war by human rights (HR) and international humanitarian law (IHL) principles. So some of my attention shifted from the mechanisms of territorial control to "humanitarian" government. Although, of course, materiality is a fundamental category in the latter book, albeit in a different way, as I tried to show how it activates law and its forums through forensics.

In any case, the investigation that culminated in my recent work started with a certain refusal of spatial research methodologies, commonly held at the time, derived mainly from certain readings of Henri Lefebvre. I thought they needed a more dynamic, elastic, topological, and force-field-oriented understanding of space, as well as an understanding of the immanent power of constant interaction between force and form. Across what I describe as the "political plastic," space is continuously in transformation—political forces slowing into form. I tried to describe war as a dynamic process of space-making. Frontier colonization is a slowed-down war, but still very elastic; the frontier is very different from a city like Paris, which has figured as *the* imaginary for a lot of spatial theory and thus often misplaced and applied to the frontier. Paris is a planned city, a very hard city, and its hardness has haunted the imagination of some spatial scholars studying very different realities today. I thought we had to get rid of Paris to liberate Palestine. And then I kept pushing toward the idea of immanent materiality on different scales; not only on the scale of the territory, but on a micro-scale, through an analysis of details and substances—water, fields, forests, hills, valleys—which all play a role in shaping conflicts, and therefore have an effect on the forensic imagination.

So, to refer to an idea you brought up in our earlier conversation, the idea of "elasticity," or what you called "plasticity"—ending at a moment of a bomb blast—I would say that I think that a blast is simply an acceleration of relations of force and form in the same way that wars in the city are an actualization and acceleration of the latent and slower processes of conflict and negotiation that define urban life and every form of development in the city. I think it is more interesting to think of the continuities between elasticities and explosions than about the differences. I was working very closely with analysts of bomb blast sites, and you see millisecond by millisecond—there is a description of this in the last chapter of the *Lesser Evil* book—what happens to a building when it is bombed. It is like taking on 15 years of gradual disintegration, which is what every building is undergoing from the moment it is built, in 5 milliseconds.

HD&ET So what you have called "the pyramids of Gaza" are just the sped-up force of the "natural" collapse of a building?[4]

EW The destruction of refugee houses has generated the pyramids of Gaza. There are many pyramids throughout the strip, mainly in the camps and neighbourhoods that ring Gaza City and along the short border with Egypt. They are a new typology that has emerged out of the encounter between a three-storey residential building, of the kind that provides a home for refugees, and an armored Caterpillar D9 bulldozer. The short shovel of the bulldozer can destroy only the columns closer to the façade of the building, but the single centre column is left intact, and it makes the peak of the pyramid. The fact that the centre column remains is what makes this new type of ruin; it is important because one can actually enter the ruin itself—very carefully—as some forensic architects have done. There are irregularities that register differences in the process of construction, the uneven spread of concrete, or the various modes of destruction, such as the inability or reluctance of the bulldozer operator to go completely around the building. A particular irregularity could be the result of a previous firefight, for example. The task is obviously to connect the differences in the patterns of destruction of concrete to the general process of war—or in this case, an attack on Gaza—to connect the micro-details to a larger, systemic violence.

Here is another example where an analysis of the composition of building materials is crucial: geological formations exist both inside and outside buildings. They are obviously the ground on which buildings stand, but also appear in construction materials, as stones or the gravel within concrete. A denser concentration of minerals within a rock will often become the line of least resistance, along which a crack will tear it, and likewise the building, apart. So seismic cracks are interesting because they connect the geological, the urban, and the architectural. Cracks are a fantastic demonstration of a shared materiality of the planet, moving from geology to architecture, and studying cracks, which is one of the tasks of forensic architecture, demonstrates the necessity to rid our thinking of the figure-ground relation—a building is not ontologically or epistemologically different from the rock or gravel in which it is anchored.

For example, Dara Behrman, a member of the Centre for Research Architecture, looked at how pirate archaeological excavations—for a biblical history project undertaken directly beneath the Palestinian neighbourhood of Silwan in occupied Jerusalem—generated cracks that travelled from bedrock formations through the voids of the underground archaeological sites, to roadwork and walls of buildings above. The cracks appear and disappear, translating force into lines of least resistance. Residents brought photos of these cracks to court, but their political and legal meaning, part of the underground colonization of Palestine, was not admitted. If Forensic Architecture refers to the presentation of structural analysis within contemporary legal and political forums, the task of this collection is to extend its scope beyond the context of property and insurance disputes to become an analytical frame and a new mode of practice, bearing upon different scales of investigation in engaging the material consequences of the most urgent political issues and contemporary struggles for justice.

HD&ET The material analyses of Forensic Architecture, such as those you mentioned, are always part of a multi-scalar, multi-centred approach. We believe that such an itinerant methodology differs from the dominant trajectory of Science and Technology Studies (STS), by its explicit relation to, or explication of, political realities. Of course, we do not mean to suggest here that scholarship in the field of science studies is not political, but instead that the work of Forensic Architecture, and more broadly, the work produced at the CRA, seems much more "interventionist," if we might use this term. Does the intervention, or interference, in political realities shape the practice of Forensic Architecture? And, presuming it does somehow inform these practices, we are interested in how such interference helps to advance certain interdisciplinary strategies.

EW Yes, we see research as a form of political intervention. It is crucial for us to be actively involved in the processes that we write (or exhibit or film) about. This is for two reasons: first, because we engage in activist research and take sides; second, because being in close proximity—in fact, being part of the subject of our research—is the only way for us to undertake the research. Political and legal activism allows one to gain unparalleled access to institutions and thus enables epistemological inquiries as well. Forensics was not the first, nor is it the only research we conduct at the Centre, although it has become the most productive because it is precisely structured by the act of taking sides, without compromising the intensity and seriousness of the research. It created a productive bridge between research and intervention, or what we call field work and forum work.

We have recently started to refer to our practice as *forensis*, which is a Latin word that means "pertaining to the forum." This is a more general term than forensic architecture: *forensis* is a new aesthetico-political condition in which research and science are employed in an activist mode as a part of a political struggle. We choose our cases to demonstrate both new methods of inquiry, and how the production of new forms of evidence can expand the political imagination and articulate new claims for justice in relation to violent conflict and climate change. But our research practice also involves raising critical questions about the role of new technologies of capture and representation in the creation and articulation of public truths.

So *forensis* departs from the methods of STS on account of the way in which political activism acts as the engine and the enabler of epistemological inquiry. In fact, we do two things that are both interdependent and contradictory. On the one hand, our members engage by practicing forensic architecture on different scales and locations, including concentration camps in former Yugoslavia, drone warfare sites in Pakistan, Yemen and Palestine, migrant movements in the Mediterranean, and environmental damage in Bangladesh, Brazil, Chile, and Ecuador, among other examples. Each of these investigations was chosen because of the urgency of the situation; however, each investigation also allows us to demonstrate how methodological innovations in the production of new types of evidence can intervene in the process. Our investigations, conducted with groups of political activists, prosecution teams, human rights organizations, and the United Nations, allow us to construct a critical epistemology that can theoretically evaluate the very assumptions, protocols, processes, and politics of knowledge production. In short, the research uses forensics both to pose political challenges and examine the tools of contemporary forensic practices.

The two modes of practice at the core of our research method—producing evidence and querying its nature—continuously pose a series of challenges that both strengthen and threaten its component parts. As we defend our findings as the truth of what has happened, our opponents could surely point to our writing on the elastic nature of truth-claims, the audacity of truth-speech, and the complexity of truth-making. And, when we are in more critical discussions, our colleagues can rightly point out that we were often in danger of becoming complicit with the very institutions and processes we have previously criticized. We see the tension between these component parts as the condition of our work. Rather than resolve these contradictions by pushing the pendulum one way or the other, we recognize the tension as productive. This is not a problem that could ever arrive at a satisfactory solution, but a mode of problematization that intensifies the research process.

As critical scholars and practitioners, we arrived at this project armed to the teeth with critique, but the only way for us to conduct meaningful research was in close proximity—in critical proximity—with the subjects of our investigation and with the empirical rigour that could only be generated through such proximity. "Critical" as a mode of practice requires a high level of self-reflexivity as we begin to inhabit the terrain of our own inquiries; but, for us, critical also means vital, urgent, and decisive.

There is another aspect. Because the CRA program is nested in the context of Goldsmiths, which is an especially multidisciplinary institution, it is also a pedagogical experiment that attempts to bring critical education together with activism using science and technology. So, another main difference with STS is that the original kernel of the multidisciplinary field for STS is anthropology or sociology of science; the kernel of our multidisciplinary field is architecture, and architecture with an activist core.

At the CRA, our research considers the role of spatial analysis and representation. Of course, when doing forensic architecture, the frame of architecture is used to refer to a more extensive set of relations and spatializations, including buildings, cities, oceans, and territories, because these fields describe the pathologies of our contemporary situation. Our scale of operation expands the frame of analysis and intervention from the house—such as when we do "building surveyor" work on houses in war zones—to the planet, through the work of some of our members, including Paulo Tavares, Nabil Ahmed, Godofredo Pereira, and Adrian Lahoud, who see the earth as both a construction site and a ruin.

Speaking about the whole earth—and I'm thinking here of the exhibition work of Anselm Franke—the starting point for our investigations was much more modest; it was inspired by the work of building surveyors, by their careful and systemic analysis of the structural and infrastructural conditions of a building.[5] The practice of Forensic Architecture starts with the presentation of such surveys in a legal forum. In relation to both war zones and the environment, surveys cannot always maintain a haptic dimension, but also rely on all sorts of sensing and measuring technologies. The single surveyor is replaced by an ad hoc network of collaborations between architects, scientists, and activists. The surveyor's snapshot, used to document the localized damage that has occurred, is then superseded by mathematical models to predict the risk of damage that *will have* occurred. Similarly, the forum may no longer necessarily be a particular courthouse, but may instead be comprised of a rather diffuse network of communications and assemblies connected through the media. Despite these transformations, and across the diverse scales and epistemic fields that the project traverses, there is still something of the relation between the surveyor, structural analysis, and the forum that remains.

HD&ET In an interview with Robin Mackay, you said in relation to the occupation of Palestine by Israel: "Every form that the occupation has taken since 1967 has been presented as an attempt to end the occupation. Perhaps the only constant thing about the occupation is that there are always attempts to end it. [...] The occupation is finally nothing but its constant end. [...] Therefore we need to be suspicious of anyone that runs under the slogan 'end the occupation'—they must have yet another spatial apparatus in mind."[6] In Decolonizing Architecture (DAAR), a residency project started by Sandi Hilal, Alessandro Petti, and yourself in Beit Sahour, you take the approach that the occupation, and its interminable end, should be reconfigured as a question of "decolonization." Can you say more about what you mean by decolonization here? Toward what kind of a future does a practice of decolonization move if there is no end to the occupation?

EW I think that one of the biggest problems in thinking about the future of Palestine, a problem that somehow defines one's "camp" within the Israeli or Palestinian anti-colonial left, is defined by what "state" you support as a solution. So we get the positions of one-statists versus two-statists versus no-statists, and a lot of very important and creative discussions are organized in relation to that. Surely, thinking politically, we are one-statists, but in DAAR, the studio that Sandi, Alessandro and I set up, we try to propose a different relation to the future, articulated through the process of decolonization.[7]

To do architecture in an area of such intense conflict is always to engage in a less-than-ideal world. This has to do not only with the violence that contaminates every aspect of life there, but also with determining the point from which speculation can begin. Conflicts create a sense of postponement and hence these future projections; we wait for the post-conflict to begin imagining. But the Palestine conflict is an endless conflict, so we feel that the "x-state solutions" are trapped in a top-down perspective. We did not start the project from the utopia of an end state in order to move backwards to the present; instead, we started from "real existing colonialism," from the trash, buildings, infrastructure, and law that it creates. Our approach has been to reuse, rather than reject, the material conditions of the present. So we want to mobilize architecture as an optical device through actually existing structures—such as a military base, a settlement, the Palestinian parliament building, a particular Palestinian house in Battir, different houses in Jaffa in what is called '48 Palestine—to study the conflict and to act within it.

HD&ET Can you talk a little more about the project where you proposed to repurpose an evacuated settlement for public use by Palestinians? One of the things that We are especially curious about is how you decide what kinds of public spaces might be useful. In the refugee camps, where most public space has been eliminated, how do you rebuild? What sort of community consultation does DAAR engage in?

EW The project started with the Palestinian Ministry of Planning in 2005, which had to advise on the fate of the settlements that were about to be evacuated in Gaza. The Palestinian Ministry of Planning became the centre of intense meetings between Palestinians and a variety of NGOs, different UN agencies, the World Bank, foreign governments, and international investors, all of whom outlined their proposed uses for the evacuated settlements. I was called on to advise. At the time we did not know whether they were going to be evacuated intact or whether they would be destroyed. We thought, or assumed at least, that they would be left intact, and because of this assumption the ministry wanted experts, or quasi-experts—architects—to partake in these discussions that were otherwise political and diplomatic. The main problem we were facing was that the land division in the West Bank and Gaza is such that most of the land is private (for many different reasons, not just the system of Israeli domination); it is owned by private families, and people do not sell land, so to have the settlements evacuated would give a precarious basis and infrastructure for a set of common areas. So this was the idea we were working with. Sandi, Ale, and I were working a lot with NGOs. They function as a kind of government, because the military rule doesn't want to deal with the occupied population, and the Palestinian government is very absent and incompetent, so a network of NGOs somehow emerges, and it was really with those NGOs that we were deciding the uses of land. And then there is another aspect, I mean, what you plan is one thing and what happens on the ground is often another. In the end, the settlement was destroyed, so we could not repurpose the buildings. We did other things instead.

But there was a lot of resistance to this project, which was not really surprising. Many Palestinians said Israel should "dismantle the houses and take them away." Or they wanted to "have a big bonfire," which at DAAR we thought was great, because access to the colonies or military outposts should be experienced differently by all people who were at this place at that time. This popular impulse for destruction sought to give a sense of relief; architecture had to burn. Through this process of repossession we were experiencing a radical condition of architecture—the moment power is unplugged, when the old use is gone and new uses are not yet defined. It is the limit condition of architecture. But whatever may happen on the ground, the possibility of further evacuation should be considered. We were also worried that the infrastructure would simply be reused to reproduce colonial power relations: colonial villas to be inhabited by new financial elites, etc. In this sense, historical decolonization never truly did away with the spatialized power of colonial domination. So we acted according to a different option that sought to propose subversion of the originally intended use, repurposing it for other ends.

HD&ET The artist Adam Harvey has developed what he calls "Stealth Wear": he manipulates the double ability of fashion to both reveal and conceal, creating clothing that shields the wearer from drone attacks by using a reflective material that effectively seals in the heat of the body so that it cannot be detected from the air.[8] You write that all architecture is a process of making and unmaking, an ideological restructuring of surfaces, yet so much of your work seems to be about making things visible, bringing injustices to light. Is it sometimes more desirable to create a surface of invisibility?

EW Yes, I understand what you are saying. I think that rather than operating on a single trajectory of increased visibility, mapping is always an intervention in the field of the visible. What is being foregrounded, what is being shown, and what is being "un-shown"—these are choices that we have to make with every map. When one thinks about the logic of sensing and aesthetics, one can understand the logic of disappearance as an aesthetics as well. For example, the resolution of commercially available satellite imagery of the kind we see in newspapers, such as suspected nuclear sites in Iran or destroyed villages in Darfur or Gaza, are limited to a resolution of half a metre per pixel, which means the size of a pixel is exactly the size, or the box, in which a human body fits. Within that logic of visibility, there is also a structured, built-in lacuna: the loss of the figure, or the human.

When one looks at facial recognition software, one understands that there are pretty simple ways of creating camouflage that is no longer a visual camouflage for the eye, but camouflage from algorithms, which now do a lot of the seeing. There are ways in which algorithms can be disturbed and confused with techniques that a human eye might have picked up on, but that an algorithm cannot discern. For example, there was a very strange accident in Dubai in 2010 where Israelis were trying to kill a Hamas operative who was using camouflage from the eye and from a certain face-recognition algorithm. Hamas thought they were camouflaged against one algorithm without realizing that the algorithm had changed! The Dubai police used different software and they were exposed. There are all sorts of counter-forensic practices.

HD&ET These counter-forensic practices seem especially related to the politics of visibility. In William Haver's recent essay on sense and the commons, he seems to argue against Rancière's analysis of the distribution of the sensible, suggesting that what is urgently needed is not a politics that reveals what is hidden—which is how Rancière's work is often read—but a philosophy that allows us to see what we already see.[9] Haver quotes Foucault to help explain that the role of philosophy "is to render visible precisely what is visible, that is, to make appear that which is so near, that which is so immediate, so immediately bound to ourselves that we for that very reason do not perceive it. Then if the role of science is to make known that which we don't see, the role of philosophy is to make us see what we see."[10] It seems to us that Forensic Architecture could be located precisely at this intersection, between science and philosophy; how does such a position relate to the politics of visibility? Of evidence? Of the Anthropocene?

EW One aspect of the idea of counter-forensics is the inversion between the state and the police. Previously, criminals were conceived as individuals or groups; the state was the police. This also meant that, in most cases, the state had a technological and epistemological advantage over criminals. In our form of forensics, it is the state that is typically the criminal, and the individuals and groups—human rights organizations, environmental activists, NGOs, etc.—who act as the "police." But this means that those perpetuating the violence also tend to control the scene of the crime. They also have an optical advantage. They can see places better, and can negate or deny by mobilizing state resources that are difficult to see. So, in a similar way to how you phrased it, we had to reveal what is invisible but also collect and analyze what is already in the public domain—visible but not seen, or seen and not well understood, like photos in social media and the low-resolution commercial satellite images from Google Earth. This means working around the evidence, not only with it. So, I identify with the way that Haver has framed the question, although this might be more complementary to the work of Rancière than you suggest, since in his philosophy and work on aesthetics and politics he has precisely called for reorganizing the way we see what is there but is not seen.

In FA, we undertake a number of investigations that are all about looking again at what exists in the public domain, organizing it, conceptualizing it, and cross-referencing it with other sources. When a killing happens in North Waziristan, there are echoes in local Pakistani media. Little of this is picked up by Western media. One of our researchers, Jacob Burns, has been trawling through these news media sites to find spatial patterns. How many homes were hit? How many people died in buildings, in cars, in cities, etc.? This requires making connections and cross-referencing different pieces of information from different media regarding these killings. All this information is in the public domain, but it is invisible because people only view this information in a cursory manner and do not sufficiently interrogate the connections.

For example, another aspect of our work on drones is to analysis mobile phone videos and still footage. Very little documentation has been smuggled out of Waziristan, which is under a state of siege, and where no one with a camera is allowed in or out. Whatever does come out is hard to trace and difficult to locate in both space and time. We have conducted an analysis of a specific strike in Miransha, evidence of which was smuggled out to US media through four different people. But the footage that was released just showed a blurry pile of rubble. We took the clip frame by frame and stuck them together to create a spatial panorama from this mobile phone sweep. Once we had the contour of the site, we analyzed it and measured the shadow to find the time of the day, then searched for the form of the building within the entire fabric of the town; we discovered the place with a high degree of probability. A part of the footage was of the room in which people died when a rocket entered through the ceiling. We analyzed the rubble and located the spread of fragmentation. We measured the pattern and density of the fragmentation and discovered gaps within them; we can assume that these gaps are the shadow of people that died in this room. There is so much data that exists in the public domain, but we need to develop ways of seeing it, ways of conceptualizing what we look for, and ways of mobilizing it. These ways of seeing rely, as you say, both on a theoretical conception and also on technological innovations. Together they turn noise into sound.

HD&ET In *The Least of All Possible Evils*, you identified a shift from thinking about genocide through primary effects toward the secondary effects outlined in a number of cases. We see this as a particularly powerful way to think about the relationships of complicity in warfare and of escaping some of the problems of "acceptable" deaths—because they have been calculated in advance—in acts of war. It also opens up the possibility of thinking about environmental catastrophe as a type of inflicted and purposeful genocide. Can you talk about this framework and how Forensic Architecture takes it up through the project on oceanic forensics and the "left-to-die boat"?

EW You are referring to the work of Charles Heller and Lorenzo Pezzani, who worked with Situ Studio on this project. Charles and Lorenzo are PhD students at the CRA and research fellows on the Forensic Architecture project, and Situ Studio is an emerging architectural firm in New York. Together with FA, they have set up an important project of accountability in the Mediterranean.[11] The "left-to-die boat" that Charles, Lorenzo, and Situ have been mapping and writing about has become an issue within IHL because, to a certain extent, it is the first time the trace of a boat on water has been mapped. Things moving in water usually leave no trace. The team discovered GPS coordinates by tracing phone calls and then worked with an ocean-ographic institute to re-create the drift pattern of the Mediterranean. The migrants on board were drifting in one of the most cluttered parts of the Mediterranean, in the middle of a siege with a lot of military and NATO vessels—and nobody inter-vened. So their idea was to reverse the regime of surveillance: if Western states claim this is the most surveyed sea in the world, they also have the responsibility to protect those people who might drown in it. According to international laws of the high seas, if you hear an SOS call you must intervene. So, there is a series of legal challenges now based on the very unique ability to trace the movement of the boat in the sea.

This research represents an important and paradigmatic moment in the forensic architecture project that I run with a great team of artists, architects, and filmmak-ers—including Susan Schuppli and Thomas Keenan—in which various fellows, students, and Situ Studio are developing different abilities to visualize, map, and sense events, as well as advance political and legal claims, or political claims in the form of legal claims.

As critical scholars and practitioners we arrived at this project armed with critique. We felt confident in our ability to detect, unveil, and analyze instances where power is camouflaged as benevolence. Not only in the fields in which we investigated war crimes, but in the operation of the forums that administered this evidence and arbitrated on the basis of it. We have no illusions about the forums: we know they internalize the power field external to them, and that they are skewed towards the powerful. We have no illusions about the politics of international humanitarian law. We know that human rights forensics can become an extension of western surveillance practices. We have seen the way in which the HR and the legal process can be abused by states to amplify violence. We assumed, however, that the only way to conduct critical research in the world today is in close proximity to, and even complicity with, the subjects of our investigation. Like the traditional *Operaist* motto, we wanted to act inside and against!

HD&ET There seems to be a tension in your work between wanting to mobilize investigative journalism to denounce individuals publicly, as in the case of the Guatemalan genocide when you listed the accused (José Efraín Ríos Montt, Héctor Mario López Fuentes, Óscar Humberto Mejía Victores, and José Mauricio Rodriguez Sánchez), but also to articulate the diffused networks of responsibility, across human and nonhuman actors, through forensic architecture. When thinking about whether you are going to take one tactic or another, is it just a question of the particular forum in which you are presenting?

EW This issue has already erupted in the context of my previous work on critical theory in the military. In 2008, one of the military commanders I was writing about hired one of the largest legal firms in Israel to threaten me and my publishers in Israel for libel. The accusations were frankly ridiculous and concerned with technical matters.[12] I had research to support my allegations, but the real aim, I think, was to scare me and my peers from further publishing critical material that involved such detailed analyses of the military that named names and suggested personal responsibility and even liability. What this suit did was to remind us in the anti-colonial Israeli left of the power of this type of investigation. Indeed, within the controversy that ensued, one of the things that was brought to the forefront was our tendency to generalize and concentrate analysis on large, depersonalized systems—the military, the state, etc.—rather than concentrating our attention on the role that certain characters might have within these systems. It is exactly this interaction between larger forces and individual intention that is necessary to examine. In order to operate simultaneously, in one text, we needed to have two machines, so to speak, a theoretical one and a journalistic one, with the latter ferociously investigating certain issues and then placing them within a large theoretical frame of the former. But we did not have the legal infrastructure, nor the money to defend ourselves (even against the most spurious of libel claims), for the journalistic machine to work completely.

So this connects to your question about forensics and the relation between the individual and larger, shaping forces. Human rights have what we call a figure-ground problem. On the one hand, human rights discourse operates very much through a process of foregrounding individual victims and perpetrators. It is a conception that is based on a single human figure who is tortured or killed, repressed by an authoritarian regime. This is a process of figuration, the extraction of a figure from a political background. The individual is the subject of human rights analysis and her or his testimony is the way of getting into the logic of the event. Retribution is too often seen as the punishment of individual perpetrators, rather than as the dismantling of all structural, shaping forces within which injustice is perpetrated. This is figuration. An individual extracted from a political field and particular history narrated as a crime—as if it were a "simple" criminal case.

However, war crimes investigations call for a more complex analysis than those in the context of domestic criminal law. War crimes, like other wartime events, are produced by a multiplicity of agents woven together by networks that further distribute action and responsibility, using technologies that now increasingly have semi-autonomous decision-making capacities. For example, militaries are themselves diffused bodies that are, in turn, governed by political, institutional, and administrative logics.

On the other hand, some current human rights techniques have shifted attention to the ground. Satellite imagery, as Laura Kurgan beautifully shows in her new book, has become a relatively recent tool for HR investigators.[13] In satellite imagery, we no longer see figures. What becomes visible in these images is the background to human action—the land, the landscape, the built fabric, the destroyed buildings, the burnt fields, deforestation, flooding, etc. Instead of the figure, we have the ground that now stands for the condition of the human. This challenges an important principle within HR work, which is traditionally about the human (state of the individual) by the human (testimony). Given that viewing is now not only undertaken by prosthetic sensors, but interpreted by algorithms, it is no longer strictly a human domain. So, by inverting figure and ground in this gestalt, we have turned the ground into the object of study. We have "figured" the ground.

In our analysis of Operation Sofia—what is called "the last Indian massacre"—during the Guatemalan Civil war in the early 1980s, our team (including Situ Studio, Paulo Tavares, Daniel Pasqual, and myself) has sought to extend the understanding of genocide by shifting our attention to the ground condition, using maps and remote sensing of the region. We are trying to produce maps of the processes of large-scale deforestations, of road-building, and concentration-towns, of destruction of the villages of the native Ixil people, of fencing and "privatizing" their mode of cultivation in fields that were common property, to account for the changing of plant species, especially maize, that led to the massive destruction of this protected group and their way of life. We seek to account for the reorganization of people and material that has resulted in the destruction of the conditions that would sustain life. Indirect killing, which occurs more slowly and not by direct trauma such as bullet holes or machete wounds, challenges traditional forensic work.

This is what we call *field causality*, which is tied to debates around the entanglement of politics and the environment. Unlike the direct linear causality of criminal law, field causality does not seek to connect a chain of events. Instead, causes are understood as diffused aggregates that act simultaneously in all directions. They are shaping forces and they affect the formation of larger territories and political events. In other words, rather than looking simply at mortality, we take an epidemiological approach and look at patterns.

From the mid-nineteenth to the beginning of the twentieth century, the most important foundation of forensic science was the understanding that every contact leaves a trace and therefore if something touches something, one can actually recreate the moment of encounter. Adrian Lahoud, my successor at the Centre and member of our research team, has continuously insisted that we must look at the ways in which contact and trace have become separated and scattered, that is, that an action might happen in a certain place—an emission, for example—but its consequences might be felt across oceans and air currents.

This goes beyond the simple gestalt that concentrates on the human figure. We have lost sight of the ground, the political and environmental context; but while looking at the ground, we have lost the figure, as in the lacunae in satellite surveillance that I mentioned earlier. The task is to articulate new relationships between figure and ground, to find ways of understanding and illustrating rapid shifts in scale and the importance of events.

In the case of Guatemala, as in previous work on Palestine, this brings in all kinds of different actors—architects, road builders, agriculturists, farmers, bankers—who are all a part of a much more diffuse responsibility that must be addressed in a fashion outside of the usual legal system. Indirect, aggregate, or field causality seeks to undo another important distinction between different kinds of values we attach to death. There were people that were killed and people that died. To die, in this discourse, implies a secondary, non-intentional death. Recently, more work has been undertaken by epidemiologists in relation to non-direct mortality in wars. There was even an attempt by Luis Moreno-Ocampo, the first prosecutor of the International Criminal Court (ICC), to include indirect mortality figures in his controversial charging of the president of Sudan, Omar al-Bashir, with genocide in Darfur.

HD&ET It is an incredibly poignant argument to say that genocide is not just the barrel of a gun, but that it involves, instead, a network of diffused responsibility; still, aren't there only a few legal venues to enforce these arguments? It makes us wonder what other avenues for redress there could be.

EW I agree. Moreno-Ocampo faced huge criticism for his decision to do that, as well as accusations of "inflating numbers" in the context of a very politicized campaign against Sudan. And I partially agree, but I think that this is the frontier of conflict investigation, and the consequences of such developments could be felt in different forums, as you say, not only in legal ones. Field causalities have a very different implication than direct causes for the way the forums have been made. Indeed, field causality could be the bastard's best defense in court. It would be what every perpetrator would like to claim in order to avoid conviction, and is therefore not enough as a single line or argumentation; we need to learn how to link singularity to structural conditions. However, it is very important to insist on this because field causality describes a political diagram that must be dismantled, and not just by courts. It does not necessarily imply a judgment, but rather a more radical action in changing the political force field.

HD&ET Have the kinds of arguments developed through forensic architecture been used outside of the context of recent genocides and IHL? This kind of analysis, for example, could do a lot of justice in the context of the ongoing genocide of indigenous people in North America—how governments and industry force people into settlements, the ongoing contamination of lands, and the hazardous exploitation of resources through oil and mining practices, etc. Has the project of FA been advanced in these situations?

EW The senior person on our project, Susan Schuppli, is a Canadian theorist and artist, and she is looking at new claims brought up by indigenous communities in northern Canada and the new forums that have emerged to deal with these issues. She is also helping convene a group of M.A. members at our Centre who are working with the American NGO *Three Degrees Warmer* on a case brought by the Native Village of Kivalina, Alaska against Exxon Mobil Corp. These are, strictly speaking, outside of the legal frames of human rights and international humanitarian law, but as other members in our research groups have shown, and as I briefly alluded to above, environmental issues are increasingly resembling states of conflict. And, environmental law increasingly resembles the laws of war.

HD&ET In *The Least of All Possible Evils*, you explain that part of the justification for the use of drones is that they are "emotionless." As Ronald Arkin, an American scientist and a leader in the field of weaponized robotics explained, robots have no joy in violence. It seems to me that part of the ongoing justification for extra-judicial killings by states rests not only on processes of rationalization, but also the diminishment of excess. There is, then, a fantasy about the elimination of the excesses of war. What has become distasteful to certain forms of state power in late capitalism is not "evil" or "violence," but excess, Arkin's "joy in violence." To a certain extent, the materials you are dealing with in forensic architecture, as in any environment, are also inherently excessive, they spill over their boundaries and defy easy classification. How does your work negotiate these two different ways of dealing with excess?

EW Yes, in *The Least of All possible Evils*, the argument is that dealing with the excesses of war, rather than its more structural political causes, could be abused by militaries and states. The calculated conception of violence it puts forth can justify almost any atrocity. In this way the logic of the "least of all possible evils" is invoked to justify the use of a lesser violence to prevent the excesses you mentioned. This is the principle of proportionality, which is about the "too much" of war, without ever saying how much is too much. So, the argument conjures a cold calculus, a kind of economy of ethics where good and evil are traded like commodities, and speculated on in the financial economy. But economies are dangerous and volatile, as we have seen again recently. So, proportionality always has a relation to the disproportional, or the excess you mentioned—violence beyond reason, beyond calculation, the war of the mad, like the one Israel declared when it said that they were going to apply disproportional violence to Lebanon. In other words, they were going to break the law to maintain it. But disproportional violence is also the violence of the weak, those who cannot calculate, or wish not to, and those who are kept outside the economy of calculations. This violence is disproportional because it cannot be measured or calculated, and because, ultimately, when justice is not answered by the law, violence will continuously seek to altogether restructure the basis of law.

HD&ET Anselm Franke, whom you mentioned earlier, is curating the forthcoming Forensic Architecture exhibition as part of the Haus der Kulturen der Welt's (HKW) ongoing Anthropocene-Project, an initiative involving cooperation with the Max Planck Gesellschaft, Deutsches Museum, the Rachel Carson Center for Environment and Society, and the Institute for Advanced Sustainability Studies. We are interested in how a venue like the HKW is another forum for the public consideration of the forensic practices that you have developed in architecture. While the work of Forensic Architecture seems to frequently engage the forum of the law, whether through IHL or environmental law, the forum of the public exhibition at the HKW seems to engage a different type of forum. Do you see these various forums as complementary? How does the public response to Forensic Architecture relate to its politico-juridical potential? And, how does working with a curator like Anselm Franke transform research that would otherwise be disseminated in legal or academic contexts?

EW Maybe there is an analogy to make between the presentation of spaces, landscapes, and objects in a courtroom, or in other political forums and assembly spaces, and a curatorial practice—such as Anselm's—which uses the exhibition space as a laboratory for presenting, thinking through, gathering, and re-arranging forms of knowledge. Of course, every forum in which political speech is articulated has its own sort of protocol by which a relationship between people and things—that is, politics—is organized, mediated, and reorganized. However, it is also true that presenting things in each of these forums, whether forensic or curatorial, has something important in common: the presentation rearranges what can be said and heard in each of them; and, in both cases, such presentations can even call for making a new forum.

The intersection with Anselm's work occurred much earlier than the Anthropocene Project. In 2003, we started working together on the exhibition "Territories" as a way of developing a research and curatorial practice that tried to be political and interventionist and used the exhibition, and its budget, to support research work in Palestine. The exhibition toured, and we managed to use the infrastructure of the art world to provide the research that was later recorded in *Hollow Land.*

Among other things, the conception of the forensic research was inspired by Anselm's project on *Animism*, which he developed as a major part of his PhD at the CRA. What was important in this project was how he asked a series of questions regarding the ways in which claims for the agency of objects were part of very specific political situations. Rather than a general claim, his was a call to analyze the specificity of those situations.

The first public test of the forensics project was the exhibition *Mengele's Skull* that Anslem curated with Tom Keenan, Nikolaus Hirsch, and myself. Later, several of our members were involved in events like the Anthropocene Project at HKW, where we sought to intervene by insisting on the missing politics, that is, on the way the reality of the Anthropocene must be understood through multiple conflicts that were missing from an analysis of the bureaucracies of science foregrounded in this project. Later on, several of our members participated in *The Whole Earth* exhibition, which Anselm curated at the HKW, which also helped frame our attempts, within the group, of taking the scale of forensic investigation to that of the planet itself.

I think there are probably several lessons to learn from the entanglement of exhibition and forensic practices; one of the most important, however, would be in relation to ongoing discussions about the immateriality of curating practices. I think, in fact, that a very precise empirical and material presentation is the best mode to instigate and mobilize political situations because politics is itself a process of materialization on different scales.

Notes

1   After a series of advanced seminars at Duke University in February 2013, Eyal generously agreed to sit down with Heather Davis to discuss his recent work on forensic architecture, international human rights law, and the relation of critical thinking and artistic practice to political interventions. A partial transcript of this conversation appeared as "Proportionality, Violence, and the Economy of Calculations: Eyal Weizman in Conversation with Heather Davis," *Scapegoat: Architecture | Landscape | Political Economy*, Issue 05 – Excess, ed. Etienne Turpin (Summer/Fall 2013): 130–147. Eyal, Heather, and Etienne later developed the concepts and concerns further for this publication.

2   Craig Whitlock, "Drone Warfare: Niger Becomes Latest Frontline in US War on Terror," *The Guardian*, 26 March 2013, http://www.guardian.co.uk/world/2013/mar/26/niger-africa-drones-us-terror.

3   Jan Zalasiewicz, Mark Williams, Will Steffen, Paul Crutzen "The New World of the Anthropocene," *Environmental Science & Technology* 44, no. 7 (2010): 2228–2231.

4   For a detailed description, analysis, and illustrations of the "pyramids of Gaza," see Eyal

Weizman, *Forensic Architecture: Notes from Fields and Forums* (Ostfildern: Hatje Cantz, 2012), 4–5.

5 Diedrich Diederichsen and Anselm Franke, eds., *The Whole Earth California and the Disappearance of the Outside* (Berlin: Sternberg Press, 2013).

6 Eyal Weizman, "Political Plastic (Interview)," *Collapse* VI (January 2010): 279–80.

7 For a full list of DAAR projects, as well as theoretical reflections on those projects, see http://www.decolonizing.ps/site.

8 This project can be found at http://ahprojects.com/projects/stealth-wear.

9 William Haver, "A Sense of the Common," *The South Atlantic Quarterly* 111, no. 3 (Summer 2012): 439–452.

10 Michel Foucault, "La philosophie analytique de la politique," in *Dits et* écrits, 1954–1988, Vol. 3, 1976–1979, ed. Daniel Defert and François Ewald (Paris: Gallimard, 1994), 540–41.

11 "In the case of what is now referred to as the 'left-to-die boat,' 72 migrants fleeing Tripoli by boat on the early morning of 27 March 2011 ran out of fuel and were left to drift for 14 days until they landed back on the Libyan coast. With no water or food on-board, only nine of the migrants survived. In several interviews, these survivors recounted the various points of contact they had with the external world during this ordeal. This included describing the aircraft that flew over them, the distress calls they sent out via satellite telephone and their visual sightings of a military helicopter which provided a few packets of biscuits and bottles of water, and a military ship which failed to provide any assistance whatsoever." For their complete analysis, see Forensic Oceanography, http://www.forensic-architecture.org/investigations/forensic-oceanography.

12 For a complete analysis of these events, see David Cunningham, "Walking into Walls: Academic Freedom, the Israeli Left and the Occupation within," *Radical Philosophy* 150 (July–August 2008): 67–70, http://www.radicalphilosophy.com/news/walking-into-walls-academic-freedom-the-israeli-left-and-the-occupation-within.

13 Laura Kurgan, *Close Up at a Distance: Mapping, Technology, and Politics* (Cambridge, Mass.: Zone Books, 2013).

Landscapes of San Francisco Bay:
Plates from Bay Lexicon

Jane Wolff

Mixed Media

What brings water to the city?

a. river: a natural watercourse, flowing in a line from higher to lower ground.

b. delta: a landscape created by rivers as they approach the sea. In the California Delta, the Sacramento and San Joaquin Rivers split into a series of winding, slow-moving channels that converge at the Carquinez Strait and flow into San Francisco Bay.

c. dam: a barrier built across a river to create a reservoir.

d. aqueduct: a pipe or channel engineered to bring water to the city from far away.

San Francisco lives on borrowed water.

The city's watershed is defined twice, once by topography and once by engineering. The steep west slope of the Sierra Nevada sends rain and melting snow to San Francisco Bay. Water travels in streams and rivers down the Central Valley, through the California Delta, and past the Carquinez Strait, always moving toward the ocean. Since the 1920s, an aqueduct has carried some of that current on a different route. The Tuolumne River is captured behind Hetch Hetchy Dam and gradually released into pipes that run straight to San Francisco. Every spigot in the city is connected to the mountains.

The aqueduct is good and bad. It protects San Francisco from local scarcity, and it provides clean water, uncontaminated by the farms and factories that lie between the mountains and the coast. But what comes out of the tap is used at the expense of the estuary. Before plumbing stretched across the state, that water belonged to the fish.

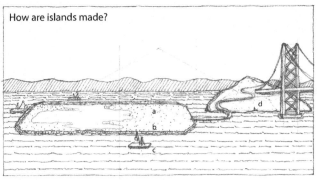

How are islands made?

a. shoal: a place where the bay floor is close to the surface of the water.

b. seawall: a wall built to contain filled land and protect it from erosion.

c. dredge: a boat equipped with machinery to lift and transport sediment from the bay floor.

d. bedrock: solid rock that lies below the surface of the ground. The bedrock of the Coast Ranges was pushed into low mountains by the movement of tectonic plates that underlie the Pacific Ocean and North America.

Yerba Buena Island and Treasure Island make a pair, but they are not twins.

Yerba Buena belongs to the geological formation of the Coast Ranges, a consequence of the movement of tectonic plates that make up Earth's outer layer. Thirty million years ago, the plate under the Pacific Ocean began to slide northward against the edge of the plate that supports North America. Folded and crumpled by the friction, the North American sea floor was pushed up into a line of low mountains on the edge of the continent. Ten thousand years ago, when the last ice age ended, Yerba Buena was separated from its neighbors by rising water in San Francisco Bay. The mountain became an island.

Treasure Island is a younger construction, the product of dredges and siphons. Until the 1930s it was Yerba Buena Shoals, a high patch of bay floor just north of Yerba Buena Island. It presented a significant navigation hazard—some parts lay just a few feet below the water—and in 1936, the federal government's Works Progress Administration undertook its transformation into useful ground. Sand and sediment dredged from around the bay were piled behind a seawall built of rubble blasted from the Yerba Buena Tunnel. The new land was dedicated almost exactly a year after the Bay Bridge had connected San Francisco to Oakland. Treasure Island is a closer relative of the bridge than of the old island: both projects were undertaken to expand the territory of a watery metropolis.

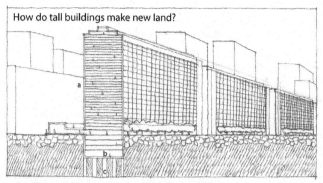

How do tall buildings make new land?

a. vertical land: new surfaces constructed as the multiple floors of high-rise structures.

b. underground land: new surfaces excavated from fill and contained in the bases of towers.

c. foundation: the lowest part of a tall building, constructed to transfer its weight from the ground's unstable surface to the solid rock that lies below soil, fill, gravel, and mud.

Once, new land at the edge of the bay was built horizontally. Piers extended streets into the mudflats of Yerba Buena Cove. Rubble and sand were placed beside and between the piers to raise the surface of the flats. The seawall was constructed to stop the filled ground from eroding. Land was made for access to the water because the city lived on maritime commerce.

Today, new land is made vertically. The stacked floors of the Embarcadero Center multiplied the surface of the ground dozens of times, and its garages made inhabitable space underground. Built between 1967 and 1981, as ship traffic was moving from San Francisco to Oakland, the center's towers defined a new world on the waterfront. Office workers replaced longshoremen, and access to the bay was less important than easy connections to subways and freeways. Sometimes cities are remade gradually, but the Embarcadero Center was part of a rapid process of urban renewal fueled by suspicion of the old, enabled by public policy that swept away anything decrepit, and bankrolled by real estate speculation. The compound and its neighbors, high-rise buildings linked by walkways two stories above the street, crowded out the warehouses of the Produce District.

In this vertical city, the filled land at the shore is uncertain ground. It does not have the structural strength to support tall buildings, and earthquakes have the power to shake it into a liquid. The Embarcadero Center's towers extend far below the surface of the waterfront. Their foundations reach through sixteen stories' worth of rubble and mud to bedrock, and their bases are designed as giant shock absorbers.

Like many iconic places, San Francisco Bay is loved better than it is understood. Its power as scenery has obscured its ecological complexity, its natural and cultural dynamics, and its ongoing evolution as a metropolitan centrepiece. The products of long, reiterative interactions among human intentions, geographic circumstances, and environmental processes, its landscapes are ecological hybrids. They are hard to describe, and so they are hard to apprehend: language is the first tool for perception, and we cannot recognize what we cannot name. An illustrated field guide to San Francisco's shoreline, *Bay Lexicon* offers a nuanced, place-based vocabulary that makes the hybrid circumstances of San Francisco Bay apparent—and legible—to the range of audiences with a stake in the landscape's future.

A collaboration with the Exploratorium of San Francisco, this project emerged from work over the last five years with curator Susan Schwartzenberg to develop exhibition content and teaching materials for a new museum gallery about the landscape and ecology of San Francisco Bay. *Bay Lexicon* uses illustrated flash cards to examine and define elements of the landscape visible from the gallery and along San Francisco's Embarcadero. It builds on the principles of the Exploratorium's founder, physicist Frank Oppenheimer, who believed that a citizenry informed about science comprised the best defence against the catastrophe of nuclear warfare. Today, as we face the spectres of immediate and long-term ecological disaster, environmental literacy is an essential skill. Events like Superstorm Sandy and Hurricane Katrina demonstrate this need. The havoc that the storms created was the predictable outcome of reciprocal influences between dynamic environments—the Hudson River estuary and the Mississippi Delta—and engineering interventions people made in order to live there. No surprise to landscape scholars and ecologists, the catastrophes came as shocks to the general public. Few people had the ability to read the landscape, to translate its physical circumstances into representational terms that could explain what had happened or suggest how to move forward more sustainably.

Using methods and tools from landscape scholarship, design, and science education, *Bay Lexicon* aims to encourage observation and enquiry about the natural world and its relation to culture. By defining and questioning a series of sights and situations along San Francisco's shoreline, the lexicon articulates relationships between visible, tangible artefacts and the complex (and often invisible) processes that shape the bay and its edges. It asks how the physical landscape has been transformed by practices of inhabitation and because of ideas about meaning and value. It locates observations of local conditions in the context of the region, and it reminds readers that the present always contains traces of the past and clues to the future. The project uses a specific place to raise general questions: *Bay Lexicon* considers San Francisco Bay as a subject, but it raises issues that exist in every hybrid landscape.

Architecture's Lapidarium

by Amy Catania Kulper

On the Lives of Geological Specimens

> As intelligence and language, thought and the signs of thought, are united by
> secret and indissoluble links, so in like manner, and almost without our being
> conscious of it, the external world and our ideas and feelings melt into each
> other.
>
> —Alexander von Humbolt, *Cosmos* (1849)

I Vital Matter: Architecture's Material Life

Written over ten years before its publication in
1981, Aldo Rossi's *A Scientific Autobiography*
constitutes a peculiar point of departure for
an essay in a collection devoted to architecture in the Anthropocene. On the first page of
the text, Rossi writes:

> Certainly a very important point of
> reference is Max Planck's *Scientific
> Autobiography*. In this book, Planck re-
> turns to the discovery of modern physics,
> recapturing the impression made on
> him by the enunciation of the principle
> of the conservation of energy; he always
> recalled this principle in connection with
> the schoolmaster Mueller's story about
> a mason who with great effort heaved a
> block of stone up on the roof of a house.
> The mason was struck by the fact that
> expended energy does not get lost; it
> remains stored for many years, never
> diminished, latent in the block of stone,
> until one day it happens that the block
> slides off the roof and falls on the head of
> a passerby, killing him.[1]

GEOLOGICAL SPECIMEN ONE

"The Parthenon, Athens," figure 17 from
Aldo Rossi's *A Scientific Autobiography*,
1981

Fig. 01

Though Rossi's anecdote constitutes an inauspicious beginning for an autobiography, his capacity to draw autobiographical, physical, and building practices com-
pellingly into each other's orbit succinctly establishes the claims of this essay. In
the following architectural investigation of ten geological specimens, the collected
examples will support the following arguments. First, a vitalist theme historically
emerges at the intersection of architectural, scientific, and philosophical discourse.

Second, as a result of these vitalist tendencies, the situation of architecture—that which historically was conceptualized as "site," and its material constitution—ceased to be represented as a static or benign entity. Third, the influence of vitalism also introduced the term "life" as the chronological measure of agency, both human and inhuman, organic and inorganic, facilitating the comparison of human and geological agencies that is characteristic of the Anthropocene. Fourth, this metric—"life"—emerges from the overlap between the introversion of biological discourse (searching for the smallest unit manifesting life), and the inner investigations of autobiographical work (examining how a given character has come into being, how an individual life acquires meaning). In biology and autobiography, "life" is both the unit of measure and the evidence of immanence. And fifth, the ten geological specimens in architecture's lapidarium construct a foundation for an understanding of life as the measure, and immanence as the operative condition, of architecture in the Anthropocene.

Returning now to the first specimen, Rossi cites two primary influences for his autobiography: Planck's *Scientific Autobiography* (published in German as *Wissenschaftliche Selbstbiographie,* in 1948, and in English in 1949), in which the physicist narrates the events leading up to his formulation of the principle of the conservation of energy; and Stendhal's *The Life of Henry Brulard* (written between 1835 and 1836, and published posthumously in 1890), a thinly veiled fictitious account of the author's unhappy childhood.[2] Stendhal's work interested Rossi for its strange mixture of autobiography and architectural plans—Stendhal elected to illustrate this account of his life, not with perspectival vignettes, but rather with planimetric fragments.[3] Of Stendhal, Rossi writes:

> It was perhaps through Stendhal's drawings and this strange mixture of autobiography and building plans that I acquired my first knowledge of architecture; they were the first seeds of a notion which ultimately ends up in this book. I was struck by the drawings of plans which seemed to be a graphic variation of the handwritten manuscript, and principally for two reasons: first, because handwriting is a complex technique that lies between writing and drawing [...] and second, because these plans disregarded or ignored formal and dimensional aspects. In some of my recent projects, or ideas for projects, I try to stop the event just before it occurs, as if the architect could foresee—and in a certain sense does foresee—the unfolding of life in the house.[4]

In this sense, the autobiographical account and the architectural plan are parallel operations for Rossi in that both are activated by a vital energy, manifesting itself either as an event or a formal configuration. Here, it may be worth noting that Stendhal is a *nom de plume* for Marie-Henri Beyle, selected in hommage to Johann Joachim Winckelmann, who was born in Stendal, Germany. Winckelmann is known for bringing natural historical taxonomy to art historical discourse, and in this sense his categorization of cultural artifacts into periods and styles could be similarly characterized as a moment of fixity within a fluid historical continuity.[5]

What is the common ground between cultural artifacts and the categories that house them, between disparate pseudonyms and the author who creates them, between the architect and the spatial configurations he imagines, and between the autobiographer and the narrative he recounts? In each of these instances, the common ground resides in the conceptualization of "life" as *the* critical unit of chronological measure. In his essay "Of Crystals, Cells, and Strata: Natural History and Debates on the Form of a New Architecture in the Nineteenth Century," architectural historian Barry Bergdoll observes that the three defining texts of nineteenth-century architectural theory—Ruskin's *Stones of Venice* (1851–1853), Viollet-le-Duc's *Dictionnaire raisonné de l'architecture française* (1854–1868), and Gottfried Semper's *Der Stil* (vol. 1, 1861, vol. 2, 1863)—are all "shot through with geological references that seek to bring the century's fascination with the study of the history of civilization into line with the new insights into the expanded time-line of the history of the earth itself."[6] Bergdoll's characterization of this desire for the synchronization of human time and geologic time is supported by Martin J. S. Rudwick's reminder that geology and biology are terms both coined at the start of the nineteenth century, and that their emergence occasioned a reorientation of the map of knowledge.[7] Rudwick writes: "The relations between the various natural sciences, and between them and the social sciences and humanities [...] are not in-trinsic to the natural and human worlds: all our maps of knowledge are themselves human constructions, embedded in the contingencies and specificities of history."[8] Rudwick's framing of historical contingency as that which unites the sciences and the humanities proffers a unit of measure for the attempted synchronizations of nineteenth-century architectural theory—a life.

In his 1995 essay "Immanence: A Life…," Gilles Deleuze draws the distinction be-tween a life, and an immanent life: "A life is everywhere, in all the moments that a given living subject goes through and that are measured by given lived objects: an immanent life carrying with it the events or singularities that are merely actualized in subjects and objects."[9] Somewhere in Deleuze's formulation of immanent life lurks Rossi's desire to "stop the event just before it occurs"—both characteriza-tions allude to potential, prior to its realization. In Jane Bennett's interpretation of Deleuze, her attention focuses on the philosopher's use of the indefinite article "a," and his reference to "a life," because, "[a] life inhabits that uncanny nontime existing between the various moments of biological and morphological time."[10] Like Bergdoll, Bennett points to the reckoning of human and geological time, but unlike Bergdoll, she establishes "a life" as the potential interface between the two. Bennett continues: "A life thus names a restless activeness, a destructive-creative force-pres-ence that does not coincide fully with any specific body. A life tears the fabric of the actual without ever coming fully 'out' in a person, place, or a thing. A life points to what *A Thousand Plateaus* describes as 'matter-movement' or 'matter-energy,' a 'matter in variation that enters assemblages and leaves them.'"[11] Alternatively, Giorgio Agamben's interpretation of Deleuzean immanence concentrates not on the indefinite article preceding life, but rather on the semantic connotations of Deleuze's punctuation, specifically the colon and the ellipsis in his title. Agamben argues: "If we take up Adorno's metaphor of the colon as a green light in the traffic of language, [...] we can say that between immanence and a life there is a kind of crossing with neither distance nor identification, something like a passage without spatial movement."[12] For Agamben then, the colon intimates a departure from immanence as a state of being towards something like "immanation" (Deleuze's term): activated possibility that is not yet actualized, catalyzed potentiality that is not yet realized—in other words, virtualization. With respect to the ellipsis dots following "a life" in Deleuze's title, Agamben reasons: "Here the incompletion that is traditionally thought to characterize ellipsis dots does not refer to a final, yet lacking, meaning [...] [R]ather, it indicates an indefinition of a specific kind, which brings the indefinite meaning of the article 'a' to its limit."[13] According to Agamben, taking the colon and ellipsis together, "a life..." is "pure potentiality that preserves without acting."[14] Thus, to conclude the interpretation of this first geological specimen, if the vital force that inhabits Max Planck's example of the schoolmaster Mueller's stone is conserved energy, and the vital force that Rossi identifies in Stendhal's plan fragments resides in its capacity to stop an event before it has occurred, then Rossi's geological specimen frames this vitalist immanent life as pure potentiality.

II Geological Life: Some Mythological Narratives

The second specimen explores the notion of geological life through four mythological (or at least mythical) narratives that consider the intertwining of the earth's history with human history. The mythological account is a useful vehicle for exploring the idea of geological life, largely because it is pre-scientific, so its tendency is to narrate through engagement, rather than to explain from a distance. The subject of Louis-Ernst Barrias' sculpture is the Egyptian goddess Isis, identifiable by the green scarab perched upon the cloth beneath her breasts. Isis was a seminal figure for the Romantics, and Friedrich Schiller wrote about her in the poem "The Veiled Image at Saïs," published in 1795 and translated into English by Sir Edward Bulwer Lytton in 1866. In the poem a young man travels to Egypt and is told that behind the veil of Isis lays the truth, but he is cautioned not to lift it. Why this admonition against lifting the veil? Jean-Paul Sartre writes: "What is seen is possessed; to see is to *deflower*. If we examine the comparisons normally used to express the relation between the knower and the known, we see that many of them are represented as being a kind of *violation by sight*."[15] For Sartre, visual examination is critical to the scientific paradigm, and the Romantic caution against lifting the veil is directly linked to the desire to preserve the participatory, connective, and immersive dimensions of knowing affiliated with the mythological paradigm. Similarly, Karsten Harries writes:

> The look tends to degrade the seen by transforming it into an object. Objects have their foundation in the subject. To wish to know or see something as object is to wish to appropriate and process it. The desire to see the truth is a desire to be its master and thus master of all. The young man in the poem is

GEOLOGICAL SPECIMEN TWO

Ferdinand Cheval, *Palais Idéal* (1879-1912), Louis-Ernest Barrias, *Nature Unveiling Herself*   Fig. 02
Before Science (1899), John Collier, *Priestess of Delphi* (1891), Sir Edward Coley Burne-Jones,
Sisyphus (c. 1870)

unwilling to accept the fact that man, although transcending known objects,
is in turn transcended by an unknown reality and is not the author of his
being. By knowing all, he wants to become his own foundation and to put
himself as pure knowing subject in the place of God. [16]

The Romantic obsession with the veil of Isis, then, is a cautionary tale about the human desire for omnipotence, a desire that in Barrias' sculpture is combined with the scientific gaze. And yet, this representation of Isis seems to willingly and without coercion lift her veil, as if nature is eager to reveal her secrets to the inquiring scientist. What the narrative of Isis demonstrates is the precariousness of mythopoeic propinquity in the modern advent of the distanced scientific gaze.

John Collier's depiction of the *Priestess at Delphi* represents the oracle perched on a tall stool, hovering above a chasm in the earth that appears to be emitting steam or gas. In his discussion of the Delphic oracle, Steven Connor observes that the association of females with the earth is commonplace in many cultures. He writes: "The female earth is thought of as valuable enclosures or interiorities. In particular, vases which hold grain, oil, or wine, and ovens that transform grain into bread. This emphasis upon valuable interiority made openings in the earth extremely significant. Such openings, in the form of chasms and caves, were at once the confirmation and transgression of the earth's power to hold and store items of value."[17] The oracle's power is derived from her proximity to the earth, both physically and metaphorically, and from this proximity comes her ability to speak for the earth, to interpret its emissions. Page duBois alludes to the tradition of the oracle being a post-menopausal woman, a figure who "must remain pure potential, never having their interior filled up by sex or pregnancy, so that other processes of thesaurization can occur."[18] Poised upon a golden-footed stool that straddles a fissure in the earth's surface and ensconced in the emitted vapours, Collier's oracle is a metaphysical trope, translating and rendering immanent the unleashed generative potential of the earth.

Another mythological narrative that takes up this theme is Albert Camus' *The Myth of Sisyphus* (published in French in 1942, and English in 1955). Captured in Edward Burne-Jones' painting (c.1870), Sisyphus is condemned, by the gods, to the futile physical labour of continually pushing a boulder up a hill. Upon reaching the apex, his onerous task accomplished, he is then fated to witness the boulder's retreat, secure in the knowledge that his labour was entirely in vain. Camus writes:

> It is during that return, that pause, that Sisyphus interests me. A face that toils so close to stones is already stone itself! See that man going back down with a heavy yet measured step toward the torment of which he will never know the end. That hour like a breathing-space which returns as surely as his suffering, that is the hour of consciousness. At each of these moments when he leaves the heights and gradually sinks toward the lairs of the gods, he is superior to his fate. He is stronger than his rock.[19]

In his analysis, Camus isolates this hiatus from labour, this moment of consciousness, as an instance of affinity between the anthropological and the geological, and moment of identity, or even empathy, between man and stone. The two are at once the same and yet different—Sisyphus is already stone, yet he is stronger than rock—and a vital exchange has occurred between the life of the boulder and the life of the man whose fate is inseparable from this geological burden.

Finally, a mythical (if not mythological) exemplar of geological life resides in the urban legend of the French postman, Ferdinand Cheval. In April 1879, Cheval tripped on a stone along his typical route, and was so taken by it, that for the next 33 years he collected specimens during his mail rounds, and with them constructed the *Palais Idéal*. Once again, the respective fates of man and rocks are inextricably intertwined. Embraced by the surrealists, and particularly by André Breton, Cheval's masterpiece came to epitomize the ambitions of automatism—a seamless connection between reality and dream. If, in Camus' hands, the myth of Sisyphus encourages the reader to contemplate some sort of vitalist exchange between man and rock, Cheval's *Palais Idéal* conjures another manifestation of these generative forces as they ignite the postman's material imagination in the implementation of a geological dream world.

III Generative, Taxonomical, and Mathematical Immanence

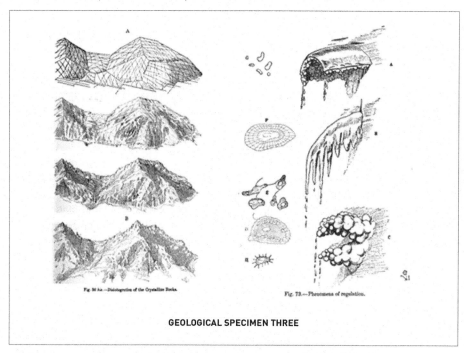

GEOLOGICAL SPECIMEN THREE

Eugène-Emmanuel Viollet-le-Duc, Disintegration of Crystalline Rock, *Mont Blanc* (1876)   Fig. 03
Eugène-Emmanuel Viollet-le-Duc, Phenomena of Regelation, *Mont Blanc* (1876)

Width: 20 meters ⎱ calculated from arch to axis
Length: 34.5 meters ⎰ of the former columns
Column thickness (bottom): 0.977 meters
Column thickness (top): 0.873 meters
Column height: 9.504 meters
Additionally, column height: ca. 19.5 modules
Entablature height: 3.7 modules

Front norm, following the old canon:

$$\frac{4 \times 5.85 = 23.4}{(19.5 + 3.7) = 23.2}$$

Side norm, following the new canon:

$$\frac{5 \times 5 = 25}{(19.5 + 3.7) = 23.2}$$

Leaf frieze on the
temple at Aezani

GEOLOGICAL SPECIMEN FOUR

Fig. 04   Gottfried Semper, "Temple of
Panhellenic Zeus at Aezani," from
*Style in the Technical and Tectonic
Arts* (1860-63)

In 1876, French architect, theorist and restoration specialist Eugène-Emmanuel Viollet-le-Duc wrote a lengthy tome on Mont Blanc, on its geological and geodesical formations and transformations, as well as on the current and past state of its glaciers.[20] The first image of Viollet-le-Duc's text is neither scenic nor pictorial; rather, it is a diagram depicting the process of geological upheaval in its before and after states. This is significant in that Viollet-le-Duc elects first to demonstrate nature's behaviour before representing nature's appearance to his readers. In his description of immanence, Deleuze writes: "Absolute immanence is in itself: it is not *in* something, *to* something; it does not depend on an object or belong to a subject."[21] In his depiction of this geological phenomenon, Viollet-le-Duc is representing a process, the process of upheaval, and in this sense his diagram of forces has no subject—it is all verb. Viollet-le-Duc's other texts equally reveal this propensity for the representation of immanent natures. His 1875 *History of Human Habitation* examines the perennial practices of domestication, while *Learning to Draw* (1879) and *The History of a House* (1873) are thinly disguised *Bildungsromans* in which the process of cultivation is emphasized over the cultivation of an individual.[22]

In "Disintegration of the Crystalline Rocks," Viollet-le-Duc depicts the morphological "life" of Mont Blanc. Interestingly, however, none of the four images depicted in this mathematical regression is an actual representation of Mont Blanc. Viollet-le-Duc renders this drawing as if the process of crystalline disintegration had a life of its own, independent of Mont Blanc or the specificity of any other geological formation. Similarly, his illustration of the phenomenon of regelation is revealing. Here, Viollet-le-Duc attempts to taxonomically depict matter that is undergoing a change of state. Anticipating Henri Bergson's vitalist assertion that "form is only a snapshot view of a transition," Viollet-le-Duc produces stop-motion imagery at both micro and macro scales, making the process of glacial formation immediately intelligible.[23] In thus depicting geological formation (the process of upheaval), geological erosion (crystalline disintegration), and glacial changes of state (regelation and compression), Viollet-le-Duc's representations of Mont Blanc epitomize Deleuzean "immanence": a process that is always yet "in the making."[24]

IV Technical and Tectonic Immanence

By contrast, in Gottfried Semper's hands, the subject of geology is always already categorized through the material specificity of stones of a particular sort, and through the tectonic lens of stereotomy. In his seminal text, *Style in the Technical and Tectonic Arts or, Practical Aesthetics* (1860–63), stone is conceptualized as a building material inseparable from the techniques through which it is prepared for construction. When Antoine Picon addresses architectural construction, he describes it as being "on the verge of speaking," but in Semper's case, the techniques of stereotomy are both *a priori* and prescriptive, and in this sense, the stone already knows what it is going to say. Paradoxically, Semper discusses the techniques of stereotomy before he ever considers the materiality of stone, exacerbating this omission by positing the question: "But did stereotomy, in fact, have no original domain to it?"[25] What follows this question is a historical discussion of the hearth, indicating that Semper is operating under the assumption that the ontology of stereotomic technique can be traced back to the central element of a primitive building form.

Following a similar logic, Semper then discusses the foundation wall:

> The lifeless crystalline-mineral quality that characterizes the foundation wall makes it a formal manifestation of stone construction; its nature corresponds completely to what is placed on top of it. The two combine to form a self-contained whole, what one might call a representative of a *crystalline universe*. Stone turns eurythmically inward on all sides and denies any external existence. We cannot contemplate it except as a regular and complete form.[26]

With respect to the geological specimens under consideration, Semper's prioritization of stereotomy and its attendant mathematization of stone epitomizes technical and tectonic immanence. The characterization of a foundation wall as a "lifeless," "self-contained whole," that "denies any external existence," articulates a moment in which technique eclipses material possibility, in which the "how" of stereotomy's mathematical capacity to fashion stone supplants the "what" of traditional material iconography. In Semper's hermetic world of construction, in his "crystalline universe," any vitalist aspirations for the generative capacity of stone are channelled into the mathematical proprieties of stereotomy; the stoniness of stone capitulates to the human techniques through which it is fashioned towards technical and tectonic ends. The life of Semper's stone is mathematically predetermined as it succumbs to the exigencies of construction practices. For Semper, geological knowledge is thus confined to the epistemological horizon of stone as building material, and this horizon is squarely located between column base and frieze in the mathematical and tectonic expression of stereotomy.

V Aesthetic Immanence

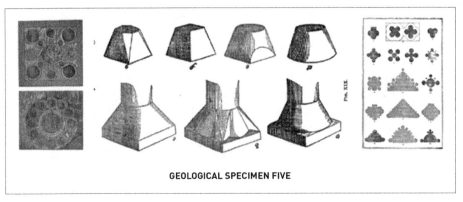

GEOLOGICAL SPECIMEN FIVE

Fig. 05   John Ruskin, *Wall Veil Decoration*, from *The Stones of Venice* (1851-53), John Ruskin, *Peers*, from *The Stones of Venice* (1851-53), John Ruskin, *Plans of Peers*, from *The Stones of Venice* (1851-53)Joseph Michael Gandy, *Architecture: Its Natural Mode* (1838)

The first chapter of John Ruskin's *The Stones of Venice* (1851–53) is entitled "Quarry," a rubric that definitively established the inextricability of human and geological history, given that the chapter is primarily concerned with the political and religious history of Venice. The first image of Ruskin's book, a "Wall Veil Decoration," illustrates the story of an ambassador who arrived in Venice in the fifteenth century and immediately recognized a change in its architecture. Here, Ruskin argues that Greek architecture was "clumsily copied" by the Romans. Following on the heels of this anecdote, Ruskin admits his desire to establish a law for architecture, like the one that exists in painting, which would allow for a distinction to be drawn between good architecture and bad. He writes: "I felt also assured that this law must be universal if it were conclusive; that it must enable us to reject all foolish and base work, and to accept all noble and wise work, without reference to style or national feeling. [...] I set myself, therefore, to establish such a law."[27] Ruskin rationalizes his search for such a law by revealing his aspiration to establish the very foundations of architectural criticism.

Given that Ruskin would like these foundations to be discerning and capable of eschewing the clumsy copy with which his text begins, his language then takes up the tropes of geological formation: "And if I should succeed, as I hope, in making the Stones of Venice touchstones, and detecting, by the mouldering of her marble, poison more subtle than ever was betrayed by the rending of her crystal"—his description concludes with the promise to access a more vital truth.[28] Here, Ruskin's language of geological decay (mouldering), geological examination (touchstones are assaying tools used to identify precious metals), and geological formation (the process of crystallization) lays the foundations for an aesthetic law that will not falter in the face of substandard stylistic copies. Though the operations of geological formation and human cultural production may parallel one another, aesthetic judgment should emulate nature's generative processes in order to fulfill its universal aspirations. Ultimately, the moralizing tone of Ruskin's nascent architectural criticism emanates from this desire for aesthetic law to mimetically replicate natural law, ensuring historical continuity and safeguarding against stylistic anomaly.

VI Origins: The Inception of Immanence

GEOLOGICAL SPECIMEN SIX

Joseph Michael Gandy, from *Architecture: Its Natural Mode* (1838)   Fig. 06

Architecture: Its Natural Model (1838), specimen six, is Joseph Michael Gandy's pictorial narrative on the entanglements of human and geologic time. In the foreground, a group of primates (an obvious allusion to human evolution) crafts a primitive hut through the bending and lashing of tree branches. In front of the hut, a primate with a simian head and human body perches, "unaware of the basaltic fragment on which he is seated, the faceted and monumental ruins of this Classicizing geology spilling all around him."[29] Here, the primate evolving into a human before our eyes occupies a "Classicizing geology"—a stone poised somewhere between its geological formation and its cultural articulation as column. Behind this hut looms Fingal's Cave—a geological tourist attraction in Scotland—conveying the message, "the future history of architecture was already written in the landscape, merely waiting for human civilization to catch up."[30] The formal affinities between the manmade shelter and the geologically wrought cave attest to this.

Gandy's watercolour, the only surviving image of his *Comparative Architecture* series at the Royal Academy in London, was exhaustively described in the exhibition catalogue. It is something of a geological *capriccio*, a collection of the world's most remarkable geological formations assembled as if they occupied a single site. Etymologically linked to the word "capricious," the *capriccio* emerged as a representational genre in the seventeenth century, at a moment when the cosmological paradigm was gradually being eclipsed by modern historical and scientific paradigms, with their attendant notion of individual human agency. Here, the whimsy of the geographical imprecision of Gandy's collection—the image includes the natural arch from Mercury Bay in New Zealand and the rock formations of Cappadocia in Anatolia—meets the accuracy of the modern scientific gaze and the temporal agency of the new historical worldview. Gandy wrote: "Men who traverse this earth and examine the animal, mineral, and vegetable kingdoms find a succession of models for his artificial fabricks. [...] The philosophy of architecture is a sketchbook from nature."[31] Though the *capriccio* genre was commonplace in Gandy's time, the paradox raised by the idea of a geological *capriccio* is compelling because it posits the operations of geological formation *between* site-specificity and human agency.

Fig. 07   Joseph Michael Gandy, *A Selection of Parts of Buildings, Public and Private, Erected from the Designs of John Soane* (1818)

Perhaps Gandy's primary contribution to the genre resides in his acknowledgment that the assembled collection need not be capricious; in fact, as an aggregate it has the capacity to describe a life, as was the case in his homage to John Soane. In 1818, Gandy produced a painting entitled *A Selection of Buildings, Public and Private, Erected from the Designs of John Soane*, commemorating Soane's contributions as an architect and antiquarian. If in this case Gandy is describing an immanent history, the life he alludes to in *Architecture: Its Natural Model* is a geological life. In reference to such evocations of "life," Deleuze writes: "The life of such individuality fades away in favour of the singular life immanent to a man who no longer has a name, though he can be mistaken for no other."[32] There is little wonder that Gandy is possessed of a geopoetic imagination that allows him to speculate upon such a geological life. "Matter-movement" stilled in the process of construction or halted in the attrition of ruination had long been the ostensible subject of his representations, as evidenced by his seminal image *A Vision of Sir John Soane's Design for the Bank of England as a Ruin* (1830). With painstaking attention to detail, Gandy represented immanent life—the life of a building, the life of an architect, the life of a geological specimen—seamlessly eliding natural creation and human production, and ultimately paving the way for an architecture of the Anthropocene.

VII Resource

Contained within the ideological ruminations of Karl Marx and Friedrich Engels' *The Communist Manifesto* (1848), is this tribute to the productive knowledge of the bourgeoisie:

> The bourgeoisie, during its rule of scarce one hundred years, has created more massive and more colossal productive forces than have all preceding generations together. Subjection of nature's forces to man, machinery, application of chemistry to industry and agriculture, steam navigation, railways, electric telegraphs, clearing of whole continents for cultivation, canalization or rivers, whole populations conjured out of the ground—what earlier century had even a presentiment that such productive forces slumbered in the lap of social labour?[33]

GEOLOGICAL SPECIMEN SEVEN

Diderot and D'Alembert, *Mineral Loads or Veins and their Bearings*, from *l'Éncylopedie*, vol. 6 (1768)   Fig. 08

What Marx and Engels are witnessing, in this and other passages, is the commodification of the natural world into resources (to be used, and used up), as well as the reification of its vital forces into labour and energy. What transpired during this century of bourgeoisie rule that occasioned such a massive reconceptualization of the natural world? Between 1751 and 1777, Denis Diderot and Jean le Rond d'Alembert published the 32 volumes of the *Encyclopédie*, a comprehensive and exhaustive documentation of modern knowledge.

Part of the project of the encylopedists was to classify geological and mineralogical resources, and to document the various technologies deployed for extracting them from the earth. As a result of eighteenth-century archeological and antiquarian activities, the earth acquired a new perceptual depth, facilitating the conceptualization of the natural as immanent history, and of the earth's materials as resources that could be extracted just like archeological artifacts. Natural dispositions were reconfigured into productive knowledge, as in geological specimen seven, an illustration demonstrating the virtue of constructing galleries and tunnels according to the inclination of the veins being mined. Typically, in these encyclopedia images, a sectional view of an underworld of resource extraction supports the unfolding perspective of a productive landscape, in which the resources are utilized towards highly differentiated ends of cultural fabrication. In this sense, these types of images constitute a thickening of the epistemological horizon, as they cultivate new territories for the imposition of productive knowledge. Eventually, the technologies of extraction begin to eclipse the commodification of the earth's resources in such a way that the instrumentalization of the process and the productive knowledge it proffers become the ostensible subject of these images. The geological life depicted by the encyclopedists is a life of resource extraction, energy production, and commodity consumption, epitomizing Nietzsche's "monster of energy" in the escalating supply and demand of the emerging capitalist economy.[34]

GEOLOGICAL SPECIMEN EIGHT

Fig. 09   Giovanni Battista Piranesi,
           Foundations of the Theater of
           Marcellus, from *Antichità Romane*
           (1756)

VIII Foundations

In the context of Venice, foundations consist of wooden piles made from the trunks of alder trees, submerged in the waters of the Adriatic, sitting upon a soft layer of sand or mud, then upon a harder layer of compressed clay. Giovanni Battista Piranesi, born in Mogliano Veneto on Venetian *terra firma*, laboured under both a Venetian preoccupation with foundations and an antiquarian curiosity about the ground upon which he stood. His preoccupation with foundations, both literal and figurative, is also attributable to the aftermath of the Quarrel of the Ancients and Moderns, a late seventeenth-century literary and artistic debate over the origins and foundations of modern European culture. It is as critical to historically situate

Piranesi's work in its aftermath as it is to situate it geographically. Piranesi's desire to excavate a legitimate and appropriate historical past to substantiate his contemporary culture; his ambition to make the unseen geological substrate, laying beneath the horizon, into a visible and intelligible traditional footing; and his attempt to exaggerate archeological legacies; all point to an explicit aspiration to construct cultural foundations in a moment of epistemological uncertainty. In 1756, he produced a volume on the architecture of Roman antiquity, *Antichitá Romane*, which warrants some comparison with Michel Serres' text *Rome: The Book of Foundations*.

Piranesi, "Mausoleum of Cecilia Matella," from *Antichità Romane* (1756)   Fig. 10

Serres writes: "*Ad urbe condita.* Foundation is a condition. The condition is union—that which is situated or put together, stored away, held in reserve, locked up in a safe place, and thus hidden from the gaze, beyond understanding."[35] If, for Serres, foundations are hidden from the gaze beyond understanding, the horizon of epistemological intelligibility has expanded into subterranean territories for Piranesi.

In her seminal text *Body Criticism: Imaging the Unseen in Enlightenment Art and Medicine*, Barbara Maria Stafford describes the corrosive process of Piranesi's etchings as a parallel operation to an archeological imagination that sees under and through, visually dismantling the surface of things. She writes: "Piranesi's radical experimentation with etching, a corrosive chemical process for biting a copperplate, permitted him to perform perceptual rescue work. He artistically unearthed the mutilated corpse of Italian antiquity."[36] Aspects of Piranesi's "perceptual rescue work" can be seen in his "Foundations of the Theater of Marcellus," (geological specimen number eight) in which the scalar exaggeration of the monument manifests certain cultural foundational anxieties. Lurking beneath the sterilizing tendencies of the Enlightenment *tabula rasa* and the new epistemologies it would support, Piranesi literally unearths a history both experientially distant and immanently present. The intelligibility of human history parallels the intelligibility of natural history—the foundations for both are accessible and understandable. As Stafford eloquently states, "There was an intimate connection, then, between the etching process and the exploration of hidden physical or material topographies. Important, too, was the entire panoply of probing instruments, chemicals, heat and smoke, revealing and concealing grounds."[37]

In a quite different representation of foundations from the same text, Piranesi stumbled upon a pile of rocks on the site of the ancient Mausoleum of Cecilia Matella, and became curious about the peculiar notches carefully cut into the discarded stones. These markings allowed Piranesi to reconstruct the monument and speculatively represent the complex block-and-tackle system he imagined was deployed in its construction. This depiction of foundations is consistent with the enlightenment ethos in which progress began to slowly eclipse providence, and technology took up the eschatological agenda of making a better world—a man-made and immanent creation. For his part, Serres describes the foundations of Rome not as a static system of support, but rather as a fluid and fecund cultural substrate: "The foundation is the theory or practice of movement. Of fusion and melange. Of the multiplicity of time. Indeed, all foundation is, in the original sense, current. The dike was built between nature and culture. Along it one could easily return."[38] For Piranesi, the intelligibility of the foundation stones of ancient Rome manifest such a fusion or mélange—a current that renders history immanent and foregrounds the elastic imagination of the architect.

IX Formations

GEOLOGICAL SPECIMEN NINE

Fig. 11   Athanasius Kircher, *The Eruption of Mount Etna, 1637,*
from *Mundus Subterraneus* (1664)

On a visit to Messina in 1638, Jesuit scholar Athanasius Kircher witnessed Vesuvius as it began to reverberate and smolder. Overcome by curiosity, he hiked to the rim of the active volcano, and this is what he later wrote about the experience: "When finally I reached the crater, it was terrible to behold. The whole area was lit up by the fires, and the glowing sulphur and bitumen produced an intolerable vapour. It was just like hell, only lacking the demons to complete the picture!"[39] Despite this formative experience, Kircher's geological imaginings, pursued in his 1664 text *Mundus Subterraneus*, decidedly tilted more in the direction of nature's generative capacity than its destructive tendency. In this text, he advanced a hermetic and interiorized worldview of geologic formation: "Kircher repeated an ancient animistic theory important to both British and French materialists that found support among reputable eighteenth-century natural philosophers; namely, *that all earthly bodies grow and develop from within.*"[40] Kircher's interest in the vital forces of geologic formation shifted in scale from those forces that animated and shaped the earth's surface, to those that contributed to "physiographic metamorphoses"—the natural appearance of images and pictograms on stones.[41]

In this scalar shift from the geologic forces animating the subterranean world to the vital stimuli that produce physiographic expressions, Kircher articulates the operations of immanent life. Of these pictorial stones, Barbara Maria Stafford writes:

> Thus the patterned moth or flower, like the fossil script, or even man himself, exists nowhere else but in the particular and concrete container, envelope, or carapace of its matter. Design is not a separable or removable imprint or impresa stamped on the surface. It does not rest on the plane but permeates the medium and grows along with it. Design is a succinct picture or real symbol of the actual development of that medium.[42]

In this sense, for Kircher, geological configuration is an act of design, and more broadly, within the development of any medium resides this immanent formational impulse. By explicating the process of formation in this way, he strongly anticipates subsequent appropriations of the generative capacities of the natural world.

X Transmutations

GEOLOGICAL SPECIMEN TEN

Basil Valentine, The Twelve Keys (1678), Ernst Rutherford in his Laboratory   Fig. 12

Perhaps nowhere is the thirst for the knowledge of creation more apparent than in the alchemical pursuit of the Philosopher's Stone, a legendary substance allegedly capable of turning inexpensive metals into gold, and believed to be an elixir of life useful for rejuvenation and possibly achieving immortality. For a long time, it was the most sought-after goal in Western alchemy. Possession of the Philosopher's

Stone, in the form of a yellow, red, or grey powder, was ultimately not about the possibility of accumulated wealth, but rather the power to transform. Precious metals were merely the outcome of the transmutation. The vital force—the life within the stone that facilitated the transformation—was either controlled for purposes of transmutation, or simply possessed as a form of rejuvenation or immortality. The outcome of the experimental procedure was far less important than the instrumental capacity to direct and control the vital force harnessed within the Philosopher's Stone.

Working together in a laboratory at McGill University in 1898, chemists Ernest Rutherford and Frederick Soddy discovered that radium emits radioactive particles, developing the concept of half-life – a period of time over which half of the substance is emitted and lost.[43] It did not take long for the scientists to make the connection between this material transformation of Radium, with that of their alchemical predecessors. Soddy, who apparently studied alchemy as a hobby, had the temerity to describe the transformation they were witnessing as transmutation. Rutherford responded: "For Mike's sake, Soddy, don't call it transmutation. They'll have our heads off as alchemists."[44] This tenth and final geological specimen in architecture's lapidarium, then, brings us full circle. In this case, the life depicted, or perhaps more accurately, the half-life, conforms to Deleuze's description of life as "matter in variation that enters assemblages and leaves them."[45]

Conclusion

This foray through ten specimens in architecture's lapidarium has attempted to advance the following five-point argument. First, a vitalist theme emerges historically at the intersection of architectural, scientific, and philosophical discourse. Second, as a result of these vitalist tendencies, the situation of architecture typically engaged through the category of "site" ceased to be represented as a static, mute, or indifferent condition. Third, vitalism introduces the term "life" as a chronological measure of existence, facilitating the elision of human and geological agency characteristic of the Anthropocene. Fourth, in biology and autobiography, "life" is both the unit of measure and evidence of immanence. The metric of life emerges from the overlap of introverted biological discourse, searching for the smallest unit manifesting life, and the inner investigations of autobiographical work, examining how a given character came into being and how an individual life acquires meaning. Fifth, these ten geological specimens construct a foundation for the understanding of "life" as the measure, and immanence as the operative condition of architecture in the Anthropocene era.

Within architecture's lapidarium, "life" is explored as an incremental measure of immanence—the life of a resource, the life of a material, the life of a building and the respective lives of its inhabitants, the life of the architectural conceits of "siting" and "material imagination," and the historiographical life of a disciplinary engagement with stone—all contribute to the constitution of geological life in the Anthropocene. Each of the ten geological specimens represents such an immanent life, and the exploration of each attempted to expose the particular vehicles of immanence that attempt to explicate life's vital generative forces through the lens of the scientific paradigm, often translating formerly metaphysical concepts into immanent ideas.

In the case of Aldo Rossi's *Scientific Autobiography*, geological specimen one, the plan and the autobiography are both examined as vehicles of immanence, through the lens of parallel lives. Utilizing Max Planck's conservation of energy, Rossi draws his scientific autobiography into dialogue with that of the renowned physicist, as well as Stendhal's *bildungsroman*, *The Life of Henri Brulard*. For Rossi, Planck and Stendhal influenced his architecture through the idea of the conservation of energy and the notion that plans are integral to autobiographical narratives. In drawing this comparison, Rossi moves the possibility of immanent life across three registers: matter's capacity to conserve energy, the archi-

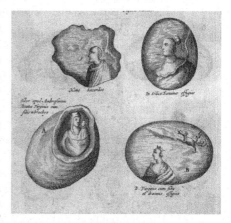

tectural plan's capacity to capture an event before it unfolds, and the autobiography's capacity to narrate without definitively concluding. The mythological figures of Isis, the Delphic Oracle, Sisyphus, and Ferdinand Cheval, geological specimen two, consider the recovery of myth's cyclical narratives in a historical moment in which science's linear narratives dominate. The re-telling of these narratives through the lens of the scientific paradigm explicates numerous vehicles of immanence. In the case of Isis, the veil that once mediated between the Romantics and nature's secrets has been removed by the prying analysis of the scientific gaze. As for the Delphic Oracle, her ability to speak for the earth, translating the desires of the gods, is rendered immanent in a process of thesaurization that taxonom-

Athanasius Kircher, detail from *Pictorial Stones with Human Faces* (1664)

Fig. 13

ically represents difference. In Camus' hands, Sisyphus becomes a figure through which anthropological identity and geological identity are elided in a single, if not singular, immanent life. While in the urban myth of Ferdinand Cheval, the surrealists identify a material imagination capable of operating between the real and the oneiric.

Viollet-le-Duc's images of Mont Blanc, geological specimen three, deploy the serial representational strategies of morphology to capture the immanent life of a mountain. In his hands, mathematics becomes a critical tool of abstraction, which leads to speculation about geological decay and formation. The use of taxonomy to represent material phase changes is another vehicle of immanence deployed by Viollet-le-Duc, bringing the fixity of the categories of human knowledge into dialogue with the fluid formation of matter.

Gottfried Semper's discussion of the techniques of stereotomy in *Style in the Technical and Tectonic Arts* (1860-63), geological specimen four, examines the mathematical operations that impose form on matter as a vehicle of immanence. Semper grounds the epistemology of the techniques of stereotomy upon the ontology of the hearth and foundation walls, theorizing a "crystalline universe" in which the *a priori* mathematics of geological formation gives rise to architectural tectonics.

John Ruskin's *Stones of Venice*, geological specimen five, achieves immanence in the attempt to formulate a universal aesthetic law capable of distinguishing good architecture from "clumsy" copies. Ruskin's law incorporates the tropes of geological decay (mouldering), mineralogical assaying (touchstones), and geological formation (crystallization) as developmental models ensuring the legitimacy and authenticity of the aesthetic outcomes.

Joseph Michael Gandy's *Architecture: Its Natural Model* (1838), geological specimen six, deploys hybrid logics as a vehicle of immanence, operating between the activities of humans and primates, and between the formal logics of geology and architecture. Gandy's *capriccio* is a collection of natural wonders that positions geological "life" between the site-specificity of the individual formations and the agency of the human imagination capable of gathering them together. Within this *capriccio* we witness the seamless merging of natural creation and human production.

In geological specimen seven, *Mineral Loads or Veins and their Bearings*, from Diderot and d'Alembert's *Encyclopédie*, geological life is rendered immanent through the commodification of the earth in terms of its resources and the human labour required to extract them. The project of the *Encyclopédie* is fully entangled with the instrumentalization of culture and the productive knowledge that it occasions. Within the *Encyclopédie*, immanence is achieved through the exhaustive cataloguing of disparate techniques of cultural production and their capacity to establish new epistemological horizons.

In Piranesi's examination of the foundations of ancient Roman culture, geological specimen eight, immanence is located between the almost mythological exaggeration of the "Foundations of the Theater of Marcellus" and the scientific explanation of the construction of the "Mausoleum of Cecilia Matella." Through the parallel subtractive practices of archeology and etching, life (the life of a building, the life of a ruin) is made immanent in Piranesi's work, through its analogy with the processes of discovery and representation.

Athanasius Kircher's *Mundus Subterraneus* (1664), geological specimen nine, presents an interiorized view of geological formation in which all development emanates from within. In Kircher's oeuvre, generative creation is mapped from the scale of geological formation to the scale of physiographic metamorphosis, leading to the conclusion that geological configuration is an act of design. Here, the vehicle of immanence resides in the belief that within the development of every medium, a formational impulse can be made intelligible.

Finally, in the transition from alchemical transmutation to nuclear physics, geological specimen ten, the vehicle of immanence is scientific explication. The Philosopher's Stone was a trope that aligned the possibility of human transformation and change with the possibility for physical change in the material world—it registered a condition of intrinsic development against a condition of extrinsic development, utilizing the observation of one to theorize changes in the other. The deployment of this same term in the context of nuclear physics produced a vehicle of immanence that was ever more interiorized, and ever more radicalized in terms of its implications.

In architecture's lapidarium, the immanent life of geology is made manifest; the complicity of mineralogical crystallization and human mathematization is expressed; the intelligibility of natural formation and human fabrication is articulated. Within this collection of geological specimens, the intermingling of the earth's generative forces and human productive ambitions become one, anticipating the architecture of the Anthropocene.

Notes

1   Aldo Rossi, *A Scientific Autobiography*, trans. Lawrence Venuti (Cambridge, Mass.: The MIT Press, 1981), 1.

2   Stendhal actually wrote two autobiographical accounts, and both were published posthumously. *The Life of Henry Brulard* was published as a fiction, whereas *Souvenirs d'égotisme (The Memoirs of an Egoist)*, published in 1892, was framed as a more standard autobiographical account. But there is agreement amongst scholars that *The Life of Henry Brulard*, though posited as a fiction, is the more autobiographically accurate of the two. For the purposes of this argument, the metric of "life," even Stendhal's own life, operates seamlessly between fictional and realistic accounts.

3   Erich Auerbach persuasively argues that Stendhal's writing is not influenced by the pervasiveness of historicism; though he places the events of his life in perspective and is aware of the constant changes around him, this does not result in an evolutionary understanding. Auerbach writes: "[H]e sees the individual man far less as the product of his historical situation and as taking part in it, than as an atom within it; a man seems to have been thrown almost by chance into the milieu in which he lives; it is a resistance with which he can deal more or less successfully, not really a culture-medium with which he is organically connected." Erich Auerbach, *Mimesis: The Representation of Reality in Western Literature* (Princeton, NJ: Princeton University Press, 1968), 463–465.

4   Rossi, *A Scientific Autobiography*, 6.

5   Beyle wrote under at least one hundred different pseudonyms, and in this fact resides the relationship between a fluid life and the static name that stabilizes it for a moment in time.

6 Barry Bergdoll, "Of Crystals, Cells, and Strata: Natural History and Debates on the Form of a New Architecture in the Nineteenth Century," *Architectural History* 50 (2007): 6.

7 Martin J. S. Rudwick, *Bursting the Limits of Time: The Reconstruction of Geohistory in the Age of Revolution* (Chicago: The University of Chicago Press, 2005), 9.

8 Ibid.

9 Gilles Deleuze, *Pure Immanence: Essays on a Life*, trans. Anne Boyman (New York: Zone Books, 2001), 29.

10 Jane Bennett, *Vibrant Matter: A Political Ecology of Things* (Durham: Duke University Press, 2010), 53.

11 Ibid., 54.

12 Giorgio Agamben, *Potentialities: Collected Essays in Philosophy*, ed. and trans. Daniel Heller-Roazen (Stanford: Stanford University Press, 1999), 223. Agamben goes on to stipulate that "the colon represents a dislocation of immanence in itself, a characterization suggesting that this crossing or passing is not relational, but rather autonomous.

13 Ibid., 224.

14 Ibid., 234.

15 Jean-Paul Sartre, *Being and Nothingness*, trans. Hazel E. Barnes (New York: Simon & Schuster, 1956), 738.

16 16 Karsten Harries, *The Meaning of Modern Art* (Evanston: Northwestern University Press, 1968), 50.

17 Steven Connor, *Dumbstruck: A Cultural History of Ventriloquism* (Oxford: Oxford University Press, 2000), 52.

18 Page duBois, *Sowing the Body: Psychoanalysis and Ancient Representations of Women* (Chicago: University of Chicago Press, 1988), 107–108. Elsewhere, duBois describes thesaurization in this way: "It locates the female as a potential for producing goods or protecting them. She becomes the locus of inscription, the folded papyrus that signifies the potential for deception." See: Page duBois, "The Platonic Appropriation of Reproduction," in *Feminist Interpretations of Plato*, ed. Nancy Tuana (University Park, PA: The Pennsylvania State University Press, 1994), 139.

19 Albert Camus, *The Myth of Sisyphus and Other Essays*, trans. Justin O'Brien (New York: Vintage International, 1983), 121.

20 See Eugène Emmanuel Viollet-le-Duc, *Mont Blanc: A Treatise on Its Geodesical and Geological Constitution; Its Transformations; and the Ancient and Recent State of Its Glaciers*, trans. B. Bucknall (London: Sampson Low, Marston, Searle, & Rivington, 1877). Originally published in French in 1876.

21 Deleuze, *Pure Immanence*, 26.

22 *Histoire de l'habitation humaine, depuis les temps préhistoriques jusqu'à nos jours* (1875), published in English in 1876; *Histoire d'un dessinateur: comment on apprend à dessiner* (1879); and *Histoire d'une maison* (1873).

23 Henri Bergson, *Creative Evolution*, trans. Arthur Mitchell (Lanham, Md.: University Press of America, 1983), 302. (First published in French in 1907, and in English in 1911.)

24 John Rajchman, introduction to *Pure Immanence: Essays on A Life*, by Gilles Deleuze (New York: Zone Books, 2001), 13. Rajchman writes: "For immanence is pure only when it is not immanent *to* a prior subject or object, mind or matter, only when, neither innate nor acquired, it is always yet 'in the making;' and 'a life' is a potential or virtual subsisting in just such a purely immanent plane."

25 Gottfried Semper, *Style in the Technical and Tectonic Arts or, Practical Aesthetics*, trans. Harry Francis Mallgrave and Michael Robinson, Getty Texts and Documents Series (Los Angeles: The Getty Research Center, 2004), 726.

26 Semper, *Style in the Technical and Tectonic Arts*, 728.

27 John Ruskin, *The Stones of Venice* (London: George Allen, 1896), 52.

28 Ibid., 48.

29 Brian Lukacher, *Joseph Gandy: An Architectural Visionary in Georgian England* (London: Thames and Hudson, 2006), 189.

30 Ibid.

31 Ibid.

32 Deleuze, *Pure Immanence*, 29.

33 Karl Marx and Frederick Engels, *The Communist Manifesto* (London: Verso, 1998), 40.

34 In *The Will to Power*, Nietzsche describes the monster of energy as follows: "And do you know what 'the world' is to me? Shall I show it to you in my mirror? This world: a monster of energy, without beginning, without end; a firm, iron magnitude of force that does not grow bigger or smaller, that does not expend itself but only transforms itself; as a whole, of unalterable size, a household without expenses or losses, but likewise without increase or income; enclosed by 'nothingness' as by a boundary; not something blurry or wasted, not something endlessly extended, but set in a definite space as a definite force, and not a space that might be 'empty' here or there, but rather as force throughout, as a play of forces and waves of forces, at the same time one and many, increasing here and at the same time decreasing there; a sea of forces flowing and rushing together, eternally changing, eternally flooding back, with tremendous years of recurrence, with an ebb and a flood of its forms; out of the simplest forms striving toward the most complex, out of the stillest, most rigid, coldest forms striving toward the hottest, most turbulent, most self-contradictory, and then again returning home to the simple out of this abundance, out of the play of contradictions back to the joy of concord, still affirming itself in this uniformity of its courses and its years, blessing itself as that which must return eternally, as a becoming that knows no satiety, no disgust, no weariness: this, my *Dionysian* world of the eternally self-creating, the eternally self-destroying, this mystery world of the twofold voluptuous delight, my 'beyond good and evil,' without goal, unless the joy of the circle is itself a goal; without will, unless a ring feels good will toward itself—do you want a *name* for this world? A *solution* for all of its riddles? A *light* for you, too, you best-concealed, strongest, most intrepid, most midnightly men?—*This world is the will to power—and nothing besides!* And you yourselves are also this will to power—and nothing besides!" Friedrich Nietzsche, *The Will to Power*, trans. Walter Kaufman and R. J. Hollingdale (New York: Vintage Books, 1967), 549–550.

35 Michel Serres, *Rome: The Book of Foundations*, trans. Felicia McCarren (Stanford: Stanford University Press, 1991), 259.

36 Barbara Maria Stafford, *Body Criticism: Imaging the Unseen in Enlightenment Art and Medicine* (Cambridge: MIT Press, 1991), 58.

37 Stafford, *Body Criticism*, 70.

38 Serres, *Rome*, 275.

39 Paula Findlen, *Possessing Nature: Museums, Collecting, and Scientific Culture in Early Modern Italy* (Berkeley: University of California Press, 1994), 186.

40 Barbara Maria Stafford, "Characters in Stones, Marks on Paper: Enlightenment Discourse on Natural and Artificial Taches," *Art Journal* 44, no. 3 (Autumn 1984): 233.

41 Ibid.

42 Ibid., 235.

43 David Orrell, *Truth or Beauty: Science and the Quest for Order* (New Haven: Yale University Press, 2012), 72.

44 Ibid.

45 Bennett, *Vibrant Matter*, 54.

Erratic Imaginaries

by Jane Hutton

Thinking Landscape as Evidence

Kidston Lake Rocking Stone, Kidstone Lake, Nova Scotia. Gardner Collection of Photographs, Harvard College Library

Fig. 01

In 1882, the Rev. D. Honeyman wrote about a peculiar geological feature: "The Rocking Stone of Spryfield has long been regarded as an object of interest. [...] I was astonished at its imposing appearance. Having reached its top by a ladder, which is placed against it for the convenience of visitors, I enjoyed a strange rock in this wonderful cradle. My conductor and companion, Simon D. Macdonald, F.G.S., seeing me seated at the top, went to the end of a lever, also placed in position, and commenced operations. The mass began to move, the motion increased and the rocking commenced, and was continued until I was satisfied."[1] A similarly pleasurable experience of rocking the Rocking Stone at Kidston Lake in Spryfield, Nova Scotia, was described 60 years previous in an article in *The Glasgow Mechanics Magazine*. After "rocking and inspecting this wonderful stone for some time," the author recorded some observations. Pivoting on a flat stone, the Rocking Stone could be moved by simply mounting it and shifting one's weight from side to side. With a short lever, the massive body could be moved about 12 inches in an east-northeast to west-southwest direction "by a child of 12 years."[2] Noting that there were no nearby rocks that the Rocking Stone could have broken from, the author concluded that the anomaly "clearly evidences the skill and power of an Almighty hand!" By Honeyman's time, a tall, wooden ladder and a lever were on hand to help rockers mount the stone and instigate movement. [Fig. 01] Picnickers laid out their spreads on the flat top and enjoyed the gentle motion produced by their very presence. But years of recreational rocking eventually wore down the base of the stone, and it stopped moving. In the 1890s, one group of garrison soldiers allegedly rocked so hard that the stone became lodged in place. In the 1990s, as part of a clean-up effort of the surrounding land, members of the local heritage society removed impeding materials from beneath the stone, freeing it to rock freely once more.[3]

Even without human force, the boulder was known to move; a strong gust of wind could trigger its vibration.[4] But long before, the Rocking Stone had moved, or had been moved, even more significantly. In fact, it had been picked up, transported, and deposited by retreating glaciers about 20,000-26,000 years ago at the end of the Last Glacial Maximum, or Wisconsin Glaciation Period, when vast ice sheets extended across North America, Northern Europe, Northwestern Asia and much of the Andes.[5] Honeyman, who was familiar with the local geology and the principles of glacial transport that were well-known by 1882, took a hammer to the rock to investigate its mineral composition and posited that the boulder had probably been moved by some nine or ten miles.

Terrain Erratique

N° 1. PIERRE DES MARMETTES.

Fig. 02   Pierre des Marmettes, from Jean De Charpentier, *Essai Sur Les Glaciers et Sur le Terrain Erratique du Bassin du Rhone* (Lausanne: Imprimerie et Librairie de Marc Ducloux, 1841).

Landscapes conspicuously strewn with boulders of foreign origin in the southern Jura Mountain region were described by German-Swiss geologist Jean de Charpentier as *terrains erratiques*.[6] The term was later used to describe not the landscape, but the individual thing—an *erratic*. Charpentier himself lived not far from one such rock—the *Pierre des Marmettes*—a ten-metre-tall granite boulder in the Swiss Rhône valley. [Fig. 02] Based on its unique granitic composition, the rock appeared to have come from 30 kilometres up the valley.[7] The supposed journey of such a behemoth confounded expectations and served as the basis of inquiry, and later as evidence, for Charpentier's contributions to the development of glacial theory. This aligns with the trajectory of discovery described by Thomas Kuhn, who, in *The Structure of Scientific Revolutions*, writes that "discovery commences with the awareness of anomaly, i.e. with the recognition that nature has somehow violated the paradigm-induced expectations that govern normal science."[8] While Charpentier investigated, public fascination with the boulder proliferated; a tourist pavilion was erected on top, a version of which remains today.[9] [Fig. 03] When the rock went up for sale to an extraction company in 1905, a nation-wide campaign was launched to save it. The ultimately successful case for preservation was based entirely on the rock's crucial role in the development of glacial theory.[10]

Postcard, Pierre des Marmettes, (1905)   Fig. 03
R. Heyraudt, Publisher, St. Maurice, collection of Vincent Franzen

Scientific and lay observations of erratic boulders have served as critical, distributed evidence for the development of the theory of glaciation; by implication, ideas of geologic time and the location of humans within it are also entangled in such a theory. Erratics attracted a wealth of curiosity through their alien lithology and their unexpected patterns of distribution, both of which were crucial aspects of the evidence needed to reconstruct an Ice Age. Still, long after they played a role in establishing modern geohistory, individual boulders persist as cultural artefacts for provoking and inscribing ideas about time. Certain erratics maintain a dual status as physical fragments of deep time and contemporary cultural objects that relay more recent histories. They are curious things—in size, shape, and position. They are visible and climbable relics of glacial processes too vast to otherwise experience. They are prone to being used as markers of human events and spaces, yet are also markers of deep time, having travelled long distances in nearly unimaginable environments. It is through this conflation of vastly different timescales that erratics bridge a seemingly unbridgeable divide between geological time and human action.

Flowing ice acts as a massive material conveyor, plucking and transporting fragments of rock as it advances. Glacial melt water enters fractures in the earth's surface, freezing, expanding, and loosening angular fragments, or blocks, of bedrock. Rather than being tumbled like river stones, blocks are dragged by the weight of the glacier, honing angular surfaces. Bound tightly by the ice, they scour the surfaces that they pass over, and abrade deep parallel grooves in the direction of the ice flow. In North America, melt water from the toe of the shrinking Laurentide Ice Sheet carved the Missouri and Ohio River systems, radically modifying the drainage patterns of the whole continent. The rebound of land released from the weight of ice, the action of melt water on different types of rock, and the deposition of conveyed debris formed the moraines, drumlins, eskers, and kettle ponds that characterize glacial surficial geology. The majority of this rock material is deposited near where it is picked up; a small fraction of it, usually composed of harder minerals, travels further and ends up deposited elsewhere, often on bedrock with a totally different mineralogical composition.[11] When not embedded in local till, large boulders will appear curiously on the surface of the land.

The Last Revolution

In the first half of the nineteenth century, efforts to reconstruct geologic time oscillated between two predominant hypotheses: one according to which the earth had existed for a very short time, estimated at 4000 B.C. by James Ussher; and another that suggested the earth had an unlimited timescale of repeated cycles of geologic change.[12] Georges Cuvier, then a professor at Paris's Museum of Natural History, proposed in his *Researches on Fossil Bones* (1812) a middle-ground and modern position, namely that the earth had a vast, non-repeated history, the great majority of which had occurred before humans existed. Cuvier described successive periods of calm, interrupted by periods of violent change, which he called "revolutions" and analogized to the recent political revolution in France.[13] The character of the "Last Revolution" was the most urgent to understand, as it distinguished between the present (human) world and a vaguely defined past.[14]

Among the most puzzling features of the Last Revolution were growing accounts of far-displaced erratic blocks and underlying bedrock scratched with directional markings. Massive boulders had been found on German plains originating in Scandinavia, in Brandenburg from across the Baltic Sea, and in St. Petersburg from somewhere near Finland.[15] As early as 1787, Horace-Bénédict de Saussure described "indicators," boulders with such particular lithology that they could be traced to the area from where they had likely originated.[16] Straight lines could then be drawn on a map between the site of an erratic and its probable origin. A widely circulated explanation was found in William Buckland's *Relics of the Deluge* (1823), which credited the changes to a mega-tsunami or catastrophic flood (which could be identified as Noah's Flood) dating back no more than 5,000 years.[17] That scattered boulders, drifts, and U-shaped valleys were evidence of a global diluvial event resonated strongly in the popular imagination. Thomas Cole's painting *The Subsiding of the Waters of the Deluge* (1829) depicts a scene after the rains of the great flood have ceased, with a human skull in the foreground and erratic boulders perched on high peaks signalling the destructive power of the waters.[18]

The everyday observations of erratic boulders and glacial processes by people living near them proved valuable for the naturalists seeking answers. Alpine shepherds remarked to early geologist visitors that large, angular boulders and abraded surfaces below existing glaciers were evidence that they had once been much larger. Field observations from one unnamed woodcutter from Meiringen and a shepherd named Jean-Pierre Perraudin ultimately allowed Charpentier to speculate that glaciers, not floods, had transported the boulders:[19] "The shepherds of the Alps have always had a better knowledge of the phenomena of the glacier than most scientific men."[20] Similarly, the Swiss naturalist Louis Agassiz credited Alpine shepherds, who had observed the landscape over time, with being the first to measure the movement of glaciers and their rate of change.[21] Eventually, the explanation that attributed erratic terrain and scratched bedrock to ice floes prevailed over the dilivual hypothesis. Building on the work of others, Charpentier suggested that a giant glacier had once extended throughout the Alps. Agassiz's *Etudes sur les glaciers* (1840) expanded on Charpentier's work, arguing that a single vast ice sheet had in fact covered much of the continent. These hypotheses were seminal in the development and communication of a widely accepted theory of glaciation.

"I hardly know anything more instructive to a student of geology," Agassiz suggested in 1860, during a lecture in Cambridge, Massachusetts, "than to watch the small physical phenomena which we see all about us, and by our imagination, conceive of them as operating on a grand scale."[22] Geologists and artists used the familiar landscape of glacial debris, erratic blocks, and scratched bedrock in New England to communicate to the public new theories of the geological past. Landscape artists of the Hudson River School socialized and conversed with geologists during the second half of the nineteenth century, as American landscape painting shifted its focus from the symbolic and allegorical to the study of natural phenomena with a more scientific lens. William Haseltine's painting *Rocks at Nahant* (1864) references the directional glacial markings on the Massachusetts shoreline, where both he and Agassiz spent time. The painting also depicts the same landscape where Agassiz's popular Sunday geology walks would take place, which Haseltine often attended.[23]

Scientific interest in erratics trailed off by the late nineteenth century, yet with their indubitable physicality and weighty presence they maintain a dual status as objects of scientific evidence. In *Things that Talk*, Lorraine Daston writes that such objects, which both "talk" through the meaning that they produce and are persistent as "things" in the world, "unsettle views about the nature of both."[24] The apparent paradoxes that surround knowledge of erratic boulders make them objects of sustained consideration. They are solid, insistent markers in space, yet they indicate a remote origin, and therefore travel between these two registers of knowing. Their movements are a result of both subsequent geologic forces and human forces, for instance in the relocation of a celebrated boulder for its "conservation." Their transient reputation destabilizes notions about the natural environment as static and also challenges assumptions about indigeneity and rights to land. Doreen Massey notes that in a campaign to promote immigration rights in Hamburg, Germany, a large, beloved boulder was identified as "our oldest immigrant," after being glacially transported from modern-day Sweden.[25] The campaign challenged residents' political claims to land through their "intrinsic indigeneity" by calling into question the stability of the very land upon which their claims were made.

Erratics refer to overlapping moments in scales of time: their original formation, their glacial deposition, and different events in human history—sometimes they are even literally carved with a date or name. Unlike the *Pierre des Marmettes*, the individual erratic cases that follow were not singled out as demonstrative evidence for the theory of glaciation in the nineteenth century, although their recorded histories overlap with the emergence and widespread dissemination of the theory. They reflect instead a range of efforts to grapple with or manipulate ideas about different geological time scales.

Rollstone Boulder, Fitchburg, Massachusetts

Just as the *Pierre des Marmettes* was almost sold and turned into dimensional stone in 1905, the Rollstone Boulder, perched on Rollstone Hill in Fitchburg, Massachusetts, was also vulnerable to imminent destruction. The vibrations of an expanding hilltop quarry threatened to destabilize the 110-ton porphyritic granite boulder, whose structural integrity had already been a longstanding and active cause for concern by area residents. From downtown Fitchburg, the boulder's silhouette was visible on the hill's ridgeline, making it an ever-present if somewhat distant marker among the town's natural scenography.[26] It was a well-known character that had "survived the ice age," "held early pilgrims on [its] shoulders," "conversed with Mohawk Indian tribes, and observed the creation of Fitchburg and its surrounding communities," at least according to *I Am The Boulder,* a poem by Robert Boucher.[27]

The boulder's feldspar and iron sulphide varies from the granite that it had landed on, but matched the composition of that found about 100 miles north, in central New Hampshire. Despite understanding that the boulder had once been a part of something much bigger, residents had been preoccupied with keeping the rock whole, lest it break apart and lose the familiar shape by which they had come to know it. To start, someone had filled the surface cracks with cement. At another point, an expedition of geologists instigated the wrapping of the rock's midriff with a solid iron belt, "to prevent further disintegration." The concern for the rock's wholeness passed between generations; in a 1902 report, a member of the Fitchburg Historical Society expressed gratitude "to the person or persons whose kindness and generosity" had taken such care to keep the rock intact.[28] Multiple postcards and photographs show the boulder in various states of repair and disrepair, surrounded by geologists, mounted with children, or being "held up" by a comedic visitor hamming it up for the camera. [Fig. 04]

In the early 1930s, when the rock stood in the way of a derrick that the quarry wanted to install, it was dragged 200 feet along the hill by a mechanical apparatus. When quarrying operations expanded on Rollstone Hill in the late 1920s, a special committee to save the rock was assembled.[29] Newspaper clippings from 1930 show the boulder's surface marked with a network of white lines in preparation for being dynamited and relocated downtown. Over the course of 13 weeks, 275 dynamited fragments were transported to Fitchburg's Upper Common and reassembled using the white lines as guides "to assume again its original famous contours." To this day the boulder remains there adorned with a plaque that details its past. The *Boston Daily Globe* did not fail to report on the rock's resting place as a confluence of both glacial and human forces: "Having been moved only twice since it was forsaken by a cold and inhospitable glacier, the Rollstone Boulder has taken up its last abode nearer than ever to the friendly and admiring citizens of Fitchburg,

Postcard, Rollstone Boulder, Fitchburg, Massachusetts
Peter Cristofono collection

Fig. 04

whose fortunes, although covering the merest instant in the history of the giant monument, are doubtless the most interesting of which it has watched."[30]

Babson Boulders, Dogtown, Massachusetts

On a visit to the landscape surrounding Dogtown, Massachusetts, in 1858, Henry David Thoreau described "the most peculiar scenery of the Cape. [...] We could see no house, but hills strewn with boulders, as though they had rained down, on every side."[31] The area, later known as Dogtown, was the Commons between significant villages in the mid-seventeenth century; eventually people settled there amongst the densely bouldered *terrain erratique.* Smaller glacial rocks were used to build walls and houses, but larger boulders were steadfast and speckled the landscape. The town prospered until the mid-eighteenth century, eventually reaching a population of 80 families; it was only as residents migrated to the coast to take advantage of abundant fish stocks that the population saw a decline. As the population dwindled, buildings decayed, trees colonized the clearings, and dogs ran free, giving the town its current name.[32]

Among the descendants of Dogtown's first English settlers, Roger W. Babson, born in 1875, maintained a connection with the mostly abandoned town. He built a summer cottage in the area and made telling its history a lifelong project. The Boston millionaire businessman, presidential candidate for the Prohibition Party, author, and founder of three colleges had famously predicted the 1929 stock market crash. He found particular interest in studying the economic rise and decline of his familial land. "Connected with the story of Dogtown is a great economic lesson as well

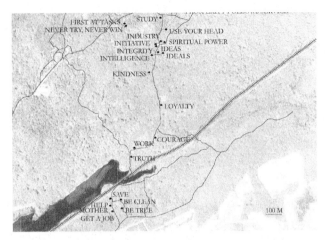

Fig. 05   Babson Boulders Map

Fig. 06   Babson Boulder, Courage, Dogtown, Massachusetts

as a story of romance," he wrote.[33] His autobiography, *Actions and Reactions*, involved an especially direct appropriation of Newton's eponymous theory, which he applied to Dogtown as an example of the causal relationship between morality and prosperity:[34] "Dogtown teaches me clearly that progress comes only slowly and from developing within the individual self-control, high ideals and other fundamental immunities."[35] Babson saw the landscape, then associated with decline and the subject of ghost stories, as an opportunity to record and communicate his lessons.

Having located and mapped all of the remnant stone cellars from pre-existing houses in the village, Babson marked them by hiring stone workers to carve numbers into nearby large erratic boulders. He later hired quarry workers to carve slogans into the boulders, following a circuit through the woods surrounding his property. [Fig. 05] Among the slogans, always inscribed with capital letters to emphasize their imperative nature, are the following: SAVE, IDEAS, STUDY, INTEGRITY, LOYALTY, NEVER TRY / NEVER WIN, PROSPERITY FOLLOWS SERVICE, KEEP OUT OF DEBT, USE YOUR HEAD, INTELLIGENCE, KINDNESS, COURAGE, WORK, INITIATIVE, INDUSTRY, TRUTH, BE CLEAN, GET A JOB, BE ON TIME, BE TRUE, HELP MOTHER, SPIRITUAL POWER, IF WORK STOPS VALUES DECAY. At a time when billboard advertisements were beginning to sprout up everywhere, to which Babson was adamantly opposed and called "debauching outdoor poster talk," he constructed a constellation of rock mottoes. He called the project his "Life's Book," and wrote that, "my family says that I am defacing the boulders and disgracing my family with these inscriptions, but the work gives me a lot of satisfaction, fresh air, exercise, and sunshine. I am really trying to write a simple book with words carved in stone instead of printed on paper."[36] [Fig. 06]

The erratic boulders of Dogtown were convenient media for Babson's distributed lessons. They insisted on personal moral responsibility at the exact moment of systemic economic collapse in the United States. The boulders scaled appropriately for such messages were those too large to be cleared or used for other construction purposes; as such, they were pre-colonial and had witnessed the complete economic cycle of the village. Babson enlisted their reference to the past generations' economic decline as a way of provoking better moral action in the future.

Medicine or Prayer Rock, Ipswich, South Dakota

While Babson marked boulders to incite moral behaviour, the "Medicine or Prayer Rock" in Ipswich, South Dakota, outside of the Marcus P. Beebe Memorial Library, is marked as a static monument to a naturalized indigenous past, while patronizing its significance. The embossed sign standing next to the rock reads: "Found near Mobridge, the impression was tediously incised by some old Indian intent on building himself up as a medicine man. Once formed it was a symbol of great power and was venerated by the Indian who believed it was the work of the 'Wakan' or Great Spirit. – Erected 1962, Ipswich Commercial Club." The rock was removed from its location southeast of Mobridge, and taken 68 miles to the main walkway of the public library. On one side of the rock is an impression of two hands, spread apart as if the body they belonged to was leaning heavily into the surface. A plaque bolted to the street-facing side of the rock commemorates the library—not the rock—named in memory of Beebe, the first president of the bank of Ipswich. [Fig. 07]

Other boulders with similarly incised handprints are on display at the Marshall City Prayer Rock Museum in Britton, SD. Not only does their relocation raise serious questions about rights and repatriation, display efforts sometimes assume the need to physically preserve the rock in its "found state" by encasement or weather proofing. Linea Sundstrom writes that this instinct is odds with northern Plains conceptions of rock art, which is not understood as a static media: "Instead, it changes constantly (or one's perception of it changes), so that one sees something different each time the rock art is examined."[37] It is expected to weather, deteriorate, and eventually fall apart. Sundstrom distinguishes this overzealous preservation from the importance of protection from desecration and vandalism.

The rock is featured as one of Ipswich's main tourist attractions. It is in the foreground of a local mural that depicts the elements central to the town's history, including the founding of the Yellowstone Trial and the extension of rail lines to the town. Apart from tipis in the distant corner of the mural, all traces of the Lakota or Dakota populations have been erased. At the library, not only does the installation erase the rock's significance by using it merely as a means to point to the building, it

Fig. 07   Medicine or Prayer Rock, Ipswich, South Dakota
Photo courtesy of J. Stephen Conn

assumes that the rock is no longer of significance to the populations from which it came, and for whom it is an important element in creation myths. In a study of rock art significant to Native American groups in South Dakota, Sundstrom writes that such rocks are, in certain cases, still sacred to single or multiple groups; accordingly, the Ipswich library site and other civic landscapes in South Dakota are "not very appropriate locations for traditional religious activities."[38] The transportation and representation of the Prayer Rock have manipulated and inverted time such that the indigenous people confronted by both early colonial expansion and contemporary violence are erased and relegated to a naturalized pre-history.

Plymouth Rock, Plymouth, Massachusetts

The Yellowstone Trail, whose ambitious founder came from Ipswich, South Dakota, imagined it as "A Good Road from Plymouth Rock to Puget Sound." As in this slogan, Plymouth Rock typically signifies much more than the rock itself. Visitors today are often surprised by its modest size and complete encapsulation in a caged enclosure. At the time of the arrival of British Separatists in Plymouth Harbour, the Plymouth Rock, which *may* have been used to prop up a disembarkment plank, weighed 200 tons.[39] As Alexander de Tocqueville wrote, "A few poor souls trod for an instant on this rock, and it has become famous, it is prized by a great nation; fragments are venerated, and tiny pieces distributed far and wide."[40] Over the course of 400 years, the rock has been split so it could be displayed at alternate locations, fractioned and sold, mortared, trimmed, and in 1920, waterproofed. Fragments of the rock reside in Los Gatos, California, Brooklyn, the Nevada State Museum, the Smithsonian in Washington D.C., and exist as paperweights, tie clips, and cufflinks.[41]

The piece that remains in Plymouth is a five-by-six-foot rounded fragment, enclosed in a shrine within a granite and iron portico. [Fig. 08] The granite boulder's origin has been often traced close to Boston. John McPhee notes how claims that the rock may have travelled from the area associated with British Canada caused enough anxiety to elicit further official study.[42] The rock's symbolism is highly mutable and transferable, being recalled as a symbol of stoicism by Daniel Webster, of freedom from oppression by abolitionists, and signifying the protection of immigrants.[43] At the first meeting of the Organization of Afro-American Unity, Malcolm X also took on the origin myth of the rock, quoting Cole Porter: "We didn't land on Plymouth Rock. The rock landed on us."[44]

The first National Day of Mourning was held in 1970 overlooking the fiftieth annual costumed, re-enactment of the "Day of Thanksgiving" at Plymouth Rock. Wampanoag leader Wamsutta, whose speech had been invited and then censored by the Commonwealth of Massachusetts, delivered it on nearby Cole's Hill where a boulder monument for the National Day of Mourning has been installed. [Fig. 09] Mahtowin

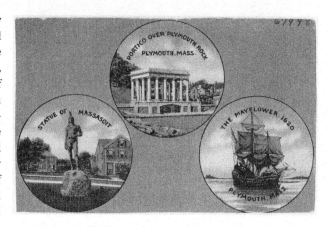

Postcard, Massasoit Statue, Portico over Plymouth Rock, The Mayflower. 1930-45. The Tichnor Borthers Collection, Boston Public Library

Fig. 08

Munro and Moonanum James of The United American Indians of New England, organizers of the Day of Mourning, refute the official history:

> We object to the "Pilgrim Progress" parade and to what goes on in Plymouth because they are making millions of tourist dollars every year from the false pilgrim mythology. That money is being made off the backs of our slaughtered indigenous ancestors. [...] And no, they did not even land at that sacred shrine called Plymouth Rock, a monument to racism and oppression which we are proud to say we buried in 1995.[45]

In Charles Lyell's *Principles of Geology,* under the heading, "Prejudices arising from our peculiar position as inhabitants of the land," the author acknowledges the difficulty of inhabiting "almost exclusively a theatre of decay, and not of reproduction." In his words:

> He who has observed the quarrying of stone from a rock, and has seen it shipped for some distant port, and then endeavours to conceive what kind of edifice will be raised by the materials is in the same predicament as a geologist, who, while he is confined to the land, sees the decomposition of rocks, and the transportation of matter by rivers to the sea, and then endeavours to picture himself the new strata which Nature is building beneath the waters.[46]

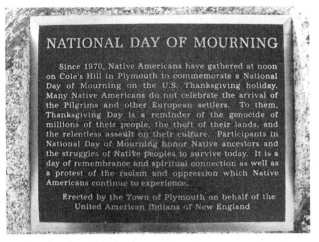

NATIONAL DAY OF MOURNING

Since 1970, Native Americans have gathered at noon on Cole's Hill in Plymouth to commemorate a National Day of Mourning on the U.S. Thanksgiving holiday. Many Native Americans do not celebrate the arrival of the Pilgrims and other European settlers. To them, Thanksgiving Day is a reminder of the genocide of millions of their people, the theft of their lands, and the relentless assault on their culture. Participants in National Day of Mourning honor Native ancestors and the struggles of Native peoples to survive today. It is a day of remembrance and spiritual connection as well as a protest of the racism and oppression which Native Americans continue to experience.

Erected by the Town of Plymouth on behalf of the United American Indians of New England

Fig. 09   National Day of Mourning plaque, Plymouth, Massachusetts
Photo courtesy of Gerald Azenaro

That we witness just fragments of physical matter at single moments of time, yet seek to understand the world of dynamic materials over deep time, is a perpetual conundrum when visualizing and understanding geological processes. While confined to the land and a particular time, erratic boulders have helped resolve some of the paradoxes of geology by allowing scientists to piece together a cohesive theory about the earth's distant past, as well as understand, ponder, and re-write time at multiple scales. Beyond their role as scientific evidence, their glacial history, pervasive distribution, and curious shapes and sizes have made them enigmatic characters. These characteristics include the ability to move or rock, thereby echoing their earlier glacial motion, as with the Kidston Lake Rocking Stone; to become affectionate local characters and produce human desires to maintain them as "whole" figures, as with the Rollstone Boulder; to be media for the transmission of ideas about more recent cycles of human history, as with the Babson Boulders; to be used to encapsulate, make static, and efface a poorly understood indigenous history, as with the Medicine or Prayer Rock; and finally as a tool for myth-making and myth-contesting, as with the Plymouth Rock. While each of these boulders has been used in specific and instrumental ways by humans, it is their concurrent references to multiple scales of time, to multiple agents of change—both human and non-human, both scientific and popular—that makes them potent figures.

Not long after the theory of glaciation had become widely accepted, George Perkins Marsh's 1868 publication *Physical Geography as Modified by Human Action* introduced the idea of human action as a force of change at the scale of the landscape: "As we have seen, man has reacted upon organized and inorganic nature, and thereby modified, if not determined, the material structure of his earthly home."[47] The scientific and lay interest in erratic boulders is nestled between Marsh's observation that humans had agency in the transformation of the world around them, and the newly theorized proposition that glacial processes had transformed the world at scales previously unimaginable. Through these two entry points, erratics manage to link the seemingly irresolvable chasm between human and geological action.

Acknowledgments

Many thanks to Senta Burton for her assistance and insights, as well as to Joyce Rosenthal and Shantel Blakely for their comments on the text. This project stemmed from research for an exhibition that I curated in 2009, the theme for which was originally proposed by Charles Waldheim, whom I'd like to thank introducing me to the topic.

Notes

1   Rev. D. Honeyman, "Nova Scotia Geology (Superficial)", *Proceedings of the Nova Scotian Institute of Science*, Vol. 5, Part 4 (Halifax, 1882), 329.

2   "Description of the Rocking Stone, in Nova Scotia," *The Glasgow Mechanics Magazine; and Annals of Philosophy*, 1 (1824): 349.

3   Elizabeth Eve, "Rockingstone Road," in *Halifax Street Names: An Illustrated Guide*, ed. Shelagh Mackenzie and Scott Robson (Formac Publishing Company: Halifax, 2004), 137.

4   Ibid., 136.

5   Peter U. Clark et al., "The Last Glacial Maximum," *Science* 325, no. 5941 (August 2009): 710–714.

6   Jean de Charpentier, *Essai sur les glaciers et sur le terrain erratique du bassin du Rhone* (Lausanne: Imprimerie et Librairie de Marc Ducloux, 1841).

7   Martin J. S. Rudwick, *Worlds Before Adam: The Reconstruction of Geohistory in the Age of Reform* (Chicago: University of Chicago Press, 2008), 510.

8   As pointed out in Timothy Mitchell, "Frederic Church's 'The Icebergs': Erratic Boulders and Time's Slow Changes," *Smithsonian Studies in American Art* 3, no. 4 (1989): 12.

9   Rudwick, *Worlds Before Adam*, 511.

10 E. Reynard, "Protecting Stones: Conservation of Erratic Blocks in Switzerland," in *Dimension Stone*, ed. R. Prikryl (London: Taylor & Francis, 2004), 5.

11 Richard Foster Flint, *Glacial Geology and the Pleistocene Epoch* (New York: J. Wiley & Sons, 1947), 75.

12 Rudwick, *Worlds Before Adam*, 12.

13 Ibid., 13.

14 Ibid., 190.

15 Ibid., 502.

16 Flint, *Glacial Geology And The Pleistocene Epoch*, 117.

17 Rudwick, *Worlds Before Adam*, 83.

18 Rebecca Bedell, "Thomas Cole and the Fashionable Science," *Huntington Library Quarterly* 59, no. 2 & 3 (1996): 365.

19 Martin Rudwick, "Essay Review of Studies on Glaciers, preceded by the Discourse of Neuchatel by Louis Agassiz, translated and edited by Albert V. Carozzi," in *The New Science of Geology: Studies in the Earth Sciences in the Age of Revolution* (Ashgate: Variorum, 2004), 142.

20 Ralph W. Dexter, "Historical Aspects of Agassiz's Lectures on Glacial Geology (1860-61)," *Earth Sciences History* 8, no. 1 (1989): 77.

21 Ibid., 78.

22 Ibid., 75.

23 Rebecca Bedell, *The Anatomy of Nature: Geology & American Landscape Painting, 1825-1875* (Princeton, N.J.: Princeton University Press, 2001).

24 Lorraine Daston, ed., *Things That Talk* (New York: Zone Books, 2008), 15

25 Doreen Massey, "Landscape as a Provocation: Reflections on Moving Mountains," *Journal of Material Culture* 11, no. 33 (2006): 33–48.

26 William Andrew Emerson, *Fitchburg, Massachusetts, Past and Present* (Fitchburg, Mass.: Blanchard & Brown, 1887), 18.

27 Robert Boucher, "I Am the Boulder."

28 Fitchburg Historical Society, *Proceedings of the Fitchburg Historical Society and Papers Relating to the History of the Town Read by Some of the Members, Vol 3* (Fitchburg, Mass.: Sentinel Printing Company, 1902), 151.

29 "Rugged Rollstone Boulder Moved with Great Effort Now Wants Plaque Back," *Fitchburg Sentinel*, 20 December 1938, http://home.iprimus.com.au/metzke/rollstoneboulder.html.

30 "Fitchburg's Historic Bowlder Moved with Care to Site in Park," *Daily Boston Globe,* 25 December 1930..

31 Bradford Torrey, *The Writings of Henry David Thoreau, XI, July 2 1858-February, 1859,* (Boston: Houghton Mifflin and Company, 1906), 179.

32 Fred Woods, "Keep Out of Debt Help Mother," *Boston Globe*, 19 August 1973.

33 Elizabeth Martin, "Deconstructing Marginality: Exploring the Foundations of Dogtown Common, Massachusetts" (PhD diss., City University of New York, 2011), 141.

34 Roger W. Babson, *Actions and Reactions: An Autobiography of Roger Babson* (New York: Harper & Brothers, 1935), 337.

35 Woods, "Keep Out of Debt Help Mother."

36 Ibid.

37 Linea Sundstrom, "Rock Art and Native Americans: A View from South Dakota," *Plains Anthropologist* 44 (1999): 74.

38 Ibid., 71.

39 John McPhee, "Our Far Flung Correspondents: Travels of the Rock," *The New Yorker,* 26 February 1990, 108.

40 Sargent Bush, "American's Origin Myth: Remembering Plymouth Rock," *American Literary History* 12, no. 4 (Winter 2000): 745.

41 McPhee, "Our Far Flung Correspondents," 130.

42 Ibid., 109.

43 Christiana Morgan Grefe, review of *Memory's Nation: The Place of Plymouth Rock,* by John Seelye, *Journal of Popular Culture* 38, no. 1 (Aug. 2004): 212–214.

44 Thanks to Amy Kulper for pointing this out.

45 Moonanum James and Mahtowin Munro, "Thanksgiving: A National Day of Mourning for Indians," United American Indians of New England, http://www.uaine.org/dom.htm.

46 Charles Lyell, *Principles of Geology or, the Modern Changes of the Earth and its Inhabitants* (London: John Murray, 1854), 81.

47 George Perkins Marsh, *Physical Geography as Modified by Human Action* (New York: Charles Scribner, 1864), 8.

Swimming in It (2012)

Chester Rennie

Mixed Media

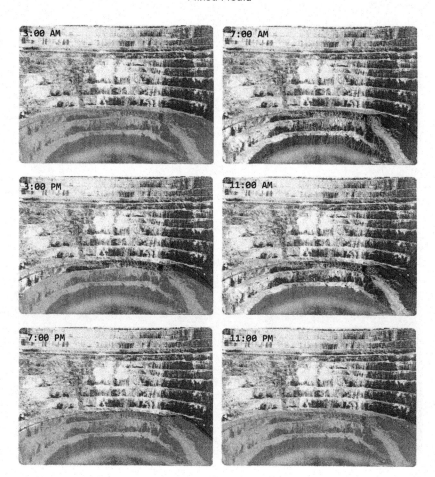

The project *Swimming in It* is a site-specific exploration of the transition of a former open-pit iron mine and current aggregate production site into a hydro-electric pumped storage facility. The site was originally developed as an iron mine by Bethlehem Steel but was decommissioned after 30 years of production because of the incursion of water from the surrounding karst landscape. In the time since its decommissioning, the pit has gradually filled with water, trembling aspen and goldenrod have colonized the overburden,

and the remainders of equipment have rusted into ruin. Soon the pit and overburden will be connected through the electrical grid to an entire province of distributed electrical objects that will move the water into the upper reservoir and back into the pit every day. This project creates two swimming pools within the pit which provide visitors with amplified material and physical access to the infrastructure of consumption which helped produce the site.

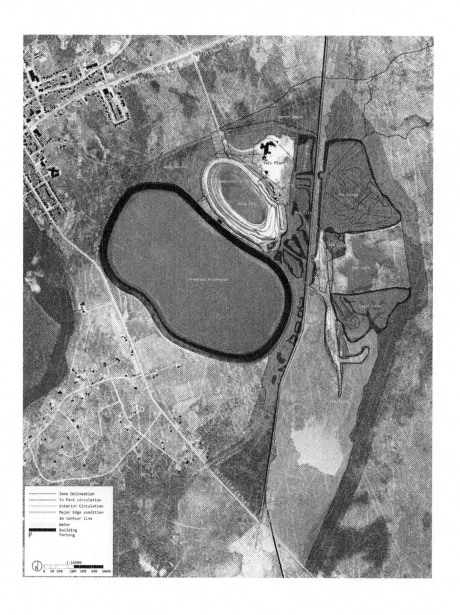

Time Matters

Elizabeth Grosz in Conversation with Heather Davis and Etienne Turpin

On Temporality in the Anthropocene

Architecture is often, and for readily apparent reasons, considered through spatial perspectives, but its intersection with the Anthropocene—what the Anthropocene *demands*—is nothing less than a reconsideration of architecture's temporal qualities. In an era where we see intense changes in weather, species, and geology at an unprecedented rate, the question of time is increasingly impinging on us. Indeed, the ways that architecture shifts, changes, transforms, degrades, breaks down, and evolves herald particular kinds of futures through its various territorializations and movements over time.

Elizabeth Grosz has been engaging with precisely these questions of duration, life, transformation, evolution, and time for at least the past decade. In her own book on architecture, *Architecture from the Outside: Essays on Virtual and Real Space* (2001), she suggests that architecture's outside, that which affords a perspective, is precisely the question of time. Time is that which both subtends and expands or dilates space, and its consideration can push spatial practices such as architecture in different directions, towards different ways of living or inhabiting. Grosz tackles the subject of architecture again in her 2008 book *Chaos, Territory, Art: Deleuze and the Framing of the Earth*, but with a different emphasis. Here, architecture is placed as the "first art," in Deleuze's sense, as the marking of a territory that temporarily and provisionally allows chaos to slow enough for new intensities to be felt and to emerge.[1] This framing of the earth signifies the origins of architecture, which provides the basis upon which other arts manifest themselves. It is, like all the other arts, not exclusively human, but is a property of life itself— its endless proliferation in and through difference.

Time, as the condition for the emergence of difference, is central to Grosz's thought. As she says in her most recent book, *Becoming Undone*, "I would prefer to understand life and matter in terms of their temporal and durational entwinements. Matter and life become, and become undone. They transform and are transformed."[2] It is this capacity for transformation, for self-overcoming that, she insists, is the "condition for the emergence of art, for the eruption of collective life, and for the creation of new forms of politics, new modes of living."[3] It is precisely through the privileging of evolutionary time that life can be understood through its excessiveness, through its continual transformation, offering a mode of self-overcoming. And it is an overcoming of philosophy, of the humanities, by way of thinking the human *in its place*—as simply one species among many which emerged, flourished, and will eventually go extinct—that Grosz asks us to consider. By looking at the human through the lens of deep time, Grosz offers a new approach to philosophy, as well as to architecture. Her clarity and unflinching vision, which avoids both romantic and nihilistic pitfalls, continues to profoundly mark contemporary philosophy. It was with considerable pleasure that we posed to her these questions on how to think through architecture under contemporary geologic conditions.

Heather Davis & Etienne Turpin In the essay "Technical Mentality," Gilbert Simondon advances a schema whereby processes of individuation occur on the level of objects themselves. In his words, "if one imagines an object that, instead of being closed, offers parts that are conceived as being as close to indestructible as possible, and others by contrast in which there would be concentrated a very high capacity to adjust to each usage, or wear, or possible breakage in case of shock, of malfunctioning, then one obtains an open object that can be completed, improved, maintained in the state of perpetual actuality."[4] In many ways, this objective of being maintained in a state of perpetual actuality, in a continual process of individuation, seems to be one of the goals of architecture, or architectural projects broadly speaking. At the same time, we live in an era where the obsolescence of buildings is increasingly expedited, even as their accumulation, sedimentation, and transformation into landfills becomes a contributor to what we have come to know as the Anthropocene. In our contemporary moment, what is the evolutionary force of architecture?

Elizabeth Grosz Architecture is both an evolutionary invention, one not made by man but one that perhaps made man's emergence possible (the human requires architecture, protection, territory in its loosest sense, a non-possessable milieu, to become man and perhaps even to move beyond man). And it is itself always open to evolutionary forces, forces of destruction even more than of construction or reconstruction, always being re-contextualized, transformed both within and in its architectural and natural contexts. A building has a finite life, even if it extends beyond its currently living occupants; it tends to become rubble without active intervention. What Simondon suggests about the technical object is that its parts may be replaceable, but to the extent that an object can evolve, change its design, become something else, it must still retain some kind of form, a plan, a finality, a functionality. The object, whether a technical object or a natural or cultural object, is no less prey to evolutionary forces than any other identity or form of cohesion. But as a technical object (like a building), many of its parts can be "upgraded," "renovated" without fundamentally transforming it; or equally, it is capable of being thoroughly transformed, a new building on an old foundation, a new building behind an old façade, in a more or less continuous movement. Evolution, as opposed to invention, always proceeds through continuity, just as invention involves the sudden cohesion or a new way of operating of many parts that may preexist the invented object.

HD&ET In *Architecture from the Outside*, you write: "Architecture relies on a double nature—nature as standing reserve, as material to be exploited and rewritten, but also a nature that is always the supersession and transformation of limits and thus beyond the passivity of the reserve or the resource, nature as becoming or evolution."[5] In the time of the Anthropocene, a period that marks itself by human intervention as much as by a surpassing of the human, how does the place of architecture change? Given the current force of evolutionary momentum, torqued and sped up to the point of human time, what futures can architecture create or inhabit? Does this necessitate an engagement with the untimely in architecture and design? Do the pressures of the Anthropocene force an evolutionary becoming of architecture at the same rate as the rest of the biological world, or as a creative gesture of futurity? Or, does our continued (biological, cultural, and economic) reliance upon nature as standing reserve draw architecture back into a necessarily reactive position?

EG This is a very complex set of questions. Architecture as we know it, human architecture, is one of the products or creations of, as well as one of the preconditions for, the age of man, if such a thing exists. It depends, of course, on how long one dates the Anthropocene, whether from the industrial revolution or from the emergence of human civilization in Africa, Asia and elsewhere. In linking the Anthropocene to the industrial revolution and beyond, for example, architecture becomes a possession; it becomes fixed, and linked less to the marking of territory than to its inhabitation. It becomes the place where living becomes separated from the lives of others. It becomes the place for the worker who produces commodities. It becomes a commodity, and then one that signifies as well as functions, that can be read just as much as it can be used or inhabited. Architecture, like all art, has the potential, or capability, of addressing and bringing into existence new qualities, new forces, new ways of living, new forms of connection and disconnection from social relations. But equally, it tends to function, like most forms of art, as a commodity more than as a mode of art. As such, the cheaper and more appealing to buyers and renters, the more consumable architecture is; the more driven by commodity production and consumption, the more "successful" it is. So architecture, in short, has the capacity to both extend man's destruction of the environment, but also, at its best but much more rarely, it retains the capacity to invent new modes of co-existence, more sustainable ways of living and more aesthetic experiences of inhabitation.

Nature as standing reserve is nature as an endless resource to be consumed without thought. Here nature is not seen as having a force of its own, but as raw material for human ends or goals that may be imposed on or extracted from it. Clearly, we are at an historical moment when this raw resource will no longer be capable of sustaining billions of people in the same way that socially and nationally privileged subjects live. It will be only through an invention, not only at an architectural but also at agricultural and environmental levels, that new kinds of building, and new kinds of coexistence, might become possible. I don't want to suggest, however, that the age of man can be overcome by man. This is perhaps the very same arrogance that produced the Anthropocene, the human tendency to believe in its own power, its problem-solving capacities, even as it has undertaken ruinous activity that imperils other forms of life. It is only hubris that leads us to believe that if the human has polluted and nearly destroyed vast environments, it can somehow restore what it has destroyed. It may be that we have not only summoned up a new architecture, new arts, new ways of living, but new forms of self-destruction, new ways of overcoming the human, new ends for architecture.

HD&ET How do we think the time of the future without humans? In other words, is the time of the future, that is, the becoming of humankind and its speculative evolution, an encounter with the virtual of the human as species? Is the future of humanity, as a nonhuman future, thus a time of the virtual? Does the nature of the virtual change if there is no time of the present, at least to humans?

EG Time exists without us. It is we who cannot exist or conceive of ourselves without it. Time continues whether we exist or not, for it is the condition of every existence, every object, natural or technical, every universe, and even the origin of all universes. The future may not involve an encounter with the human; its virtualities may just as readily be left un-actualized as a future life form elaborates them according to its interests. Will the human be an object of reflection for that which replaces the human? Who is to know? The past, the present, and the future do not require the human to exist and to function: just as the human emerged, gradually, through the elaboration and evolution of primates, so too the human will disappear, as an inevitability, given an indeterminate time span. Whatever the human provides for the future, or for any future species, will only emerge from what that species may require; otherwise the human will remain an un-actualized virtuality, no different than any other extinct species. Time, as simultaneously virtual and actual, past and present, will continue in precisely its own way, even without the presence of the human. The present abides, continuously, ceaselessly, whether observed, or experienced, or not.

HD&ET What brings you back, again and again, to questions of time? For at least the past decade, you have been reading and writing on Bergson, Darwin, Deleuze, and Irigaray, talking about the evolutionary time that subtends other systems, but with variation and difference in each of their iterations in your latest books. What happens to thought itself in this process of durational unfolding? How does thinking change against, or in relation to, the changing horizon of deep time?

EG One of the things that attracted me to Bergson in particular was his idea that the present contains all of the past within it, carrying it as it continuously transforms itself. The earliest events—even those bound up with the very origins of the universe, long before the evolutionary emergence of life—do not cease to have their effects on everything that is subsequent, even if they are restructured, given new impact and force, made meaningful, in their present effects. In other words, every actual present is subtended by the virtual entirety of the past. So deep time, the time of the universe's unfolding, the construction of the earth and all that appears on it, the eruption of life forms, all the momentous and unpredictable emergences never cease; they function both as an historical horizon but also as unspent forces, forces whose effects have not been used up by all the time that has separated the present from its primordial past. Thinking can appear only at a certain moment within this evolutionary framework, as an effect of a certain degree of complexity of the body, or, as Simondon might suggest, as a result of a set of tensions at the level of the organism that requires a new order, a new mode of existence to be invented or individuated. Thinking is made in durational flow, but, as Bergson suggests, that which can think does not necessarily think its own durational invention and elaboration. Thinking is a product or effect of life lived in a hazardous world; its emergence solves a problem by creating a new level at which the problem might be addressed, if not solved. So it is not clear, as Bergson suggests of intelligence, whether thought can adequately think duration, even as it exists only as an effect of evolutionary duration. This is what I have struggled to address in the last decade: how to think time, given that time's force is more lived, more qualitative than it is measurable, countable or mappable, which are all spatial qualities?

HD&ET Even within the writing itself—your particular aesthetic, that is—there are moments when your texts feel like a kind of musical score, with a refrain that gets repeated, both to induce a feeling of difference as well as produce something new. Deleuze and Guattari talk about the refrain as a particular kind of repetition that has the capacity to create thought, and mark the territory of thought. Is it possible to think of this kind of repetition in architectural terms—not as a scaffolding, nor in the sense of infrastructure, but in the sense of processes of territorialization?

EG Yes, I do think that there is something of the refrain, and of rhythm, in architecture, in the flows of movement, of bodies, practices, but also of air, heat, cold, electricity, and the internet, as well as the flow of materials that are used in construction. Each of these forms a refrain, a melodic tracing out of space to form a bounded territory within which qualities, particularly rhythms and temporalities, can emerge. Repetition, or perhaps seriality, is a condition of architecture, and there can be great beauty in the orders of repetition, through the spacing, materials, and movements that architecture creates. It is significant, though, that Deleuze and Guattari's concept of the refrain places architecture in a different position than music. As the "first art," the art that enables all the other arts to emerge, architecture has a more primordial connection to the earth, to location and territory, than any other art. It is only through the "construction" or creation of a circle of safety that the refrain can emerge as such and condition the eruption of music, painting, dance and the other arts. This is architecture in its most primitive and animal form—the marking of land, whether by scent, through walking trails or a fence, and its forms of occupation, whether nomadic or sedentary. At this most elementary level, architecture is rhythm attached to the earth, a rhythm that enables other rhythms to escape their location, to deterritorialize themselves, to function elsewhere, anywhere.

HD&ET Since writing *Architecture from the Outside*, have you seen any shift in the relationship of architecture to gender or political economy? The postcolonial theorist Dipesh Chakrabarty, in his essay "The Climate of History," emphasizes that while the Anthropocene has consequences for the whole species—especially in relation to climate change—it is perpetuated unevenly among the species.[6] That is, within a patriarchal, capitalist system, those who create new risks by accelerating climate change are rarely those closest to their consequences. How would you articulate the significance of gender in the context of the Anthropocene and its political economic consequences?

EG The simple answer is no, I haven't seen much of a change in the relationship between architecture and gender, though no doubt there are more women in architecture than ever before, and more women winning big commissions and projects. But along with Irigaray, I would say that architecture and its associated disciplines—design, urban planning, engineering—are just as male-dominated, as gender-, race-, and class-privileged as any cultural practice, and more so than most of the arts. There is no reason it must be this way, except for a history that has privileged certain kinds of practices and certain kinds of subjects over other possibilities. Climate change, the poisoning of the atmosphere, the extinction of countless species, has undoubtedly been effected by those who regulate large amounts of energy, something rarely accessible to most women throughout human history. The history of human accomplishment thus far is primarily both a history of self- and other-destruction, and a history of masculine privilege (among other things). If men and privileged masculine practices are responsible for climate change, this does not mean that, as usual, women should be assumed to be those who nurture, restore to health and heal the world (and humanity). Nor should be assumed that masculine privilege can somehow fix or overcome the harm it has produced, even if it could do so.

HD&ET The theorist Tom Cohen uses the term "telemorphosis"[7] to describe how, within the context of contemporary environmental collapse, the spatial and temporal distance that humans once held between themselves and their actions is rapidly diminishing. In your own work, you've argued, contra Kant, that "space and time remain conceivable insofar as they become accessible for us corporeally."[8] While our corporeal experience of the Anthropocene seems to be largely at odds with our biological survival (by way of chemical contamination, toxicosis, radiation, extreme weather events, etc.), do you think there is an embodied relation that can be productive of an ethics or a politics for the contemporary?

EG That is *the* question of the present. I don't know. I don't know how we can mobilize, nor which ethical and political terms may be useful for such a mobilization of human energy toward a given goal and the prevention of such a collapse. All ethics and politics are always already embodied, lived and enacted by bodies of various types in different social and geographical spaces. But we have not found an ethics or politics adequate to the overwhelming problems the human—or at least,

134

the dominant forms of the human—has produced. No one seems to have provided a strategy for collective action, as there seems to be no way these large, almost intractable problems can be addressed without broad collective agreement. The polarization and (party) politicization of responses to problems like climate change ensure that there is no immediately foreseeable ways of addressing these questions as shared dilemmas and collective responsibilities.

HD&ET Gilles Deleuze, in his reading of Spinoza, argues for the necessity of an ethology of affects that can preserve the specificity of the body outside of more abstract concepts of genera or species. This is precisely what Deleuze and Guattari, in *A Thousand Plateaus*, call *ethics*. Just as you have inquired about an ethology of language, we would like to ask if there could be an ethology of architecture? Can architecture produce an ethics—perhaps an "untimely" ethics—that could leverage a kind of ethology of buildings or the built environment?

EG The question of an ethics of affect in the field of architecture is a complex one, one that at least some architects are attempting to address, in whatever inventive ways they can—see, for example the adventurous architecture of Arawaka and Gins, which challenges the body out of its habitual modes while bringing about a new, almost counter-intuitive body—the way architecture impacts on and transforms the body to bring out joyous affects and to diminish sad affects, to extend life or inhibit it. This is not, however, typical of most architecture, which aims at a functionality that is as inexpensive and open to ready transformation (including its own redundancy) as possible. There are two quite different directions that an ethics or ethology of architecture may take: one is the direction of responsible, sustainable housing, in which the environment is impacted as little as possible and the costs of production are as small as possible. This produces an architecture that tries to serve a common good, to bring about a functionality that is practical for large and growing populations. The other direction is more experimental, where buildings are produced not as cheaply and functionally as possible, but rather through innovative, often unrepeatable designs that address engineering, construction, or aesthetic qualities in inventive ways. This is an ethics with a different orientation, without a clear-cut moral imperative, an ethics of the new, aligned more with art than politics. Sometimes—rarely—these two orientations are seen in a common project. More commonly, though, they tend to be two ethical or ethological directions (perhaps the two directions that also mark natural and sexual selection) between which architects must chose. The second approach is no doubt more untimely than the first, which orients itself precisely to the needs of the present and the immediate future.

HD&ET Could architecture, in your view, produce evolutionary-*becomings*? You have written that "[t]he living body is itself the ongoing provocation for inventive practice, for inventing and elaborating widely varying practices, for using organs and activities in unexpected and potentially expansive ways, for making art out of the body's capacities and actions."[9] The pressures that produce or provoke these becomings are both internal and external to the body itself, and to the body's own processes of territorialization, which themselves could produce further becomings. Is this an approach we can use to determine how architecture is interiorized, how it is entangled in the evolutionary process itself?

EG Yes, I have no doubt. The built environment is for most of us in the developed world the context in which "natural selection" occurs, the frame through which the world impacts the body, whether it is through natural events, like various disasters, hurricanes, earthquakes, storms, or cultural, economical or political events, wars, and crises. Cities have become our "habitats," putting as much external pressure that we must internally regulate as natural selection does within a purely natural order. Social and cultural life does not transform natural selection; it simply orients it to different criteria that are economic and social rather than biological. Architecture produces at least some of the key elements that constitute the milieu in which forces affect living beings. It is also one of the objects of evolutionary-becoming itself, always developing new forms, new materials in new ways. This is the political and ethical potential of architecture that we discussed earlier.

HD&ET Despite the increasing tendency of architecture, as a discipline and profession, toward advertisement, spectacle, and self-promotion, there remains an important struggle to articulate connections between architecture practices and the world within which the human attempts to survive, which, at the same time, it also produces. In this regard, can architecture contribute to the generation of critical ecologies?

EG Of course it can. Architecture at its best is about providing a constructed environment which, on the one hand, contributes as little as possible to further ecological destruction, and on the other produces spatial and aesthetic experiences that enable new forms of subjectivity and new forms of social engagement to emerge. Architecture is capable of not only developing new forms of design, but also new materials that are attentive to the habitat from which they are taken, as well as the habitat to which they now contribute. This is an architecture in which humans, designers and builders, as well as inhabitants, come to acknowledge the debt they owe to the natural forces that make their endeavours possible. Such an architecture is not only possible, but actual, even though it tends to defy the usual conditions under which architecture is commissioned and built.

HD&ET The human, as a type of body (one that obviously contains a huge variety of forms and variations), possesses the corporeal and technical capacities that enable us to radically transform the earth in ways that were even a short time ago quite unimaginable. This is due, in large part, to the scale of the human as a species. In the turn to the Anthropocene, can we begin to see the collective enunciation of the human? Could we read this as a kind of evolutionary death drive?

EG This capacity for radical transformation is a function of scales of population, but even more it is a function of the scale of technologies that are now capable of terra-forming any region, leveling everything to even out a terrain in a very rapid period of time. We can now clear a forest in a matter of days, if not hours, with drastic repercussions for all forms of life sustained there, including, indirectly, the human itself. I don't think that it is a death drive, although it is a drive that will in the longer term result in extinction: in this situation, death—extinction—is an inevitable Malthusian conclusion from the rise in populations rather than an orientation or drive from within species and individuals. The concept of the Anthropocene, in noting human exceptionalism, also participates in it. Man is not a more dangerous species than any other; but like all other species, whose species-existence is finite, this species will inevitably, over time, evolve or become extinct. Species come into existence and become extinct. Their activities may imperil the lives of those that share their environment. Man is no different. His technology increases the rate of change, the scale of change and the feedback consequences of ecological upheaval; but it does not change the nature of extinction. We have no need to posit an internal death drive that regulates humans from within, to the extent that humans already have an external limit on the ability of any environment to support their activities, for any sustained length of time.

HD&ET We are thinking here of how you describe Darwin's account of evolution as "each species, each bodily form, orients the world and its actions in it, according to its ability to maximize action in the world, the kinds of action that its particular evolved bodily form enables."[10] At the same time, the death drive is not a simple desire for death; it is, at least according to the accelerationism of Nick Land, a tendency to dissipate energy in ways "utterly alien to everything human."[11] Is this creative, extravagant excess, this energetic dissipation, not also part of the evolutionary process? Could it be a part of an ethology, or ethics, of the human as it encounters itself, and its own aggregate force, in the Anthropocene?

EG Yes, I believe that it is: evolution is not only the operation of natural selection, the struggle of life and death, the "survival of the fittest" (to use A.R. Wallace's definition of natural selection), but also the operation of sexual selection which generates often extravagant, spectacular, and excessively perceptible organs, bodily characteristics and capacities that are linked to attraction and taste, a tendency not entirely compatible with natural selection. This means that not only is there an excess of life over death in the existence of species (a function of natural selection), but there is also an excess of features characterizing life that have little do with survival and much to do with sexual attractiveness. This is indeed part of evolution as Darwin conceived it, although there is a strong tendency in contemporary biology to reduce sexual selection to natural selection and to seek in such features a secret discernment of survival and reproduction (beauty equals healthiness). I don't know how this might guide an ethics of ethology; it is very difficult to generate an ethics that incorporates not only everyday relations of sociality but also sexual and intimate relations, which perhaps function according to a different logic. Does excess and extravagance generate the possibility or actuality of an ethology? And what might such an ethology look like?

Notes

1   Elizabeth Grosz, *Chaos, Territory, Art: Deleuze and the Framing of the Earth* (New York: Columbia University Press, 2008), 3.

2   Elizabeth Grosz, *Becoming Undone: Darwinian Reflections on Life, Politics, and Art* (Durham: Duke University Press, 2011), 5.

3   Ibid., 8.

4   Gilbert Simondon, "Technical Mentality," trans. Arne de Boever, *Parrhesia* 7 (2009): 4.

5   Elizabeth Grosz, *Architecture from the Outside: Essays on Virtual and Real Space* (Cambridge, Mass.: MIT Press, 2001), 101.

6   Dipesh Chakrabarty, "The Climate of History: Four Theses," in *Critical Inquiry* 35 (Winter 2009): 197–222.

7   See Tom Cohen, ed., *Telemorphosis: Theory in the Era of Climate Change, Volume 1* (Ann Arbor: Open Humanities Press/MPublishing, 2012).

8   Grosz, *Architecture from the Outside*, 32.

9   Grosz, *Becoming Undone*, 20.

10 Ibid., 22.

11 Nick Land, *Fanged Noumena: Collected Writings 1987–2007*, ed. Robin MacKay and Ray Brassier (London: Urbanomic, 2011), 283.

Fortune Head Geologies (2013)

Lisa Hirmer

Photographs from Fortune Head Ecological Reserve,
Newfoundland, Canada

Fortune Head is the location of a "Global Boundary Stratotype Section and Point." This means it is an internationally recognized reference point in the geologic record, a moment in time and space marked by either a real or theoretical golden spike. A reference point, of course, permits the discussion of one location by describing its relationship to another. In this case, the reference is the line drawn between the Cambrian and Precambrian periods, which provides a way for scientists to navigate the nebulous waves of deep time as they crash together, hinting at the formation of the earth.

On a windy spring day I photograph the rocks, but I cannot see the dividing line. Perhaps the golden spike is invisible to the untrained eye. The strata of rock, like the ticks of a clock, suggest a great passage of time, but still appear indistinct. The dark gray band near the bottom of the rocks is only the result of waves crashing against them.

The Precambrian-Cambrian division is significant in the history of the earth. The period preceding the Cambrian, the Ediacaran, was an era of soft-bodied and frond-like creatures.[1] The Cambrian was a period of great change; it is even described as an explosion, although explosions in geological time still take millions of years. It was a time of massive earthquakes and continental change. New landmasses, oceans, and mountains formed. The very chemistry of the earth system changed. It was also a time of great evolutionary surges, an explosion of new life forms that brought to the world novel biological features, including skeletons, predation, and sexual reproduction.

One important signal that confirms rocks from the Cambrian era is the evidence of "bioturbating" organisms. These small, soft-bodied animals burrowed through the ocean strata while eating the sediment that collected there. Their burrow patterns leave distinctive, fossilized traces in the geologic record, and are abundant in the rocks of Fortune Head.

Our human burrowing activities are marked in the landscape here, too. A rusty orange stain crumbles out of a gully between the grey strata and into the ocean. The men in the lighthouse apologize for its presence, explaining that it is the remains of an old garbage dump which served the town of Fortune before the geological significance of the site was known, that is, before it was re-marked as a reference point.

Notes

1 See Don McKay, "Ediacaran and Anthropocene: Poetry as a Reader of Deep Time," in *Making the Geologic Now: Responses to Material Conditions of Contemporary Life*, ed. Elizabeth Ellsworth and Jamie Kruze (Brooklyn: Punctum Books, 2012), 46-54.

Utopia on Ice

by Mark Dorrian

The Climate as Commodity Form

Promotional image from the indefinitely postponed Sunny Mountain Ski Dome project, Dubai　　　　Fig. 01

In the lead-up to the 2008 Beijing Olympics, media outlets reported that the Chinese government intended to use weather modification techniques to ensure favourable conditions for the games. Playing on the story's science fiction-like strangeness, Western articles tended to locate it as lying somewhere between an amusing manifestation of cultural eccentricity and a much more worrying deployment of a weird and even alien technology, replete with military implications. Such reports show that weather manipulation remains something that is popularly imagined—like thought control, with which it has an obscure relation—and situated within the phantasmagoric domain of the other. Yet it is an idea that is deeply sedimented within the West's intertwining utopian, military, technological, and science fiction imaginaries. It is striking that in Thomas More's fable, Utopia is first established in an act of what we would today call geo-engineering, the radical reconstruction of environment by culture, when the isthmus connecting it to the mainland is severed by the legendary founder Utopus.[1] As the island was not already one, and had to be made so, Utopia is from the start presented as a project, a society established within environmental conditions that are at least specified, and might even be "designed." And this in turn poses other questions, not least those concerning weather. It is an issue that would weigh ever more on utopian speculation, to the point where we find Le Corbusier in 1933 declaring: "But where is Utopia, where the weather is 64.4°...?"[2] In general terms, this increasing centrality of atmospheric concerns for utopian thought was closely related to the shifting environmental conditions and contexts to which modernization gave rise and within which it was pursued; more specifically, it had much to do with the post-Enlightenment social vision of Charles Fourier.

Fig. 02   Image from Buckminster Fuller and Shoji Sadao's "Cloud Nine" project, ca. 1960

As is well known, the architectural fulcrum of Fourier's social system was the Phalanstery. Home to his associational community bound together through "passionate attraction," it was a people's palace that assumed the form of—in Walter Benjamin's characterization—a "city of arcades."[3] Importantly, however, it was also a climatological mechanism that took its place within Fourier's larger providentialist schema, which envisaged the transformation of the global climate through human cultivation.[4] In other words, this was a vast, divinely ordained project of planetary air-conditioning. In his treatise *The Theory of the Four Movements* (1808), Fourier depicted the aurora borealis as a seminal effusion that could not enter into creative conjunction with its southern counterpart until humankind completed the requisite preparations. These involved increasing the global population to two billion, and the subsequent cultivation of land as far as 65° north. This, Fourier declared, would trigger the emergence of the "Northern Crown," a fluidal ring, ignited through contact with the sun, which would pass light and heat to the earth and melt the northern ice. With new land thus released for cultivation, the destined human population of three billion could be fully realized within a newly equalized and temperate global climate.[5] In a Land of Cockaigne-like touch, Fourier claimed that grapes would be grown in St. Petersburg, while boreal fluid would infuse the sea with citric acid, giving it the pleasant flavour of lemonade.[6] All restrictions having been removed, the epoch of the Earth's harmonic creations could then, at last, begin.

Commenting on Fourier's followers in pre-Civil War America, William B. Meyer notes that they "made 'earth subduing' one of their goals. [...] They looked forward to the transformation of the planet, to the removal of 'those excesses of climate which make a scourge of so large a part of its surface,' to the eradication of 'the ices of the poles, and the fatal heats and miasmas of the tropics.'"[7] It was a theme that would be taken up in science fiction novels at the turn of the century, such as *A Journey in Other Worlds* (1894), written by the hotel founder, property tycoon, and inventor John Jacob Astor IV. Set in 2088, the book envisages various weather control technologies, including rain production induced by atmospheric explosions, and so-called "aeriducts," tubes through which moist air is sucked up then discharged to cool and condense at great heights. Most interesting for a discussion of the Anthropocene, however, is its idea of eradicating seasonal extremes and stabilizing temperature within given latitudes by straightening the global axis, a feat that would be achieved through moving ballast, in the form of water, between the poles. Too much even for 2088, this had not yet been accomplished, al-

Rainmakers Irving Langmuir, Vincent Schaefer, and Bernard Vonnegut at work on cloud seeding in a GE Laboratory. 1947

Fig. 03

though an association dedicated to the project—the Terrestrial Axis Straightening Company—had been formed. Rather ironically, the ice that Astor's protagonists battle would also become their author's nemesis, for he was to become the richest fatality in the *Titanic* disaster.

Clearly, axis realignment was in the air at the time, for Astor's scenario received a twist only five years later in Jules Verne's *The Purchase of the North Pole* (1899), in which a group of American investors gains the right to mine the Arctic's mineral deposits, entailing the melting of polar ice. Although they present this as a prodigious and benevolent act of climatic engineering, public opinion turns against them when it is revealed that they were artillerymen during the Civil War and that they plan to reorient the world's axis through the recoil of the world's largest cannon, which they propose to construct and fire.

Utopian climatology is, of course, only part of a much longer history of weather control. Securing beneficent rainfall is one of the most familiar objectives of archaic magic and ritual practices, in which the weather is influenced through its emblems and homologues. Such was the "serpent ritual" of the Pueblo Indians—subject of a celebrated lecture by the art historian Aby Warburg—in which the lightning of the thunderstorm was induced through the manipulation of its symbolic counterpart, the snake.[8] Perhaps too, weather supplies us with our most fundamental idea of weaponry; or at least that of the weapon in its mythic, godlike form—the weapon that is instantaneous and kills at a distance (close to the idea of being able to kill another by willing it) through some kind of discharge. All those flashing spears of the epics carry implications of lightning, as does, even more explicitly, the rifle's thunderous discharge. In Western narratives of contact with "primitive peoples," such as Daniel Defoe's *Robinson Crusoe* (1719), it is the ability to use a gun—to will death across distances, to instantaneously kill with thunder—that marks its possessor as divine in the eyes of the subaltern.[9]

It is, however, in Jonathan Swift's *Travels into Several Remote Nations of the World, by Lemuel Gulliver* (1726), a book in which utopian, scientific, satirical, and travel literatures coalesce into something very much like science fiction, that we find the first imaginings of a new kind of meteorological weaponry, one that anticipates the "atmoterrorism" that Peter Sloterdijk has—surely too restrictively—located in the twentieth century.[10] The relevant section is the journey to the levitating island of Laputa, an enormous, flying saucer-like landmass that dominates the unfortunate kingdom beneath it, through, among other measures, a form of bellicose weather control whereby the island hovers above the land underneath, modifying its climate by depriving it of sunlight and rainfall, thus subjecting its inhabitants to drought and famine.

While the utilization of gas in World War I brought a new focus on battlefield climatology, it was in the immediate aftermath of World War II that speculation and research on the weaponization of weather escalated. At the end of 1945, the Princeton University mathematician and game theorist John von Neumann convened a meeting of leading scientists, who concluded that, with new climate modeling techniques, intentional modification of the weather might be possible and that this could have a major impact in another war, for example by forcing the collapse of Soviet food supplies by creating drought.[11] The military potential of weather modification would find a powerful advocate in Irving Langmuir, whose assistant at the General Electric Corporation's research and development laboratory, Vincent Schaefer, had in 1946 discovered the still-controversial principle of cloud seeding. Although research projects proliferated in the following decades, public consciousness of the issue remained low until the early 1970s, when the news broke that the US had used weather modification techniques in Vietnam.[12] A strong domestic backlash followed, with the events the affair set in motion leading eventually to the framing of the UN Convention on the Prohibition of Military or Any Other Hostile Use of Environmental Modification Techniques (known as ENMOD), which entered into force on 5 October 1978 (though it did not come into effect for the US until 17 January 1980).[13]

But it is clear, especially from the 1996 report "Weather as a Force Multiplier: Owning the Weather in 2025"—one "chapter" of the multi-volume study *Air Force 2025* commissioned by the US Air Force Chief of Staff to speculate on the future of air war over a thirty-year period—that the story of the weather as a weapon continues in contemporary forms of military violence. Significantly, this report is concerned not just to set out what might be technologically possible, but also to project political scenarios in which it could become so, thus placing the question of international treaties and public opinion at the fore. Most striking here is that our contemporary environmental crisis is imagined not as a constraint, but rather a lubricant for public acceptability, whereby civil concerns drive cultural and technological developments to the advantage of the military. In the narrative constructed by the authors, the demands of globalized business lead to the ever-greater refinement of weather observation and prediction mechanisms. Against this background, the world experiences what are increasingly intolerable stresses resulting from population pressures and environmental degradation (shortages of water and food, etc.). As the report puts it: "Massive life and property losses associated with natural weather disasters become increasingly unacceptable. These pressures prompt governments and/or other organizations who are able to capitalize on the technological advances of the previous 20 years to pursue a highly accurate and reasonably precise weather-modification capability."[14] With states veritably forced by public opinion in the direction of weather modification, old treaties are revised and less prohibitive new agreements put in their place, opening the door to new military opportunities and their attendant forms of capital accumulation.

Promotional Poster for Dubailand   Fig. 04

Implicit in the phrase "owning the weather," and explicit in the business-based scenarios presented in the Air Force report, is not just mastery over the weather, but also its commodification, a process that we can sharply bring into focus by examining development strategies over the past decade in Dubai. In his celebrated "retroactive manifesto for Manhattan," *Delirious New York*, Rem Koolhaas characterized the early twentieth-century amusement parks of Coney Island as proleptic testing grounds for Manhattan and its "culture of congestion," and it might be supposed that in the Dubai developments we have been witness to the emergence of a similar dreamscape, although one that this time anticipates a new, atmospheric urbanism of the future. Interestingly—perhaps bizarrely—pre-credit crunch Dubai seemed to channel aspects of the visual culture of the US that effloresced in the period before the oil crisis of the early 1970s, which it absorbed and retooled for the era of postmodern global finance. In the Palms developments, the state developer Nakheel took up land art, morphing Robert Smithson's *Spiral Jetty* (1972) into a brand image visible to satellites. In more specifically atmospheric terms, there was Dubai Sunny Mountain Ski Dome, which, although eventually put on hold, was to contain an artificial mountain range and a revolving ski slope together with other—as the official description put it—"Arctic experiences" (which apparently would have included polar bears).[15] The ski dome in particular clearly expressed the development idea of an array of different encapsulated "experiences" as conveyed in the advertising material for the vast Dubailand project, of which it was to be part, but also that of weather control and escalated climate differential—the conceit of a ski dome in the desert—as a commodity attraction in its own right.

The ski dome, although structurally dissimilar, is an afterimage of Buckminster Fuller's geodesics with all their complex connotations of autonomy, encapsulation, and world imagery—expressed most potently in the floating globes of Fuller and Shoji Sadao's "Cloud Nine" project (ca. 1960). A recurring notion within the political history of air-conditioning, in which Fuller's work participates, is that of weather control as a remedial activity. It is almost as if weather—at least in the imaginations of certain white men—*is* alienation, or at least is a fundamental expression thereof, and that to make reparation, to get back together again, to melt the ice in whatever way we mean (with one another, with nature, with ourselves), we need to get the climate right. From this point of view, air-conditioning in its utopic form might be said to aim at a climatological erotics. Air-conditioning becomes necessary once we are outside paradise (*le temps*, weather and time, beginning together), but it is also the technological remediation whose promise is to either get us back there again or to deliver it to us for the first time. There is something of this in the ice-cap melter Fourier's otherwise unreasonable emphasis on the glasshouse-like street galleries of his Phalansteries, but also in Le Corbusier's equally obsessive dream of an ideal internal temperature that should be globally observed (which, in its aim of universal climatic equalization, is a kind of glacial melting by proxy).[16] This is equally evident in Fuller's famous encapsulation projects such as the Manhattan dome, which were intended to produce interiors with, in his words, a "Garden of Eden" climate.[17] And it comes as no surprise that technologically facilitated returns to Eden are at the same time returns to Mother, as unmistakably expressed in Reyner Banham and François Dallegret's *Environment Bubble* (1965), an inflatable amniotic sac in which the hum of Mother's body is replaced by that of the sustaining air-conditioning unit whose output keeps the whole pneumatic structure inflated.

It is in this last project that we glimpse an important point, which is that climatic remediation inevitably involves ideas of a "making free" of air. On the surface, it seems a counterintuitive argument to make—that Banham and Dallegret's project might in some way be invested in a discourse of air and freedom, of air as the epitome and emblem of freedom, given that it is clearly predicated on atmospheric engineering and manipulation. So what is at stake is such a presupposition?

There is a very specific kind of anxiety associated with the subjugation of air, an anxiety especially evident in responses to instances when air is commodified, privatized, or militarized. At the core of this lies air's enduring role as a cipher for radical freedom, such that the poignancy of its incremental but ever-increasing submission to technology arises from the sense of a final historical closing-off of what it has stood for—that is, of an externality beyond instrumental manipulation. As

Adorno might have put it, in the unease we feel at air's subjugation, there endures a protest against domination, no matter how mythically grounded our belief in air's freedom is.[18] Moreover, perhaps what contributes most importantly to this felt significance of air's enchainment is its status as the pre-condition for terrestrial life: something that in being free is also freely given, and, by extension, a commons that, through its nature, seemed hitherto uncloseable, unable to be stockpiled, and indeed beyond all object-relations. This anterior availability of air is stressed in Luce Irigaray's well-known reflections on Heidegger's "forgetting of air." Here Heidegger's "clearing of the opening" in which thought begins is characterized not as an emptiness, but as a "field, or open space, where air would still give itself."[19] Irigaray writes: "No other element is to this extent opening itself—to one who would not have forgotten its nature there is no need for it to open or re-open. No other element is as light, as free, and as much in the 'fundamental' mode of a permanent, available 'there is.'"[20]

Airborne Laputa preparing to menace the citizens of Balnibarbi. From a 1930 edition of *Gulliver's Travels* [Whistler Laputa]

Fig. 05

It is suggestive to articulate these reflections along with those of the American sanitary reformer John H. Griscom, who, in his 1848 book *The Uses and Abuses of Air*, asked: "When was a deficient supply of air ever known, except through the agency of man himself, in his folly and ignorance? Providence has furnished us with an ocean of it, fifty miles deep, and placed us at the bottom, where its pressure enables us to obtain it in exhaustless profusion, and perfect purity." When a child is hungry, he goes on, its wailing must be heard by its mother, but "as to the air, without a care or a thought, without labor or sensation, the little animal instinctively expands its chest, and lives."[21] The implication here is clear. Our relationship with the air, in its free givenness, is the point at which something of the paradisiacal condition of the prenatal seems to continue to endure, even after birth: that is to say, an immediate and freely given plenitude, in which conditions of lack and excess are unknown, and thus the necessity for such "external" forms of communication such as the infant's cry of discomfort has not yet arisen. Banham and Dallegret's project seems to take up this understanding and rhetorically converges air, air's meaning—or at least the meaning of air's freedom—as prenatality, and the fantasy of a technologically enabled return to that state. The paradox of engineered freedom is filtered through the underlying logic of technological remediation. It is the same with Le Corbusier, who could present his fanatically engineered "exact air" as "good, true God-given air," opposed to the "devil's air" of cities.[22]

We are now in a place from which we can circle back to Dubai's ski dome in order to examine its value as an allegory of the future, a reading that would develop along several interwoven threads. The techno-utopian ideal that we have been discussing is the reconciliation, within a renovated atmosphere, of individuals with one another and with their environment. The ski dome, in its re-performance of the symbols associated with this utopian tradition, ironically reverses the practices and metaphorics of thawing in which it was so heavily invested. In so doing, the dome presents us with a depiction of the freezing over of those aspirations, of utopia "on ice." Part and parcel of this is the ski dome's divisive spectacularization of climate differential, which visibly dramatizes the question of who will be cool and who will be hot in the new global dispensation: that is to say, the difference between "cool consumption" (which is, increasingly, the consumption of coldness) and the ever "hotter" labour (or labour in the heat) upon which the former is predicated.

In the extreme climatic juxtaposition that it effects, the ski dome allegorizes the interiorization of "nature" characteristic of the Anthropocene, at least if by that we mean "pristine nature" (and for nature to be nature as it is conventionally differentiated from culture, it must always be pristine: that is, nature always appears to be most itself when it is "untouched"). Through the paradoxical logic of technological remediation, the ski dome reproduces nature as an interior condition—more pure, less polluted, and hence more "itself" than in the world beyond, albeit now as commodity. It is revealing that the advertising for the ski dome promises "Arctic experiences" rather than those offered by a resort like St. Moritz or Chamonix. Who, after all, skis in the Arctic? The reason for this displacement is that, ideologically, the development is an interiorization of a climatic zone as much as it is a resort, one that, in a broader sense, becomes emblematic of the future interiorization of nature itself, insofar as the Arctic stands for it in its most pure, untouched, virginal, and whitest state.

Moreover, it is striking how the figure of a ski dome in the desert uncannily returns us to the arid landscapes in which the encapsulated, climatic utopias of the 1960s and 1970s were characteristically set. At the time, this iconographic motif intersected with both Cold War survivalist anxieties and fantasies of interplanetary colonization: the desert might be that of a post-nuclear earth or an alien planet, or even a combination of the two—a post-apocalyptic earth become alien. The project to implant a piece of the Arctic in the desert reproduces this gesture, but re-codes it in terms of contemporary ecological catastrophe and prospective environmental collapse. The cynicism of the project is the direct and instrumental connection between the refrigerated interior as the space of consumption and the decay of the exterior environment as the space of labour. Is it too much to claim that in the fundamental conceit of this project—that is, hyperbolic climatic differential as commodity—this destruction is incorporated as a pleasure principle?

But perhaps what the ski dome ultimately points to is a shift in the "human park"—effected by pushing the logic of air conditioning to its limit—away from the utopic and singular Garden of Eden (a communal space of dedifferentiation) and toward divergent spaces of climatic simulation and consumption. This, in turn, suggests a genealogy of visual form that might have as much to do with the history of the zoological diorama or "habitat group" as anything else. The tendency has been to see the Dubai developments as radically unresponsive to present environmental realities, and one cannot help but agree with this. However, one must also admit that they represent a commodity form whose logic is absolutely attuned to them, capitalizing on the anxieties and desires that attend life on an atrophying planet. As part of Dubai's development strategy, the ski dome gives us an intimation of what a new, atmospherically based statecraft would look like, one calibrated to emergent conditions of scarcity within a planetary environment and economy.

Notes

1   Sir Thomas More, *Utopia* (New York: W.W. Norton & Company, 1975), 34–35.

2   Le Corbusier, *The Radiant City*, trans. Pamela Knight, Eleanor Levieux and Derek Coltman (London: Faber and Faber, 1967), 42.

3   Walter Benjamin, "Paris, Capital of the Nineteenth Century," in *The Arcades Project*, ed. Rolf Tiedemann, trans. Howard Eiland and Kevin McLoughlin (Cambridge, Mass.: Belknap, 1999), 17.

4   Jonathan Beecher, *Charles Fourier: The Visionary and His World* (Berkeley: University of California Press, 1986), 224.

5   Charles Fourier, *The Theory of the Four Movements and of the General Destinies* (Cambridge: Cambridge University Press, 1996), 47–48.

6   Ibid., 50.

7   William B. Meyer, "Edward Bellamy and the Weather of Utopia," *Geographical Review* 94, no. 1 (January 2004): 43–54.

8   Aby Warburg, "A Lecture on Serpent Ritual," *Journal of the Warburg Institute* 2, no. 4 (1939): 277–292.

9   See the discussion in Paul Baines, "'Able Mechanick': *The Life and Adventures of Peter Wilkins* and the Eighteenth-Century Fantastic Voyage," in *Anticipations: Essays on Early Science Fiction and Its Precursors*, ed. David Seed (Liverpool: Liverpool University Press, 1995), 1–25.

10 Peter Sloterdijk, *Terror from the Air*, trans. Amy Patton and Steve Corcoran (Los Angeles: Semiotext[e], 2009).

11 Spencer Weart, "Climate Modification Schemes," American Institute of Physics, June 2011, aip.org/history/climate/RainMake.htm.

12 Most prominently in Seymour Hersh's article, "Weather as a Weapon of War," *New York Times*, 9 July 1972.

13 See chapter 6 of James Rodger Fleming, *Fixing the Sky: The Checkered History of Weather and Climate Control* (New York: Columbia University Press, 2010).

14 Colonel Tamzy J. House et al., "Weather as a Force Multiplier: Owning the Weather in 2025" (1996), http://www.fas.org/spp/military/docops/usaf/2025/v3c15/v3c15-1.htm#Introduction.

15 See skidubai.com/dubai/mountain-ski-dome. A much smaller ski resort located in the Mall of the Emirates opened in 2005.

16 "The normal temperature of air fit for breathing is 64.4° Fahrenheit ... But where is Utopia, where the temperature is 64.4° ... Let's manufacture exact air: filters, driers, humidifiers, disinfectors ... Oslo, Moscow, Berlin, Paris, Algiers, Port Said, Rio or Buenos Aires, the solution is the same," Le Corbusier, *The Radiant City*, 40–42.

17 See, for instance, Fuller's comments on his American Pavilion for Expo 67 in Montreal, cited in John Allwood, *The Great Exhibitions* (London: Studio Vista, 1977), 169.

18 Making a similar point, he writes: "The universality of mediation has yet to be transformed into living life; and this endows the traces of immediacy, however dubious and antiquated, with an element of corrective justice." Theodor Adorno, *Aesthetic Theory*, trans. Robert Hullot-Kentor (London: The Athlone Press, 1997), 64.

19 Luce Irigaray, *The Forgetting of Air in Martin Heidegger*, trans. Mary Beth (London: The Athlone Press, 1999), 5.

20 Ibid., 8.

21 John H. Griscom, *The Uses and Abuses of Air: Showing Its Influences in Sustaining Life, and Producing Disease; With Remarks on the Ventilation of Houses* (New York: J. S. Redfield, 1848), 6–7.

22 Le Corbusier, *The Radiant City*, 40–41.

The Mineralogy of Being

by Eleanor Kaufman

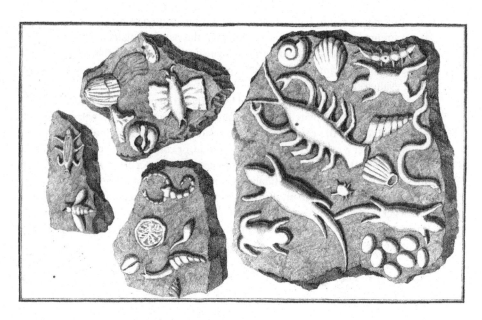

Fraudulent fossils from Johann Bartholomew Adam Beringer's *Lithographiae Wirceburgensis* (1726).   Fig. 01

There has been a substantial interest for some time in interrogating the admittedly hard to define human/inhuman polarity, and this alongside the longstanding critique of the mind-body split. From earlier works such as Donna Haraway's "Cyborg Manifesto" to Jean-François Lyotard's The Inhuman, as well as through a recent body of critical work devoted to the question of the animal, there has been a continuous call to decentre the species privilege accorded to the human and to suggest instead that the human, like the embodied mind, is necessarily infiltrated by, and coterminous with, the non-human, or, to use a term not exactly synonymous but more expressive of the very violence of designation, the inhuman.[1] While a certain, latent Cartesianism comes under fire in the attack on the mind-body opposition, a more implicit literary-philosophical humanism is the enemy of the interrogation of the human/inhuman divide. In the latter context, someone like the purportedly humanist Jean-Paul Sartre would be an enemy in no uncertain terms, and even a thinker of such ontological finesse as Martin Heidegger would be too mired in the division between a privileged human thought and what lies outside of it to be an exemplary thinker of the inhuman. To the contrary, I will claim that it is those very works that maintain the division or separation between the human and the inhuman that provide, somewhat in spite of themselves, the most detailed phenomenology of something like inhuman perception. If it is not possible for the living being to perceptively inhabit the realm of the non-living, it may still be possible to imagine an ontology of the non-living—what I will refer to, following Jean-Luc Nancy, as a "mineralogy of being"—in the very maintenance of the boundary between these two realms.

It is first necessary to highlight, through a brief reading of early interventions in the contemporary discourse of the "animal," the peculiar dialectics of the friend/enemy distinction that animates the dialogue on the animal. In other words, insofar as a series of contemporary thinkers have tried to open the question of the animal to re-evaluation and insist on the permeable boundaries between the animal and the human, this insistence is bolstered by a drive to signal just where previous critics have failed by ultimately only exposing their latent anthropocentrism in spite of their claims to the contrary. Such an argument takes the following form: even though thinker X tries to reimagine the relation, or continuum, between the human and the animal, X nonetheless cannot escape a human-centred logic. To be sure, these are compelling and textually demonstrable arguments, all the more when they are directly or indirectly affirmed by the thinker in question, in the fashion of Heidegger who compares an animal "poor in world" with the "worldless" stone and the human who is "plentiful in world" (Giorgio Agamben's extensive discussion of these Heideggerian demarcations will be taken up in what follows).

In another version of this critique, Cary Wolfe is critical of both Lyotard and Levinas, among others, for basing their respective theories of posthuman ethics on a rubric that would seem to exclude the animal. In Wolfe's unassailable reading, it is Jacques Derrida who comes the closest to successfully suspending an explicitly human-centred perspective.[2] Indeed, and seemingly paradoxically, Derrida insists that one has to respect the *discontinuity* between the human and what the human labels, after his or her fashion, the animal; not to do so would be, for Derrida, beyond stupid, or *bête.* I quote at length:

> So it will in no way mean questioning, even in the slightest, the limit about which we have had a stomachful, the limit between Man with a capital M and Animal with a capital A. It will not be a matter of attacking frontally or antithetically the thesis of philosophical or common sense on the basis of which has been built the relation to the self, the presentation of the self of human life, the autobiography of the human species, the whole history of the self that man recounts to himself, that is to say the thesis of a limit as rupture or abyss between those who say "we men," "I, a man," and what this man among men who say "we," what he *calls* the animal or animals. I won't take it upon myself for a single moment to contest that thesis, nor the rupture or abyss between this "I-we" and what we *call* animals. To suppose that I, or anyone for that matter, could ignore that rupture, indeed that abyss, would mean first of all blinding oneself to so much contrary evidence; and, as far as my own modest case is concerned, it would mean forgetting all the signs that I have sought to give, tirelessly, of my attention to difference, to differences, to heterogeneities and abyssal ruptures as against the homogeneous and

the continuous. I have thus never believed in some homogeneous continuity between what calls *itself* man and what *he* calls the animal. I am not about to begin to do so now. That would be worse than sleepwalking, it would simply be too asinine [*bête*]. [...] When that cause or interest begins to profit from what it simplistically suspects to be a biologistic continuism, whose sinister connotations we are well aware of, or more generally to profit from what is suspected as a geneticism that one might wish to associate with this scatter-brained accusation of continuism, the undertaking in any case becomes so aberrant that it neither calls for nor, it seems to me, deserves any direct discussion on my part. Everything I have suggested so far and every argument I will put forward today stands overwhelmingly in opposition to the blunt instrument that such an allegation represents. [...] For there is no interest to be found in a discussion of a supposed discontinuity, rupture, or even abyss between those who call themselves men and what so-called men, those who name themselves men, call the animal. Everybody agrees on this, discussion is closed in advance, one would have to be more asinine than any beast [*plus bête que les bêtes*] to think otherwise. Even animals know that [...].[3]

Although Derrida suggests that what might be taken to be the limits of the animal—the lack of self-consciousness, the inability to tell a complex lie—are also the limits of the human, he takes pains to distinguish this questioning of limits from an idea of some kind of simple human-animal continuum. In other words, as emphasized in the passage quoted above, he is careful to assert, and in the strongest of terms, that the division or separation between human and animal must remain in place for any well-founded interrogation of these terms to take place. Indeed, he submits the very naming of the animal, the very calling of the animal in the singular, to critical scrutiny.

Yet there is a tension that resides at the heart of this discourse, between, on the one hand, the need to assert the distinction between the human and the animal (for it would be stupid [*bête*] not to) and, on the other hand, the simultaneous need to assert that other thinkers make too much of a distinction, that they are too forthright in creating demarcations between the human and the animal. In "And Say the Animal Responded," another early formulation of Derrida's work on the question of the animal, from the 1997 Cerisy conference on "The Autobiographical Animal," the other thinker making too much of a distinction is none other than Jacques Lacan, whom Derrida accuses of falsely distinguishing the human from the animal. According to Derrida, Lacan makes such an overstrong distinction in the *Écrits* as well as *The Four Fundamental Concepts of Psycho-analysis*, where he affirms that the animal is incapable of the pretense of pretense (as opposed to simple pretense), something on the order of telling the truth to deceive the other, since the other is expecting a lie. This is a second-order lie, which requires an understanding specific to our purportedly human psychology.[4] Derrida contends, however, alluding to his own work on inscription, the trace, and the difficulty of making absolute distinctions, that "it is as difficult to assign a frontier between pretense and pretense of pretense, to have an indivisible line pass through the middle of a feigned feint, as it is to assign one between inscription and erasure of the trace."[5] While attacking the notion of a continuity between the human and the animal by underscoring the line between the two—and noting that he has always been working against such homogenizing operations—Derrida simultaneously accuses Lacan of holding too firmly to an indivisible line, holding up the counterexample of his concepts of inscription and trace, concepts that challenge such an absolute division.

Derrida's reading of the multivalence of pretense of pretense of follows directly from his citation of Lacan's anecdote of the sardine can in *The Four Fundamental Concepts of Psycho-analysis.* This story is narrated as a recollection of Lacan's experience as a young intellectual working a summer job with fishermen in Brittany. There is clearly a class awkwardness that pervades Lacan's relations with the other fishermen, leading to one of them to remark, in a fashion both jovial and barbed: "You see that sardine can, well it doesn't see you." The mature Lacan gives this anecdote a famously enigmatic gloss: "To begin with, if what Petit-Jean said to me, namely, that the can did not see me, had any meaning, it was because in a sense, it was looking at me all the same. It was looking at me at the level of the point of light, the point at which everything that looks at me is situated—and I am not speaking metaphorically."[6] Although Derrida expresses an implicit objection to the too human-centred and uni-directional focus of Lacan's notion of the gaze, it is in no way clear where he situates this anecdote of the sardine can, which would seem to go well beyond even the realm of the animal, to that of the inanimate object and its eyeless gaze.[7] Staged here by Lacan in its full social and ontological complexity is the inanimate, non-human object, the detritus of the canning industry upon which the fishermen depend, staring back: not a metaphorical gaze coming from a conscious agent, but one situated at the level of the point of light, from a vantage point reminiscent of Husserl's phenomenological reduction, yet even less encumbered by the limiting perspective of the human observer.

Thus, on the one hand, Derrida's criticism of Lacan highlights what I am signalling as the philosophical trap of accusing other thinkers of making too strong a distinction, which is an observation directed at the form of the argument—although in Derrida's case, it also reflects an earlier moment in his career, one more intensely grounded in critical engagements with other thinkers such as Foucault, Saussure, Lévi-Strauss, Levinas, and Lacan (in the case of the latter, Derrida undermines in dramatic fashion Lacan's equally dramatic reading of Poe's "The Purloined Letter," with Lacan emphasizing how a "letter always arrives at its destination," and Derrida how it "never arrives at its destination"[8]). On the other hand, and this goes more to the heart of the matter, it is puzzling that Derrida both addresses and leaves aside the anecdote of the sardine can, given that it stages—if ever it was staged in French thought—the inanimate inhuman object looking back.

Before returning to this question of the inanimate object, I wish to consider very briefly Agamben's concept of the animal in *The Open.* Far more than any text

Fraudulent fossils from Johann Bartholomew Adam Beringer's *Lithographiae Wirceburgensis* (1726).   Fig. 02

written by Derrida, Agamben's reading lends itself quite readily to the criticism that it is merely a probing meditation of the animal that ultimately serves to underscore the singularity of the human. While I do not necessarily take issue with such a critique, I nonetheless want to highlight an attribute of the animal that is, for Agamben, a superior one and therefore one that makes the animal-human relation more complex. This attribute is none other than "the open" itself, or the idea of openness. Agamben broaches the concept of the open in the chapter on Heidegger's seminar on *The Fundamental Concepts of Metaphysics*. He writes: "The ontological status of the animal environment can at this point be defined: it is *offen* (open) but not *offenbar* (disconcealed; lit. openable). For the animal, beings are open but not accessible; that is to say, they are open in an inaccessibility and an opacity—that is, in some way, a nonrelation. This *openness without disconcealment* distinguishes the animal's poverty in world [Heidegger's term] from the world-forming which characterizes man."[9] Crucial for Agamben is the two-part, relational aspect of the open. He describes it several times as an "openness to a closedness,"[10] not unlike the double structure of Lacan's pretense of pretense. What distinguishes the human is the movement of opening to what is stuck, whereas the animal is simply stuck. Or, as Agamben puts it, "This awakening of the living being to its own being-captivated, this anxious and resolute opening to a non-open, is the human."[11] We might question, as Derrida does with Lacan, whether this double movement of recognition of closedness, and the subsequent opening to it—what for Agamben makes "something like a *polis* and a politics...possible"[12]—is even fully accessible to the human. If the animal cannot accede to the double structure, is it always the case that the human can?

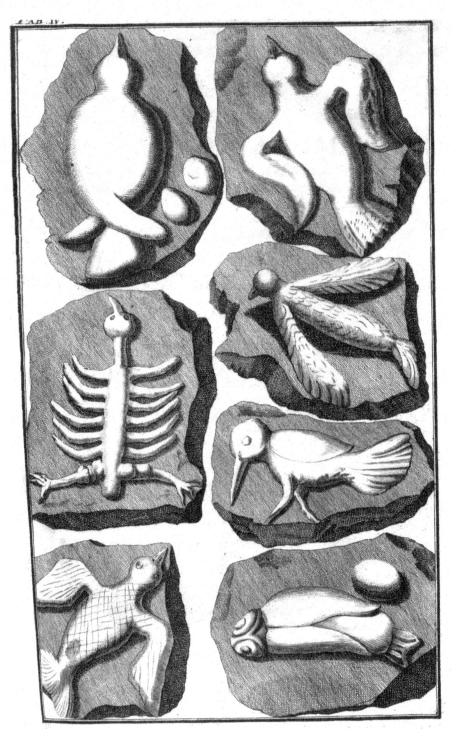

Fig. 03   Fraudulent fossils from Johann Bartholomew Adam Beringer's *Lithographiae Wirceburgensis* (1726).

Such a dynamic is also reminiscent of Sartre's distinction in *Being and Nothingness* between the "in-itself" and the "for-itself."[13] Whereas the for-itself is characterized by its dialectic of relationality with the inert in-itself, the in-itself is more purely non-relational. It seems that the merit of the for-itself for Sartre, and the human for Agamben, is the complexity of being-in-relation, the dynamic of recognition enjoyed by the for-itself and the human. But what if we were to follow the letter of Sartre's texts, and not their spirit? In doing so, we could begin to articulate a phenomenology of the in-itself, or something like thing-being, that is not accorded relationality from the perspective of the human observer. For this is what Sartre does, eminently and in spite of himself, not with the animal but more radically with the inanimate thing—represented by the stone—that Heidegger characterizes as "worldless."[14] Sartre, *avant la lettre*, explores the worldless world, the inorganic inanimate world of the stone, something that more contemporary thinkers, such as Jean-Luc Nancy and Bernard Stiegler, challenge in Heidegger's hierarchy of human, animal, and stone. But it is toward an exploration of the thingness of the thing in all its worldless, closed, stuck, and inert glory that both Sartre and Heidegger lead us, for it seems that they—above and beyond those who follow with arguably more so-phisticated meditations on the human and the animal—are actually stuck, stopped, at the level of the thing.

Like Sartre, who takes care to affirm a logic of separation between the human and the non-human, the animate and the inanimate, Heidegger, in his maintenance of the division between human, animal, and stone, actually imagines a phenomenol-ogy within which human perception might asymptotically approach something like stone-perception. In his minutely detailed example of a lizard on a rock—where the way the lizard perceives its world differs from both that of the human or the rock—Heidegger envisions a mode not only of lizard-perception but beyond that, and clearly in spite of himself, of mineral-perception and being:

> The lizard basks in the sun. At least this is how we describe what it is doing, although it is doubtful whether it really comports itself in the same way as we do when we lie out in the sun, i.e. whether the sun is accessible to it *as* sun, whether the lizard is capable of experiencing the rock *as* rock. Yet the lizard's relation to the sun and to warmth is different from that of the warm stone simply lying present at hand in the sun. Even if we avoid every misleading and premature psychological interpretation of the specific manner of being pertaining to the lizard and prevent ourselves from "empathetically" pro-jecting our own feelings onto this animal, we can still perceive a distinction between the *specific manner of being* pertaining to the lizard and to *animals*, and the *specific manner of being* pertaining to a *material thing*. It is true that the rock on which the lizard lies is not given for the lizard *as* rock, in such a way that it could inquire into its mineralogical constitution for example. It is true that the sun in which it is basking is not given for the lizard *as* sun, in such a way that it could ask questions of astrophysics about it and expect to find the answers. But it is not true to say that the lizard merely crops up

Fig. 04   Fraudulent fossils from Johann Bartholomew Adam Beringer's *Lithographiae Wirceburgensis* (1726).

as present at hand *beside* the rock, *amongst* other things such as the sun for example, in the same way as the stone lying nearby is simply present at hand amongst other things. On the contrary, the lizard has it *own relation* to the rock, to the sun, and to a host of other things. One is tempted to suggest that what we identify as the rock and the sun are just lizard-things for the lizard, so to speak.[15]

This passage reveals a thought of the being of the rock in the very act of distinguishing its "worldless" quality from the animal, which is merely "poor in world." While it is easy to critique Heidegger for his penchant for hierarchy and separation, and to assert by contrast the human-animal-thing continuum (to put it in contemporary parlance), what is less obvious is that Heidegger, much in the fashion of Aristotle, poses the problem of non-human ontology with a richness unparalleled by subsequent readings that insist on the human/non-human continuum.[16]

To develop this claim, I will attend to Heidgger's lizard-rock example in a very particular fashion. Ileidegger first asserts that it is "doubtful" that "the lizard is capable of experiencing the rock *as* rock." Yet, when there is doubt, there is the concomitant possibility that the lizard *might be* capable of experiencing the rock *as* rock, or perhaps the possibility that the rock could experience itself as rock. Heidegger continues that, although it is doubtful that the lizard could experience the rock *as* rock, still its "relation to the sun and to warmth is different from that of the warm stone simply lying present at hand in the sun." The lizard then is distinct from the stone lying "present at hand," but what does it mean to be so? Could there be a lizard or rock consciousness of being "present at hand"? Might this in fact be the point of light, here the sun-warmed stone, that gazes back in the fashion of Lacan's sardine can? Moreover, if we avoid the anthropocentric fallacy of empathetic projection onto the lizard or rock—if it is even possible to avoid this, stuck as we are in a state of humanness, just as it may be impossible for the lizard to experience the "rock *as* rock"—we still need to acknowledge a "specific manner of being" pertaining to animals and material things. But, even if we can acknowledge it, can we perceive its specificity in the way that the animal or the rock inhabits this specificity? Although the lizard cannot inquire into the "mineralogical constitution" of the rock, it nonetheless "has it *own relation* to the rock." What is its "own relation" from the perspective of the human who has a different relation to the rock?

Heidegger answers in a mode that is strikingly poetic, so I will parse the last sentence from the above citation accordingly:

> One is tempted to suggest
> that what we
> identify as the rock
> and the sun
>
> are just lizard-things
> for the lizard,
> so to speak.
>
> [*Man is versucht zu sagen:*
> *Was wir da*
> *als Felsplatte*
> *und Sonne antreffen*
>
> *das sind für die Eidechse*
> *eben Eidechsendinge.*][17]

We have in this sentence-poem, this paean to the lizard, all the complexities of voice and character to be found, as for instance, in a dramatic monologue. There is the potentially unreliable narrator ("one" [*man*]) who may not really be suggesting what he is "tempted to suggest," or may not believe it. Yet he distances himself from "we" (*wir*), presumably here the human in general, as if to indicate that he has access to something beyond the realm of the dull sublunary "we," the "we" that simply identifies rock and sun as "the rock" and "the sun." But the second stanza reveals, with its enjambment of nature and being ("sun/are"), the break between the human "we" (as narrated by the superior narrator/"one") and the lizard-thing realm, that place between the lizard and the thing as it were, the being "just" a lizard-thing (not the rock or sun of the "we") for the lizard. What does it mean to imagine lizard perception of lizard-thinghood? Is lizard-thinghood separate, and separate because impossible, from the realm of our narrator, who in his failure to narrate it nonetheless gives it a startling approximation, one signalled only in the English translation by the concluding line "so to speak" (and marked in the German more by neologism, italicization, and so forth.) For in this addendum (in translation, no less) we see staged the ambiguity and difficulty of speaking, the fact that the haughty narrator, even in his superiority over the "we" of the people, acknowledges that, with respect to the lizard and its lizard-thinghood, he can only speak approximately in his language, "so to speak." It seems that in asserting the separation of human from lizard from rock, Heidegger imagines poetically a lizard-thinghood, and in the theatrical play of its imaginative presence and structural distance comes as close as might be had—indeed closer than those who might simply propose a continuum—to an ontology of the inhuman from its own perspective.

What would it mean, then, to characterize this world-less world of the thing? Of course, this is impossible from a human-mediated framework, something thinkers after Sartre and Heidegger are all too anxious to concede. But it seems nonetheless that this thing beyond mediation still lies at the outer limit of their thought, and is perhaps none other than thought itself.

I would like to conclude by turning my attention to a quality of the thing that would seem to set it decidedly apart from the human, as well as the animal: its stuckness, its state of inanimation. To be sure, all things and all parts of things are not literally immobile; if we were to examine them closely enough there would be all sorts of movements and forces beneath our perception. But if we take the thing phenomenologically, at the level of perception, then what we confront most unsettlingly (or most delightfully, depending on one's perspective) is the thing's extreme immobility. This confrontation may be nowhere better captured than in Nancy's chapter "The Heart of Things" in *The Birth To Presence*. There, he evokes the "heart of things," where "one must not seek the living beat of a universal animation."[18] It seems impossibly difficult to deflect a will to animation, to the perception of animation, which might be equated with a perception of movement or becoming. Yet it also seems that the "being-there" of the thing is beyond such animation. Nancy writes that "this thing is nothing other than the immanent immobility of the fact *that there are* things."[19] Indeed, for Nancy this very thinking of the thing, which is thought itself, also participates in the immobility of the thing: "It is in the thought of the thing that thought finds its true gravity, it is there that it recognizes itself, and there that it collapses under its own weight. Thought finds itself at the heart of things. But this heart is immobile, and thought, although it finds itself there and attunes itself to that immobility, can still think itself only as mobility or mobilization. *There*, the heart of things creates an obstacle; *there*, it remains unmoved."[20] In these passages, Nancy touches on the obstacle that is inertia, the fact that for the human it is hard to confront inertia, that almost all of human thinking about thought is modeled on a logic of movement, on a thought that goes somewhere, travels elsewhere, becomes something other. The stone, however, does not need to *become* more inert. It just *is* inert; it has being and ontology on its side.

Even if such an approximation of inertia falls short, it strikes me that such a non-vitalist ontology—including Heidegger's "lizard-thinghood" and Nancy's "mineralogy of being"—offers human thought a more decisive confrontation with inertia than the hoped-for continuities of contemporary vitalism. "The heart of the stone," Nancy writes, "consists in exposing the stone to the elements: pebble on the road, in a torrent, underground, in the fusion of magma. 'Pure essence'—or 'simple existence'—involves a mineralogy and a meteorology of being."[21] What is a mineralogy of being if not the seemingly impossible event of pure being? It is the "it is" above and beyond the "there is" (*es gibt, il y a*) of being. Nancy links the concept of event to that of thinghood just after he evokes the mineralogy of being: "This is how a thing takes place. That is how something comes to pass. The event itself, the coming into presence of the thing, participates in this elementary essence."[22]

While it is beyond the scope of this essay to map out the various ways in which "being" and "event" are linked and dissociated in twentieth-century French thought, particularly in thinkers such as Nancy, Deleuze, Lyotard, and Badiou, it is useful here to turn briefly to Deleuze's *Logic of Sense*. Here, Deleuze situates the event within the temporal logic of Aion, the past-future conjunction, as opposed to Chronos, the time of the present. Deleuze writes of Aion, also considered as the time of the event, that "the event in turn, in its impassibility and impenetrability, has no present. It rather retreats and advances in two directions at once, being the perpetual object of a double question: What is going to happen? What has just happened? The agonizing aspect of the pure event is that it is always and at the same time something which has just happened and something about to happen; never something which is happening."[23] In mapping the conjunction of past and future that eclipses any permanence of the present, Deleuze openly favours the movement of becoming over the inertia of being. Yet in other works, he also gestures to a becoming of being, or a movement toward being. In *Cinema 1*, for instance, Deleuze locates the small as opposed to the large as the site of being, or more precisely, of "beginning to be":

> In both cases—the sublimation of the large form and the enfeeblement of the small form—Herzog is a metaphysician. He is the most metaphysical of cinema directors [...]. When Bruno asks the question: "Where do objects go when they no longer have any use?" we might reply that they normally go in the dustbin, but that reply would be inadequate, since the question is metaphysical. Bergson asked the same question and replied metaphysically: that which has ceased to be useful simply begins to be. And when Herzog remarks that "he who walks is defenceless," we might say that the walker lacks any strength in comparison with cars and aeroplanes. But, there again, the remark was metaphysical. "Absolutely defenceless" is the definition which Bruno gave of himself. The walker is defenceless because he is he who is beginning to be, and never finishes being small.[24]

Even in this somewhat rare paean to being, Deleuze situates it in the temporality of becoming: "that which has ceased to be useful simply *begins* to be"; or, "the

walker is defenceless because he is he who is *beginning* to be." It seems that to be human, or even simply to be alive, requires the need for beginning. But to not need to begin, to not need to move, to live entirely affirmatively in inanimation, is a quite extraordinary quality; this quality requires the shift of perception that the Stoics, and Deleuze following them, attributed to the mode of the incorporeal, the modality opened by the corporeal event yet also entirely separate from it.

I would like to suggest that the oxymoronic quality of inanimate being is none other than Sartre's *in-itself* and Heidegger's rock, pointing as they do toward a mineralogy of being. This is a realm not fully delineable, but it is one that at the least poses a challenge and a provocation to suspend the doubled register of human thought thinking its difference from the animal or thing, and to perceive instead the singular realm of the inhuman. This realm might also be considered a form of being as such; as Nancy writes, "We can define it: a thing is a concretion, any one whatever, of being."[25] The challenge is to perceive this concretion of being not so much as something distinct from the human but as simply what it is. I am who I am, God says; Sartre says, "if [man] could encounter pure matter in experience, he would have to be either a god or a stone."[26] This realm is, after all, a persistent literary refrain. It is the haunting and inflappable stuckness of Melville's Bartleby, who eats ginger nuts from his immobile perch in his boss' office, Kafka's hunger artist who, having found nothing he likes to eat, stays in his circus cage beyond the designated forty days, and nearly all of the characters in the fiction of Maurice Blanchot, which reliably restages scenarios where the protagonists are stuck in vexing houses, apartments, infernal institutions, and hotel rooms.[27] Why is the inert, thing-like quality of these humans so fascinating? It is time to take the directives of Heidegger, Sartre, and

Nancy in their most literal sense and shift this fascination to things themselves. Perhaps this might provoke a philosophy adequate to the event of our geological epoch.

Notes

1 Donna Harraway, "A Cyborg Manifesto: Science, Technology and Socialist-Feminism in the Late Twentieth Century," in *The Cybercultures Reader*, ed. David Bell and Barbara M. Kennedy (New York: Routledge, 2000), 291–324; Jean-François Lyotard, *The Inhuman*, trans. Geoffrey Bennington and Rachel Bowlby (Stanford: Stanford University Press, 1991).

2 See Cary Wolfe, *Animal Rites: American Culture, the Discourse of Species, and Posthumanist Theory* (Chicago: University of Chicago Press, 2003).

3 Jacques Derrida, "The Animal That Therefore I Am (More to Follow)," trans. David Wills, *Critical Inquiry* 28 (Winter 2002): 398–399. This was reprinted in *The Animal That Therefore I Am*, trans. David Wills (New York: Fordham University Press, 2008), 29 – 30.

4 The *oeuvre* of Slavoj Žižek abounds with examples of the second-order lie.

5 Jacques Derrida, "And Say the Animal Responded," trans. David Wills, in *Zoontologies: The Question of the Animal*, ed. Cary Wolfe (Minneapolis: University of Minnesota Press, 2003), 137. Reprinted in *The Animal That Therefore I Am*, 135. This discussion of Lacan is again included in Derrida's late course lectures on "The Beast and the Sovereign." See *The Beast and the Sovereign*, vol. 1, trans. Geoffrey Bennington (Chicago: University of Chicago Press, 2009), "Fourth Session, January 23, 2002," 97 – 135. For an extended discussion of *bêtise*, see also "Fifth Session, January 30, 2002," 136 – 163.

6 Jacques Lacan, *Four Fundamental Concepts of Psycho-analysis*, trans. Alan Sheridan (London: W.W. Norton, 1981), 95.

7 For a treatment of the gaze outside the realm of the visual or the scopic *per se*, see Martin Jay, *Downcast Eyes: The Denigration of Vision in Twentieth-Century French Thought* (Berkeley: University of California Press, 1993).

8 See Jacques Derrida, "The Purveyor of Truth," in *The Purloined Poe: Lacan, Derrida, and Psychoanalytic Reading*, ed. John P. Muller and William J. Richardson, trans. Alan Bass (Baltimore: The Johns Hopkins University Press, 1988), 173–212.

9 Giorgio Agamben, *The Open: Man and Animal*, trans. Kevin Attell (Stanford: Stanford University Press, 2004), 55.

10 Ibid., 65, 68.

11 Ibid., 70.

12 Ibid., 73.

13 See Jean-Paul Sartre, *Being and Nothingness*, trans. Hazel Barnes (London: Routledge, 1989). For a full analysis of Sartre's hidden ontology of objects, see my "Solid Dialectic in Sartre and Deleuze," in *Deleuze, the Dark Precursor: Dialectic, Structure, Being* (Baltimore: The Johns Hopkins University Press, 2012), and "'To Cut Too Deeply and Not Enough': Violence and the Incorporeal," in *Theology and the Political: The New Debate*, ed. Creston Davis, John Milbank, and Slavoj Žižek (Durham: Duke University Press, 2005).

14 Martin Heidegger, *The Fundamental Concepts of Metaphysics: World, Finitude, Solitude*, trans. William McNeill and Nicholas Walker (Bloomington and Indianapolis: Indiana University Press, 1995), see especially 185 – 209. Derrida provides extended and rich readings of these passages, readings which I do not attempt to do justice to here, in *Of Spirit: Heidegger and the Question*, trans. Geoffrey Bennington and Rachel Bowlby

(Chicago: University of Chicago Press, 1989) and in his later course lectures. For the latter, see especially *The Beast and the Sovereign*, vol. 2, trans. Geoffrey Bennington (Chicago: University of Chicago Press, 2011).

15 Ibid., 197–98.

16 See, for instance, Aristotle's *De Anima*, in which separations are also made between human and animal kingdoms but all within the framework of maintaining that plants have souls (albeit a usage of "soul"—*psuchē*—quite different from the modern one). See *The Basic Works of Aristotle*, ed. Richard McKeon (Modern Library, 2001), esp. 552–559.

17 See Martin Heidegger, *Die Grundbegriffe der Metaphysik: Welt—Endlichkeit—Einsamkeit* (Frankfurt am Main: Vittorio Klostermann, 1983), 291.

18 Jean-Luc Nancy, "The Heart of Things," in *The Birth to Presence*, trans. Brian Holmes et al. (Stanford: Stanford University Press, 1994), 169.

19 Ibid.

20 Ibid., 171.

21 Ibid.

22 Ibid.

23 Gilles Deleuze, *The Logic of Sense*, trans. Mark Lester and Charles Stivale (New York: Columbia University Press, 1990), 63.

24 Gilles Deleuze, *Cinema 1: The Movement-Image*, trans. Hugh Tomlinson and Barbara Habberjam (Minneapolis: University of Minnesota Press, 1986), 185.

25 Nancy, "The Heart of Things," 174.

26 Jean-Paul Sartre, *Critique of Dialectical Reason*, trans. Alan Sheridan-Smith (London: HLB, 1976), 181–82.

27 See my analysis of Maurice Blanchot and inertia, including a discussion of Deleuze's evocation of Herzog, in "Midnight, or the Inertia of Being," *parallax* 12, no. 22 (2006): 98–111, reprinted with revision in *Deleuze, the Dark Precursor*.

Amplitude Modulation (2012)

Meghan Archer

Mixed Media

ABERRANT
TRAVERSE:

THE NEW
APPALACHIAN
ITINERARY

EXPLOSIVE REVEALS

AT-GRADE CROSSINGS

[dwellings] line the roads with the hills pressed hard against their backs."

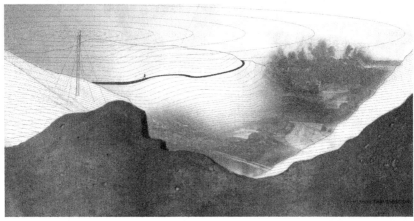

Amplitude Modulation seeks to engage with and expand the understanding of American industrial heritage while addressing the contemporary condition of resource extraction. Through various techniques, the project re-assembles the narrative of the southern coal towns of Appalachia, playing on inadvertent gaps and disjunctions within overlapping geologic, industrial, and cultural networks. The project contributes to an ecology of design practices that bridge scales from regional to local and apply friction to the current circumstances. Through research and an exploration of the operations, networks, and actors of southern Appalachia, *Amplitude Modulation* utilizes architecture as a method for tactical adjustment and the development of new strategies that question the outcomes of industrial progress.

Matters of Cosmopolitics

Isabelle Stengers in Conversation with Heather Davis and Etienne Turpin

On the Provocations of Gaïa

Isabelle Stengers' varied research interests, compelling publications, and breadth of influence make her one of the most important writers of our time. Her early training as a chemist and her collaboration with physicist Ilya Prigogine allowed her to productively and critically intervene in the discourses and practices of scientific knowledge production. She has published extensively in collaboration with other writers on topics including psychoanalysis, politics, feminism, philosophy, and science, although her primary concern remains the relation of the latter two. Attending to the specificity of laboratory work, Stengers considers this model of knowledge production to develop what she calls an "ecology of practices," thereby situating scientific knowledge as specific, local, and evolving, while extending the idea of practices and practitioners to other fields through her notion of "cosmopolitics." "One aspect of the cosmopolitical proposal," according to Stengers, "is thus to accentuate our own rather frightening particularity among the people of the world with whom we have to compromise."[1] The strength and breadth of Stengers' force as a writer comes from her training as a philosopher, particularly her careful explications of the thought of Alfred North Whitehead and William James. From these early pragmatists, she has retained *efficacy* as a central, guiding political principle, against more popular notions of choice or free will.

This philosophical position is also why her call to return to a notion of Gaïa, and her corresponding suspicion of the Anthropocene thesis, requires further consideration, especially among architects and designers. If the Anthropocene thesis repositions "Man" as the terrible end-fate of his own destiny, such a claim, in Stengers' reading, problematically retains the narrative of the "reign of Man." Instead, her thinking calls for a hesitation—an interfering idiocy, in Deleuze's sense—that can slow down the thrill of acceleration, while also insisting that what we, as humans, are facing is Gaïa, a force that interrupts our all-too-modern dreams and aspirations; Gaïa cannot be ignored, nor assimilated into our ideas of progress and knowledge. As in nearly everything Stengers writes, she is quick to indicate the consequences of a practice, and she is not afraid to discern between the worthwhile and the worthless. It is the striking movement of her thinking that is so compelling, for she carries with her a thorough understanding that it is the world that makes experience, and that has consequences; she is thus unafraid to fight for this world. We are extremely grateful to Isabelle Stengers for making the time for this interview, which took place over email following the "Gestes Speculatifs" Colloque du Cerisy in July 2013, an event she co-organized with Didier Debaise.

Heather Davis & Etienne Turpin We would like to begin with the question of education, or, more importantly, *learning*. In your recent books, including *Au temps des catastrophes* and *Capitalist Sorcery*, your writing is quite accessible; you take especially complex philosophical thoughts, and the paradoxes of contemporary political realities, and write about them in a way that is open and engaging. This resonates with us, and we read it as an attempt to move beyond the solipsism of the university system. As you are about to retire—we were told you are about to officially leave the university—would you reflect on the position of the university in relation to philosophical thought today? What concerns you at the moment regarding the university as a relay of philosophical thought?

Isabelle Stengers The books you name are indeed meant to engage thought, not to discuss philosophy. To me, this does not mean going beyond "the solipsism of the university" because there is no solipsism involved in the only thing that matters in my university job: contact with students, attempting to convey with and for them what makes philosophy worth doing. In other words, teaching philosophy involves arousing students' appetite for the free and demanding creation of problems that matter, being engaged by the consequences of the manner of creation, regardless of the disciplinary boundaries you may happen to transgress (not for the sake of transgression itself, but because unfolding the problem asks for it). Teaching is an oral practice: intonations, laughter, hesitations, even off-hand treatments of respected philosophers are part of my practice. My job is to make students feel that thinking is a vital business; that you should never lend to philosophical authorities the power to tell you what is worth thinking. That being said, I am not sure the university is the adequate relay for philosophy, at least for the kind of philosophy that turned me into a philosopher. Reading was the crucial relay for me, and it will remain the main relay for philosophy. Oral teaching can do no more than awaken the taste for thinking, which is a prerequisite for philosophical thought, but demands that students then find their own way of doing philosophy.

Coming now to the two books you name, they are also meant to awaken thought, not to try to relay what philosophy does to thought. But books also present problems that an oral practice escapes from. I have seen physicist Ilya Prigogine, with whom I worked for a long time, enthral an audience with really arcane, technical, physico-mathematical problems; his passionate relation with the problem crossed the seemingly insurmountable gap. However, in writing, artificial gaps can very easily be created. Without even willing it, an author easily selects her readers. For example, a reference to a philosopher may be sufficient for some to feel that since they do not know him or her, the book is not for them. And those readers are precisely the ones you wish to touch, not the "happy few" who use the references in order to identify and situate you. In *Au temps des catastrophes* and *Capitalist Sorcery*, there are no author references; rather, there are references to situations and experiences that the readers these books address will likely be familiar with. This is the selection principle. They address experiences which are mostly questioning ones, when one feels there is something wrong, inefficient, even lethal in the way a situation is addressed, not by the "establishment"—this is trivial—but by those who present themselves as struggling against it. Neither *Capitalist Sorcery* nor the *Catastrophe* book is about "the" situation in and of itself. They are "intervention" books, each corresponding to the conviction, right or wrong, that something may be "added" to the situation, something that could provide a line of escape from dilemmas that take us as hostages. I am thus not writing "as a philosopher" in this case, even if philosophy is an irreducible part of what enabled these interventions. Only the effects of the intervention matter, and if they work, they must be able to be relayed without philosophical references.

HD&ET Your influence within academia is substantial, and still increasing in North America as more of your work becomes available in translation. To return to our question above, we are curious about your own desire to influence, shape, or support non-academic discourses, especially those related to contemporary political struggles. Do you see your work as migrating toward, or perhaps entering into conversation with, more explicitly political assemblages outside the university system?

IS Philosophy, as I learned to practice it, is very different from philosophy as it is practiced in the English-speaking academy. There, it has always thrived on what you call "conversation" with non-philosophy, with questions and practices that come to matter at each epoch. But in reality, the philosophical tradition involves not so much a "conversing with," but is rather a risking of itself, risking its very meaning. In France, the question "What is philosophy?" or "Is philosophy still worth doing?" is asked again and again. My own starting point was to think in close contact with scientific practices. For me, it was never "philosophy of science," or "epistemology." It was about learning how to become a philosopher while not accepting the usual philosophical positions about sciences—neither judgment, nor rivalry, nor submission. Contact with political assemblages came partly through addressing the political role of sciences, partly through my discovery of how important empowered groups (i.e. illicit drugs users) could be as interveners in a situation appropriated by "experts," and partly through political conjecture, during a time when the Marxist-dominated rhetorical struggle weakened in Belgium, where I'm from, allowing for the exploration of alternative ways to inherit ideas from Marx. But again, I never had the impression of being "outside the university system." Matters are changing now with the new "management," with ranking, evaluations, etc. The trap is closing. But to me the outside was always what made me think, just as philosophy was always what enabled me to think with the outside, or try to...

HD&ET Would you comment on the direction of contemporary philosophy outside the university system, particular in aesthetic debates in the art world? We have recently seen an efflorescence of new philosophies, including the rising popularity of "accelerationism," "thing-power," and "object-oriented ontology," among other trendy brands of philosophy (and so called "non-philosophy"). Many of these upstart schools seem, at least to us, especially reactionary and politically naïve, not least because of a certain dismissive chauvinism in relation to the imminent effects of our current ecological collapse. Do these directions of contemporary philosophy concern you?

IS They do not concern me in the sense that they would interest me. I'm sorry that the art world is so vulnerable to "trends" and "brands." It seems that the so-called "French Theory"—a pure export product—has a lot of "indigenous" successors, rivalling each other to conquer such a market. But to me, they are mainly parasitic symptoms of the quite unhealthy environment we are living in, where master-discourses proliferate.

HD&ET Regarding contemporary politics, the uprisings and protests that are spreading daily to different regions of the world, especially during the past couple of years, tend to start out with a very clear demand; then, as the movements recognize the interconnections of their demands, and perhaps the incommensurability of the various demands themselves, move toward "no demand in particular." Instead, we hear a collective enunciation more along the lines of your example, with people stating, "We are not happy at all." How do you understand this tendency in contemporary politics, that is, the tendency towards claiming a collective position that refuses to clearly identify demands (demands that could then be met, or partially met, and therefore pacified) in terms of what you call "political creation"?

IS One of the only references to a philosopher I never hesitate to use is Gilles Deleuze's (oral) definition of what differentiates "left" and "right."[2] He defines the left through a crucial need that people think; that is, that people produce their own questions, their own formulation of problems that vitally concern them. To cry out "we are not happy at all" may then be the necessary starting point, together with the determinate disavowal of "pre-formatted" problems of order or priority (what the "right," including classic forms of revolutionary mobilization, needs people to accept). Obviously, the demands may then seem "incommensurable"—the need for some kind of arbiter will then be claimed. But incommensurability has nothing final about it; it simply signals the need not to identify with initial formulations, to transform one's demands into vectors that enable one to learn and connect. I like the term "divergences," as used by Deleuze, who wrote that only diverging lines communicate (meaning that communication here is creation, not redundancy). But diverging is not "from something." It designates what matters for you, and *how* it matters (in the positive sense), and therefore allows for symbiotic alliances, always lateral, never grounded on a "same" that would transcend or reconcile them.

Now, I know the new lateral character of the movements is something like an identity card, as well as the subject of many academic dissertations. But I would beg to slow down and not be so easily self-satisfied. The trap may be a certain cult for a phantom, transversality, devoid of consistence, where people connect and then disconnect, while happily claiming that "seeds" have been planted, as if no active concern for what is planted was needed. Some use the image of the rhizome, but they take it, I'm afraid, in a rather individualist manner. These connections cannot be taken for granted: once created, they need to be cared for. This does not mean that clearly identified, unifying demands should not be formulated—every demand matters. But the test—creation is always testing—is enduring, trustworthy connections, liable to produce forms of innovative mobilization for people to gather around an issue which *a priori* did not concern them, but which, they have learned, matter. Capitalism is very innovative and divisive; to become able to resist it requires becoming innovative as well. This is why I never intone refrains lauding the "new transversality"—it is still to be created. I prefer to speak about those movements, the neo-pagan reclaiming of witches, for instance, that have succeeded in enduring and connecting with others for the past thirty years.

HD&ET We are also interested in the concept of "protection," partially in relation to self-protection, but also as a question of selection, evaluation, and decision. We are particularly taken by your articulation of the way in which one must engage with the horrors that exist in the world without letting that same horror destroy oneself. How do we engage in practices of protection that resist this vulnerability to capture?

IS The idea that we do not need protection typically refers to an idealistic conception of truth: if we have truth on our side, it will protect us. One way to circumvent this habit of thought is to never divide people into good and bad, but to start instead from the fact that we all live in an unhealthy environment. We become especially vulnerable if we believe we are, by some miracle, undamaged. The rituals of neo-pagan witches are both a protection and a resource for action, for collectively becoming able to decipher what is "now" the "work of the Goddess," while never believing that they by themselves possess the capacity to determine it. But the rituals are also needed to turn horror into power. Twice I felt the need to end a book with one of their ritual songs:

Breathe deep
>*Feel the pain*
>*where it lives deep in us*
>*for we live, still,*
>*in the raw wounds*
>*and pain is salt in us, burning*
>*Flush it out*
>*Let the pain become a sound*
>*a living river on the breath*
>*Raise your voice*
>*Cry out. Scream. Wail.*
>*Keen and mourn*
>*for the dismembering of the world.*[3]

HD&ET In our estimation, the concept of protection is also related to the various ways in which one could read our differential, anthropogenically transformed global ecology—perhaps in the sense that Félix Guattari would have imagined it—in terms of psychic, social, and environmental components. Do you see the concept of protection as a necessary aspect of political practice in the era of Gaïa?

IS Guattari's *Three Ecologies* concurs with contemporary social justice movements by proposing that we think and feel with a triple devastation: psychic, social, environmental. This means giving central importance to the unknowns of a situation, as the way we formulate questions may well derive from the absence of the many voices that have already been irreversibly destroyed or silenced. Staying with the trouble, as Donna Haraway formulates it, seems to me very necessary, as does paying attention to what stories tell stories, which she takes from Marilyn Strathern.[4] The story that serves as the matrix for our stock of rather worn-out stories may well be equating Guattari's triple devastation with a kind of progress, whatever its storied versions, putting "us," their story-tellers, in a position of "guardians of truth," regardless of what this "truth" might be. Protection is, in this context, critical to helping us get along. So, I am rather dubious about the new Anthropocene story from this perspective. Who is *anthropos*?

HD&ET This concern is related to the reconsiderations of James Lovelock's Gaïa hypothesis in recent theoretical inquiry, especially in relation to the Anthropocene thesis. You turn to Gaïa as a way of figuring our current ecological crisis, as both an entity that demands a particular response and a personalization that is a form of address, as well as a way to undermine the masculinist narrative that re-centres the human as the ultimate form of destruction. But we are curious about what Gaïa, in particular, suggests, as opposed to Donna Haraway's concept of multi-critter "Becoming-with," for example? What work does this particular concept do for you? Do you think it is undervalued in most contemporary philosophy? And how does this concept resonate with what Bruno Latour calls a "political theology of nature"?

IS Gaïa does not suggest anything opposed to becoming-with. Haraway and I are both inheriting, from James Lovelock and Lynn Margulis, resistance stories that feature Man as this dangerous abstraction, as the ultimate anything. We both pay the utmost attention to scientific stories that complicate "the story" and give insistent presence to the messiness that our "theories" so easily forget. I am deeply grateful to Haraway and her innumerable and densely entangled critter stories—she daringly explores what needs to be thought, imagined, and speculated with. My use of Gaïa, as the one who intrudes, is rather addressed to our deeply ingrained habits of thought. It is distinct from Latour's "facing Gaïa." I make a strong distinction between a "Latourian us" to be composed, who might possibly become able to "face" Gaïa—that is, face the difficult task of participating in an entanglement, the ticklish, touchy character which we are just beginning to understand—and the "us" (moderns, Euro-Americans, Western, whatever) for whom the very idea of this task distastefully intrudes, for those whose hairs stick up when they hear the word Gaïa. The Anthropocene, it should be noted, is much more agreeable for the moderns, lending itself to meditations that respect their position as thinking ultimate thoughts about Man, far, far away from the sordid situation we have created for ourselves and other earthbound critters. "My" Gaïa also intrudes upon the use of the Anthropocene in trendy and rather apolitical dissertations.

HD&ET Do you think that the hesitations about Gaïa in much contemporary political theory—for example, in the political trajectory from Derrida to Rancière to Badiou, where the "environment" remains a backformation for more fundamental "human-centred" politics—are a result of a lingering modernism in philosophy? More precisely, why, in your thinking, are many political theorists so afraid of ecological positions that accept the inestimable complexity of earth systems?

IS As soon as you say the word "theory" you are in a modernist (or modern), human-centred position. Modernism is not lingering; it has many versions which concur in a quasi-negationist stance, regularly implying that what we should beware of is not the recently discovered instability of what was taken for granted, but rather the fact that this discovery could give strength to their traditional theoretical enemies. This is why I use this name Gaïa, in a deliberately provocative way, in order to incite these "modernists" and their implicit or explicit strategy of denial (their urge to deny) to come out into view. They feel that the intrusion of an Earth—no longer "ours" to protect or to exploit, but gifted with daunting powers to dislodge "us" from our commanding position—is very dangerous; not dangerous, that is, in the usual terms, but dangerous because She has no right to do so! Gaïa, as the bastard child of scientists and paganism, is encapsulating everything they gave themselves the duty to guard "truth" against. She must be taken as a trick of the Enemy, not as a question to be answered; it is part of the idealist character of theories, especially theories haunted by the salvation/damnation dualism, to identify what might confuse their perspective with such a trick. Their duty is to keep steering the rightful course, to resist the temptation to betray it. Better death than betrayal!

HD&ET In a recent article about "accelerationist aesthetics," the critic Benjamin Bratton suggested that the horizon for political thought today is thinking the "post-Anthropocene," because this trendy new diachronicism, at least in his estimation, would signal a move away from the human-centred view of the world.[5] It seems problematic, for us, that many theorists believe that we humans can so quickly slip out of the centre of things that we have so carefully and intricately placed ourselves in. In fact, given the relationship between these extensive support infrastructures and the species itself, it seems quite naïve to assume humans could exit the centre stage without serious, devastating consequences. Do you believe that this—what we could call "fear of anthropocentricism"— is creating a series of reactionary and ethically dubious positions within theory today?

IS Well, it depends on what you call "humans." Again, who is *anthropos*? Gaïa clearly heralds—the very meaning of what I call her "intrusion"—that those who believed they were at the centre desperately mess up what they, and many other earthly critters, depend upon. Now those of us who were told stories since birth that there is something really special in being "human" are at a bifurcation point: either we furiously keep to that narrative, or we accept that if there is a post-Anthropocene worth living in, those who will live in it will need different stories, with no entity at the centre of the stage. This does not preclude "responsibility," but carries the sense of being able to respond. That being said, the link between "aesthetic" and "critic" you use is not inspiring to me. The position of the critic will not get humans out of the trap. On the contrary, it will probably produce new ways of commenting on art, in a trendy race for the most radical manner of moving away from a human-centred view. This is exactly what I fear with the Anthropocene thesis; it proposes a "future perfect continuous" tense, which puts theorists into a very agreeable position. The mess can now be forgotten, swallowed in a continuity that can be theorized in a single shot. Abysmal aporia will flourish, happily confronted by theoreticians hunting down shades of anthropocentrism in other theoreticians' writings—a beautiful prospect for generations of doctoral students and aesthetic ventures in the art world. To me, science fiction is much more sustaining in this respect, from the works of Ursula Le Guin to David Brin's last novel, *Existence*. I do not perceive a race in such science fiction for the "cutting edge," but rather a cooperative imaginative and speculative exercise addressed to readers who do not need critics to grasp what is at stake in a novel.[6]

HD&ET Although often not explicitly stated along these lines in your writings, you propose a profound engagement with feminism, the necessity of a feminism that addresses the new ecological reality in which we find ourselves. What relation do you think feminism has in philosophical accounts of irreversible and catastrophic loss? What does it enable us to do in the face of Gaïa?

IS Feminism was a constitutive and vital part of my educational and affective trajectories. In the 1980s, before its theorization, eco-feminism marked the crucial beginning of "transformative politics," which has inhabited my thinking and yearning ever since. It seems that the feeling of irreversible and catastrophic loss indeed offers affinities with feminist thought, which attempts to weave together thinking, imagining, and practically enacting; that is to say, it can revitalize thinking around stakes which are irreducible to a matter of academic rivalry. I would say that the effective existence of feminism (beyond post-, queer-, and all that) depends on a culture of resolute disloyalty for those abstractions which Virginia Woolf described as turning a beloved brother into a "monstrous male, loud of voice, hard of fist, childishly intent upon scoring the floor of the earth with chalk marks, within whose mystic boundaries human beings are penned, rigidly, separately, artificially."[7] Such disloyalty must be protected in order not to produce other chalk marks, other mystico-academic boundaries. But feminism may indeed help to face what is threatening us because it dis-habituates, it dispels the anaesthesia that academic abstractions produce.

HD&ET While "accelerationists" such as Nick Land imagine that we might need to speed up to cross a threshold of capitalist exploitation, there are several reasons to remain suspicious of such a position. First, it assumes that we can tell the direction we are heading, and whether or not we are even speeding up, which seems difficult to ascertain with any definitive evidence; second, the violence produced by such an increase in velocity, if it is possible, would no doubt be levelled against the most vulnerable and the most poor, as it has been throughout modernity. Do you have concerns about the ethical tropes of political, aesthetic, or ontological accelerationism? How would you define cosmopolitics against this nihilistic heroism and its neglect of its own privilege?

IS I decline contrasting *Cosmopolitics*, whatever its shortcomings, with that trash—they are male chauvinist pigs, that's all. I am only sorry for the memory of Félix Guattari, which they deface.

HD&ET Is this why you insist, in much of your writing, on slowing down thought? We understand how this may guard against an overzealousness or a presumptuousness of knowledge and action, but we are not sure exactly what "slowness" is for you, particularly in an age when the Earth (biosphere, geology, etc.) is transforming faster than previously imaginable. How do we know when we are speeding up or slowing down? Even these referents seem capricious. In other words, what quality of slowness is articulated by the idiot, in Deleuze's sense, or the interstice, for Whitehead? Is this rather a kind of disjunctive speed, a speed that may or may not be "slow"? Why is the idea of slowness important to you, especially in relation to the relative velocity of the Anthropocene?

IS When I am speaking of slowing down, I am equating speed with mobilization. A mobilized army is an army that crosses the land with only one question—can we pass?—indifferent to the damage it causes. Whatever may inspire hesitations or attention must be banished within this framework of mobilization. What slows the army down is seen only as an obstacle. And, indeed, I see as a major challenge this sense of urgency that the fast transformation of the Earth may produce—we must stop quibbling, no time for that, we must act! This approach seems parallel to the demand to act in order to be competitive, to control market shares, or to rank our institutions. Since the nineteenth century, the sciences have been mobilized, have become "fast" sciences, with researchers regarding whatever concerns that do not directly contribute to "the advancement of knowledge" as a sinful waste of time. Now, within the knowledge economy, fast sciences are perceived as not fast enough; they are making patents and launching fabulous promises of technological revolutions that are attractive for investors but do not need reliable knowledge. The apotheosis of this paradigm is geo-engineering, the mobilization of technology against the Earth. It can also be seen as a bureaucracy deciding who deserves to live, as, for example, in Starhawk's science fiction book, *The Fifth Sacred Thing*. Slowing down, on the other hand, is multi-critter thinking, caring for entanglement, learning the art of paying attention. And it is also a matter of joy, sometimes dolorous joy, but joy indeed, when you feel your thought and imagination affected, put into (e)motion, attached to what was previously indifferent.

HD&ET There seems to be an insistence in your writing to think from within the historical present, from within our situatedness, or what Foucault called—quite provocatively at the time—the *historical a priori*. How has this insistence on the present and on a temporal immanence influenced your concept of an ecology of practices? In other words, what is the link between time, how we think about time, and how time influences thought as a practice?

IS I understand Foucault's historical *a priori* as a matter of resistance: we must give the present the power to resist the past. This also means revitalizing the past, giving it the power to escape its classification as part of the progressive history that leads to "us." All the chapters about physics in *Cosmopolitics* were written from within the historical present, turning what is heralded as the progress of physical science discovering the laws of nature into passionate, contingent, amoral reinventions of physics. I felt the need to do so in order to resist without deconstructing, without bringing so-called "progress" back to a monotonous comedy of illusions. Resistance was needed in this case because of the strong hold of the pseudo-ontology associated with physics, with all the implications about "us" being able to earn the title of the "thinking brain of humanity." But the point was to address this hold "now," with the question: "Is it possible to do so without rekindling the disastrous science war?" My bet was that physicists could give up physics as the epitome of rationality if the adventurous, demanding, and surprising character of their history, as I try to tell it, came to interest them. The concept of practice is part of that challenge. I do not mean practice in a general way, but in a speculative one; that is, against the idea that physics is a practice like any other, I try to speculate about the possibility of practitioners able to present their practice as diverging, separated from any general attribute, irreducible to other practices. Your question of thought as practice is thus a much too general one.[8]

HD&ET While many of Deleuze's concepts were quite quickly taken up in architecture discourse and practice, there is a return to his work today with a much more careful and measured sensibility. A key concept for practitioners today, and we use this term in the widest sense, is that of immanence, which is also important in your work. A second term, which is becoming increasingly important for thinking through the implications of the Anthropocene thesis (as with Bruno Latour) is intensity. Does intensity figure in your thesis on the ecology of practices? Do you agree with Latour when he suggests that the new horizon of exploration will be intensive? And, if so, how does this relate back to the concept of immanence?

IS Quickly taken up indeed! I am one of those for whom it was a matter of great unease, even suffering, as we could only imagine what Deleuze would have felt. For him, as you know, concepts could certainly migrate out of philosophy, but as tools to be engaged with, and thus transformed by the problems they would help create.

And once this transformation occurs, they would have a new life, that is, a new necessity of their own, without reference to philosophy. Some concepts from Deleuze I am able to take as tools for problems rather foreign to him, problems concerned with divergence or minority, or those of instauring a plane. Immanence is a concept I learned to think with, but cautiously, as it too easily turns into a privilege of philosophy. I take it as a constraint for the manner of divergence of philosophy. Intensity, until now, has not been a tool for me. I understand it, but using it would be like raising a Deleuzian banner. I would be grateful to hear the problems architecture faces that require immanence and intensity, as it would be an interesting manner to approach their own practice. As long as they are not banners putting them in a position of thinking through the implications of the Anthropocene thesis... And never forget that in my town, Brussels, architecture is an insult.

HD&ET In your writing about the cosmopolitical proposal, as you call it, you suggest that the difference of a cosmopolitical approach is that practitioners must learn to laugh "not at theory, but at the authority associated with [it]."[9] We are struck by the fact that you use laughter rather than another emotional or analytic response, such as anger. However, later on you describe this relation as a shrug, and then in *Capitalist Sorcery*, as a cry, writing, "We were wrong to have laughed."[10] What role do these various emotional and affective registers have in the cosmopolitical proposal? What "spell-casting" power might they have?

IS There are many kinds of laughter. The first one you allude to is the one I learned thinking and living with the feminist adventure, in my twenties. Women thinking under the rubric of the "personal is political" were laughing (and crying) together as they felt the weight of judgments and of abstract ideals dissolving away. The second one, a derisive one, is much more common. It was the laughter shared by people who "know better," judging on their own terms ideas which were indeed stupid, but this approach caused them to overlook the obstinate working of the machine which was capturing and dismembering their world. Only Foucault, as we have learned from the published Cours du Collège de France, did not laugh. He was unable to deal with the theme of his lesson of 1978–79, coming again and again to what he had discovered the previous year, and what was to shape the new horizon of "truth" in the years to come—truth, the question of which he would think with until the end of his life.

Notes

1   Isabelle Stengers, "The Cosmopolitical Proposal," in *Making Things Public: Atmospheres of Democracy*, ed. Bruno Latour and Peter Weibel (Cambridge, Mass.: MIT Press, 2005), 999.

2   Gilles Deleuze, *Negotiations: 1972-1990*, trans. Martin Joughin (New York: Columbia University Press, 1995), 126–127.

3   Starhawk, *Truth or Dare* (San Francisco: HarperSanFrancisco, 1990), 30–31.

4   See Donna Haraway, "Cosmopolitical Critters, SF, and Multispecies Muddles," (paper presented at the Colloque de Cerisy, France, 3 July, 2013); and Marilyn Strathern "Taking Care

of a Concept: Anthropological Reflections on the Assisted Society," (paper presented at the University of Cambridge, 13 November, 2012).

5   See, for instance, *e-flux* #46 (June/2013) on the theme of accelerationist aesthetics.

6   For a further elaboration of Stengers' position in relation to science fiction, see "La science fiction comme exercice speculative," March 13, 2013, http://www.erg.be/erg/?lang=fr.

7   Virginia Woolf, *Three Guineas* (New York: Harcourt, Brace and Company, 1938), 160.

8   For a further elaboration of Stengers' concept of an ecology of practices, see "Introductory Notes on an Ecology of Practices," *Cultural Studies Review* 11, no. 1 (March 2005): 183–196.

9   Stengers, "The Cosmopolitical Proposal."

10 Isabelle Stenger and Philippe Pignarre, *Capitalist Sorcery: Breaking the Spell*, trans. and ed. Andrew Goffey (Basingstoke and New York: Palgrave MacMillan, 2011), 4.

In the Furnace of Disorientation

by Guy Zimmerman

Tragic Drama and the Liturgical Force of Metal

A. Ramage and P. Craddock, *King Croesus Gold,* Archaeological Exploration of Sardis Monograph 11   Fig. 01
(Cambridge, Mass.: 2000), Fig. 4.28

> *The whole mountainous world appeared to me like*
> *an enormous theatre.*
> > – Robert Walser, "A Little Ramble" (1914)

Two recent explosions, Fukushima and Facebook, underscore the relevance of metallurgy to our historical moment. While Fukushima is analytical, based on the act of splitting, Facebook is connective, an emergent social media that has arisen from a vast meshwork of electronic interconnectivity laid down over the preceding decades and centuries. Infused with the paradoxes of subjectivity, we can nevertheless interpret Fukushima as metallurgy taking the form of toxic opponent, while Facebook—as an emergent expression of metal-based electronics—is metallurgy taking form as curative saviour (albeit in a mode of ironic trivialization). Together, these two developments support the "assertoric" nature of the modern subject as an entity constituted in language and dependent on provisional acts of repetitive self-declaration, as opposed to a solid and impermeable "apodeictic" entity.[1] In what follows, I examine some links between the assertoric quality of metal-as-subject and the "pharmacological" capacities—i.e. acting as both poison and cure—of the stage; I then consider the roots of furnace metallurgy in ancient Canaan as a way to gauge the potential of a contemporary metallurgical image of thought.

This inquiry begins with the spatial aspect of the tragic stage, and how its capacity to actualize the virtual inherently undermines the claims of what might be called the "apodeictic," or logically certain, subject. We can use Giorgio Agamben's discussion of what the French linguist Émile Benveniste calls "shifters" to see how the on-stage space is the space of "I, here and now," out of which this assertoric subject is constituted in the moment of discourse or performance. The nature of the "off-stage" is crucial to our analysis because it links the art form to metallurgical effects that, despite ancient roots, are perhaps only now becoming clear. By the off-stage I mean that diegetic world of a play we do not see and, by definition, can *never* see precisely because it is the world existing in the wings, conjured by the text and the performances, but never represented directly on stage.[2] This off-stage is analogous to the unconscious in that, if you walk up and look into the wings, you still won't see "it."[3] Just as we only come to know the unconscious mind by observing the ways it alters the behaviours we *can* observe, we only know about the off-stage of a play by the shaping force it exerts on events depicted on-stage. It is in the force this off-stage exerts on the space of the stage, and then, secondarily, on the experience of the audience, that we can locate the metallurgical effects of tragic drama.

The best way to grasp the operative role of the off-stage is through a Deleuzian lens by which it may be seen as a virtual zone that is intensively different from the relational space in which the performance unfolds onstage. Immediately, we realize that both off-stage and on-stage spaces are *also* different intensively from the "actual" space inhabited by the audience. For Deleuze, intensive differences drive processes; similarly, the nested arrangement of these three intensive spaces can be viewed as the driver of the cultural process we call "performance," "theatre," or, in this case, "tragic drama." Classically, the purpose of the tragic spectacle is to amplify intensive suffering toward an affective threshold in which the recursive operations of the self are brought to a temporary halt. Importantly, however, our attention is then drawn to an underlying *relational* capacity that is being actualized, through the action of the tragedy, toward a radical transformation. This "halting of recursive operations" is arguably a non-Aristotelian way to view *catharsis*; at least,

Fig. 02   Archaeoloical Research at Aphrodisias in Caria, 1994. R.R.R. Smith, Chrisopher Ratte, *American Journal of Archeology*, 100, no. 1 (January 1996), Fig. 23

such an operation suggests a drastic complication of Aristotle's view of catharsis as a purification or cleansing.

Mapping out a Deleuzian taxonomy of the stage, then, the three differential spaces of theatre can be read as the *virtual* off-stage, the *relational* on-stage, and the *actual* audience.[4] The zone of the relational is connected to the zone of the actual through the audience's experience of what is performed on stage. Entrances from, exits to, and reports about the off-stage, meanwhile, connect the world of the virtual to the relational and, again, by way of these appearances on-stage, to the actual experience of the audience. The three zones create a circuit that can have tragic or comedic effects, depending on certain particulars, the division of the stage space into three intensive zones echoing the basic arrangement of the metallurgical furnace:

Ore	Furnace	Metal
Off-stage	Stage	Audience
Virtual	Relational	Actual

In technical terms, the Dionysian capacity of tragic drama is *actualized* by this tripartite system of intensive differences, involving the audience in a transformative process. The dynamic plays out in classical tragedies in the dissolution of the protagonist's reified identity as a social and psychological being or, once again, as an "apodeictic subject." On-stage, this entity registers as a *resistance* to disjunction and assertoricity, a tyrannical insistence on the certainty that I-am-this-rather-than-(all)-that. "I am King," insists Oedipus, or Lear, and then the forces of the differential off-stage begin their inexorable *sparagmos* via the trajectory of the plot.

Pursuing similar objectives, dramatists from Aeschylus to Beckett and beyond arrange these three zones in different ways. Aeschylus puts the suffering *pharmakos* in the off-stage, the virtual space beyond the doors of the palace where Agamemnon (and, later, Clytemnestra) is killed.[5] The sovereign murdered off-stage creates a powerful intensive affect, drawing a *disjunctive energy* toward us from out of that radically differential space. In *The Bacchae*, Euripides personified this disjunctive energy, representing it directly on-stage by making Dionysus a "relational" character (who is this "Oriental upstart"?), rather than an off-stage virtual force. With Shakespeare's great cycle of tragedies we see Greenblattian self-fashioning as an assertoric process of self-improvisation fuelled by the "monstrous double" of the newly minted English language as it performs itself in the empty, relational space of the stage.[6] Beckett, in turn, energizes Dionysus in the audience. In Beckett, as *nothing at all* happens off-stage; the stage of *Endgame* is suspended in the ironic void described by Clov at his window. In Beckett's theatre, there is a vacuum in the wings, underscoring the autocatalytic aspect of performative appearance—the absurdity emphasizes the assertoric aspect of the theatrical spectacle—and tragedy becomes a way of investigating and embodying this process in public view. Whereas the aim of Greek tragedy is to intensify the off-stage to draw something molten toward us, Beckett reverses this process—we are intensified to draw something out of us into the off-stage—to re-animate a dead space, a world that has been drained of life.

Beckett does this by intensifying heuristic pressure, heating us through ironic aporia. The riddle is posed to *us* rather than to the characters, who understand what we do not, but whose self-knowledge is so infused with pharmacological irony it cannot help them.

It is important to remember that with tragic drama we are dealing always with the *pharmakos*, the figure in fifth-century Athens who has been, in René Girard's words, "maintained by the city at its own expense and slaughtered at the appointed festivals as human sacrifice,"[7] to cleanse the polis of this poison that is also a cure. Girard goes on to address how the *pharmakos* relates to the term "pharmakon," which plays such a central role in Derrida's critique of Plato, writing that "the Platonic *pharmakon* functions like the human pharmakos and leads to similar results...All difference in doctrines and attitudes is dissolved in violent reciprocity."[8] According to Stephen Barker, Derrida (and, in a different way, also Deleuze) attempted to "re-think the *pharmakon*" to emphasize the slippery aspects of phenomenon that resists stable signification and therefore disrupts the operation of transcendent binaries.[9] This slippery quality is embodied in the deity figure associated with tragic drama: Dionysus. From the start, the aim of tragic drama was the release of a new type of consciousness—the tragic recognition of difference's primacy—both for the protagonist on stage and, via mimetic circuitry, for the audience as well.

A case can be made that both Plato and Aristotle attempted to put this cat back in the bag, so to speak, if the "cat" is here understood to be the pharmacological energy released by the great tragedies of the previous century during the height of Athenian power. It is not representation that Plato feared, but rather what representation brings with it: the empty frame, the stage, the "unnamable" opposite of the binary of representation, its shadow, the mobile element, the *pharmakon*. Because such stagings returned written texts to presence via performance, theatre can be viewed as Plato's great rival; in Derridean terms, tragic drama is a *pharmakon*-machine, an apparatus for the activation of simulacra, mobile elements, agents of groundlessness, curative poisons, jokers-in-the-deck.

The means by which tragic drama releases these pharmacological energies requires further illumination. As a metallurgical practice, the stage operates as a kind of furnace in which the raw ore of the protagonist is heated by the mechanisms of the plot and the breath of the audience over the course of the drama, finally releasing the bright, pure flow of pharmacological *recognition*—that is, of anamnesis, or *unforgetting*. Tragedy demands that a threshold be crossed. Intensive gradients in the "ore" give way and the metal flows out in a differential flood of cathartic awareness, the scapegoat's recognition of his or her assertoric nature. Furnace and stage are thus morphogenetic spaces in which such virtual and *relational* capacities are actualized through the release of differential gradients. Importantly, the capacity of the tragic hero to suffer relates to the capacity of audiences to be moved by that suffering; our capacities for tragic recognition are interwoven and also extend beyond the boundaries of the theatre.

A. Ramage and P. Craddock, *King Croesus Gold* Archaeological, Exploration of Sardis Monograph 11 (Cambridge, Mass.: 2000), Fig. 10. 1

Fig. 03

The interpretive framework outlined above helps explain the importance of the recent work of Israeli archaeologist Nissim Amzallag, who links the emergence of copper smelting with the genesis of the deity Dionysus. More intriguing still, Amzallag goes on to position the god of the Canaanite smelters, Yahweh, also known in late antiquity as Io or Iao[10]—"the god of magicians and sorcerers"—as a homologue of Dionysus.[11] Given the trajectory of Judeo-Christian theology, it is surprising to locate evidence, controversial though it may be, of a common root between these two crucial deity figures. We see here the beginning of the con-test between tragic drama and philosophy chronicled by Nietzsche, between a

Judeo-Christian identification of the deity with "truth" or logos on the one hand and, on the other, an expression of the kind of assertoric, Dionysian desire. That these two deities have a common root, in turn, might help us understand metallurgy's conspicuous role in the processes of industrial mineralization of the planet: the Anthropocene.

In Amzallag's account, copper first announced itself via pure deposits that could be chipped off and laboriously shaped through cold- and heat-hammering. Later, around 5000 BCE, somewhere near the city of Seir in Canaan,[12] some individual or group happened upon the first proto-industrial process for heating raw ore to release a bright snake of pure copper. With this process, the enduring human relationship with metal crossed a crucial threshold. In an analysis rich in implications for the tragic stage, Amzallag identifies this as the moment when his two crucial deities are born. It is evidently an auspicious alchemical moment—the release of a pure substance from a baser one; interestingly, the development of alchemy would unfold in the Indian subcontinent under the influence of a third divine homologue: Shiva.[13] The forge reveals ore (matter) to be an arrangement of intensive gradients, an ovum that gives birth to metal; the stage, likewise, reveals a person to be pregnant with recognitions. Dionysus-

Fig. 04   Archaeoloical Research at Aphrodisias in Caria, 1994. R. R. R. Smith, Christopher Ratte, *America Journal of Archeology*, Vol. 100, No. 1 (Jan., 1996), Fig. 23

Yahweh is the deity who makes men god-like via *techne*, rather than simply deploying divine powers on their behalf; tragic drama is positioned astride the permeable boundary that separates the physical from the metaphysical. The dual nature of the god-human of metallurgy points toward a differential, disjunctive nature in keeping with the tragic off-stage; an especially transformative mode of worshipping this deity is the disjunctive performance of tragic drama.[14]

With the birth of metallurgy, the set of new capacities now adorning human subjectivity included the mirroring properties of burnished copper—the mirror that is also a weapon and a currency of exchange—capacities that have been actualized over the succeeding millennia and continue into the present. But the cultural impact of crossing this threshold cut much deeper, and with greater severity. One is left to imagine those early smelters working to explain to each other what was happening through their experimental metallurgical technologies on both affective and cognitive levels, leading to the invention of incommensurable deities. With metallurgy, the material created by the man-god is associated with a transitive element; it is as if metal were the vowel concealed within the consonant of ore, the vowel that in Hebrew cannot be depicted because it carries the divine spirit, or like the breath that inspirits the body, which in turn conceals it. "Dionysus," write Jean-Pierre Vernant and Pierre Vidal-Naquet, "is a god whose elusive countenance, though close at hand, leads his devotees along the paths of otherness, opening up the way to a type of religious experience that is virtually unique in paganism, radical self-disorientation."[15] Vernant and Vidal-Naquet are particularly eloquent when describing the alterity of this deity:

> What the vision of Dionysus does is explode from within and shatter the "positivist" vision that claims to be the only valid one, in which every being has a particular form, a definite place, and a particular essence in a fixed world that ensures each his own identity that will encompass him forever, the same and unchanging. To see Dionysus, it is necessary to enter a different world where it is the "other," not the same, that reigns.[16]

Necessarily, to worship or celebrate the disjunctive "self-disorientation" described above, humans needed an art form commensurate with a different kind of god, a god who would be an Other within the pantheon—Dionysus. The art form of tragic drama arose in response to this cultural necessity.

To worship a deity like Dionysus is to embrace contradiction. To reify Dionysus on the one hand, or to view him as pure becoming on the other, are both distortions in which the deity is seen only partially. This incommensurability is why we encounter, in both Yahweh and Dionysus, radical, oxymoronic demands for an *encoded musicality*, a *carnal dance*, the *concrete fluidity* of the serpent, a *semiology of breath* entrapped in words, a *currency of metal*, an *itinerant means of entrenchment*, a *poison that is also a cure*, the *man-god* who is transcendently immanent, and a *delirium of clarity*,[17] of the kind explored so resonantly centuries later by Antonin Artaud. Yahweh-Dionysus arose to explain the *experiential* capacity of matter, what Deleuze and Guattari would identify as its morphogenetic properties, and what Whitehead, in Steven Shaviro's reading, would link to material "occasions" in their continuous self-prehension.[18] To give this figure concrete material form is already a deeply paradoxical and transformative act; worshipping this kind of deity entails entering a double bind, an internal *sparagmos*.

If *sparagmos* is the appropriate form of worship for a deity embodying the otherness that is latent in all identity, what form—other than an orgiastic tearing of flesh—might this cataclysmic disjunction take? Given the "monstrosity" and "radical otherness" of language, *literary* form suggests itself here.[19] But, even more so, this disjunction finds its clearest expression in *theatrical* form. Agamben's recent work on the *performative* force of language, and its liturgical and sacramental aspects, suggests here a contiguity between the literary and the theatrical as well.[20]

Fig. 05   G. M. A. Hanfmann, *Sardis from Prehistoric to Roman Times* (Cambridge Mass., 1983), fig. 55 (reconstruction)

Surveying both Deleuze and Guattari's thought and Émile Benveniste's work in linguistics, Agamben focuses his inquiry on the illocutionary force of a set of "shifters"—specifically the terms "I," "here," and "now"—whose meaning depends entirely on where and when they are spoken. These proximally demonstrative terms are particularly striking because they are also the degree zero utterances of the stage. In this regard, it is interesting to consider how Dionysus, as the deity of the *I-here-now*, constitutes the focal point for a celebration of the assertoric subject, thus diffracting the celebratory worship into multiple foci. Conversely, this *I-here-now* of assertoric subjectivity can be viewed as an assertion paradoxically available to all agents—in other words, pure difference. The cathartic moment of tragic drama completes the affective circuit so that the illocutionary force of this sparagmatic *I-here-now* can be relayed to the audience. It is in our relationship to these terms that we suddenly find ourselves identical to each other in an uncanny and unsettling way; this, in fact, is the basis for the mimetic effects Girard views as a perennial source of violence that humans have learned to keep at bay through the sacrificial or pharmacological mechanisms of culture.[21]

For Agamben, the "shifters" described above carry the "liturgical force" of commandment by which the subject is constituted, a force that the different apparatuses of culture—law, religion, the various arts—organize and deploy in the service of their particular purposes. These non-lexical shifters are also legible as the subject-constituting signs pure metal seeks to embody when it emerges "assertorically" from ore in fluid form, the evidence of a poetic and a liturgical force within the material itself. The metal "performs" its emergence, the flow suggesting a subjectivity concealed in material. To make this disjunctive emergence intelligible in a form that can be celebrated, it had to be given a name: Dionysus. And with Dionysus, a furnace of disorientation, we locate a mode of subjectivity (e.g. Oedipus) that asserts itself within the intensive circuits of the stage in the moment of tragic disjunction. We see how the tragic spectacle is designed to relocate this assertoric "I," and all its relational capacity, in the virtual space of the off-stage, flooding the "actual" audience with a Dionysian experience of "here and now." The *pharmakos* can be seen as vehicle for this process, his or her disarticulation conveying differential energies from the off-stage across the threshold to reach the actual audience. The tragic spectacle is designed to restore, amplify, and bring into the open the contagious, assertoric fluidity of the non-apophantic "shifters" linked to Dionysus—non-lexical signs whose meaning depends on the proximal demonstration of discourse itself.

What is clear, finally, is that a modern form of subjectivity—fundamentally divided against itself in a dynamic, intensive way—was co-produced with ancient furnace metallurgy; in fact, both Greek tragedy and the Platonic and Aristotelian reactions to its Dionysian qualities mark important stages in the slow but steady rise of this mode of subjectivity toward its cultural hegemony. While expressions of the furnace continue to modulate the ongoing emergence of the human species, and amplify our re-making of the planet and its geology, metallurgy has also thoroughly conditioned our inner lives. Through human agents, metal has long been thinking its own capacities—for tensile strength and electrical conduction, for sharpness in weaponry and tools, for expressive use in crafts and arts, etc.—into actuality. In the present, our world is defined by the continuous flow of information along metallic circuits that supplement and, increasingly, obviate human thought. And while metal continues to actualize its material capacities by driving the human will to artifice, we should also bear in mind the tragic lessons of both furnace and stage: to allow the disorienting reality of the virtual to be made intelligible, we may require new cultural practices, narratives, and rituals—an enormous, planetary theatre—to sustain the intensity of our collective experiences of alterity, violence, and transformation.

Notes

1   Giorgio Agamben, *Animal, Man, Language*, European Graduate School, 2001, http://www.youtube.com/watch?v=KNVvvslTO8s.

2   Michael Issacharoff, *Discourse as Performance* (Stanford: Stanford University Press, 1989), 58.

3   I owe this insight to the playwright John Steppling, with whom I have frequently collaborated as playwright and director.

4   The basic arrangement of the three intensive spaces involved in theatrical work conspicuously echoes Deleuze's account of how capacities are actualized out of the virtual. Unlike properties, capacities are limitless and unbounded, their actualization entails a relational coupling. According to the Deleuzian philosopher of science Manuel De Landa, the term "affect" in Deleuze and Guattari is always shorthand for "capacity to affect and be affected." Capacities are thus related to the virtual. Properties, by contrast, are certain and "apodeictic" in nature—they can be exhaustively listed and are not in any crucial way relational. For a further explanation of these distinctions, see Manuel De Landa, *Philosophy and Simulation: The Emergence of Synthetic Reason* (London and New York: Continuum, 2011).

5   David Wiles, *Tragedy in Athens: Performance Space and Theatrical Meaning* (Cambridge: Cambridge University Press, 1997), 58.

6   Stephen Greenblatt, *Renaissance Self-Fashioning: From More to Shakespeare* (Chicago: University of Chicago Press, 1980), 245.

7   René Girard, *Violence and the Sacred* (Baltimore: Johns Hopkins Press, 1977), 9.

8   Ibid., 296.

9   Stephen Barker's comment was delivered directly on an earlier draft of this essay presented at University of California, Irvine, on 2 April 2012.

10 Jean-Pierre Vernant and Pierre Vidal-Naquet, *Myth and Tragedy in Ancient Greece,* trans. Janet Lloyd (New York: Zone Books, 1988), 389.

11 Nissim Amzallag, "Was Yahweh Worshipped in the Aegean?" *Journal for the Study of the Old Testament* 35, no. 4 (2011): 404.

12 Ibid.

13 David Gordon White, *The Alchemical Body: Siddha Traditions in Medieval India* (Chicago: University of Chicago, 1996), 54.

14 Amzallag, "Was Yahweh Worshipped in the Aegean?", 404.

15 Vernant and Vidal-Naquet, *Myth and Tragedy in Ancient Greece,* 182.

16 Ibid., 394.

17 Amzallag, "Was Yahweh Worshipped in the Aegean?", 391–397.

18 Steven Shaviro, *Without Criteria: Kant, Whitehead, Deleuze and Aesthetics* (Cambridge, Mass: MIT Press, 2009), 28.

19 Julia Kristeva, *Powers of Horror: An Essay on Abjection,* trans. Leon S. Roudiez (New York: Columbia University Press, 1982), 11.

20 Giorgio Agamben, "Animal, Man, and Language," http://www.egs.edu/faculty/giorgio-agamben/videos/animal-man-and-language/.

21 Girard, *Violence and the Sacred,* 147.

Tar Creek Supergrid (2012)

Amy Norris and Clinton Langevin (Captains of Industry)

Mixed Media

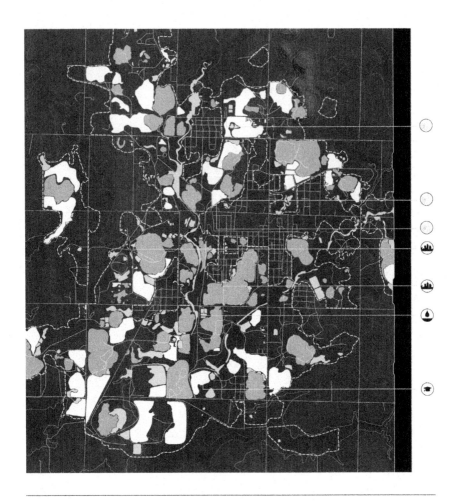

The history of Picher, Oklahoma begins and ends with the Tar Creek lead and zinc mines. Operational for nearly 80 years, the area's mines provided over 45 per cent of the lead and 50 per cent of the zinc consumed by the U.S. during World War One.[1] The by-products of this intense operation transformed the local prairie geography, creating dozens of waste rock heaps, known as "chat piles," with some extending over 30m in height. In the 1970s, the discontinuation of the pumps required to clear water from the underground shafts led to the gradual accumulation and eventual overflow of water at the surface, carrying with it lead, zinc, cadmium, and arsenic.[2]

The mines that created Picher ultimately led to its downfall. Although billions of dollars worth of ore was extracted from the Tar Creek area, the money available to clean up the environmental fallout from mining activities—in the form of the Comprehensive Environmental Response, Compensation, and Liability Act of 1980 (commonly known as the Superfund)—is extremely limited, especially when compared to the scale of the mine's impact on

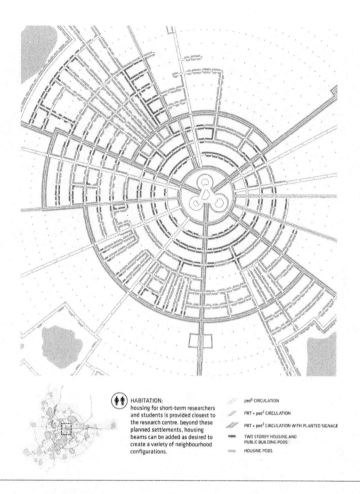

HABITATION:
housing for short-term researchers and students is provided closest to the research centre. beyond these planned settlements, housing beams can be added as desired to create a variety of neighbourhood configurations.

ped² CIRCULATION

PRT + ped² CIRCULATION

PRT + ped² CIRCULATION WITH PLANTED SIGNAGE

TWO STOREY HOUSING AND PUBLIC BUILDING PODS

HOUSING PODS

the local environment. Lacking the funds to substantially remediate the site, the majority of available Superfund money has been spent on relocating the remaining inhabitants of the area.[3]

The *Tar Creek Supergrid* emerged from our proposition that landscapes disturbed by human industry, such as abandoned mines, could become frontiers for human settlement and innovation. Solar energy generation, as part of a proposed national grid of clean energy research and development hubs, is introduced as a financial catalyst for the site, but with a twist: the addition of a structure that raises the solar energy infrastructure off the ground, creating an opportunity to host other activities on the site while treading lightly on a landscape in repair. In addition to providing an armature for energy generation, the concrete structure, pre-fabricated using waste rock material from the site, also acts as a conduit to carry water, energy, and waste to and from inhabited areas of the site.

The result is a three-tiered plan. The uppermost level is devoted to solar energy development and production: testing the latest technology and producing a surplus of energy for the site and its surroundings. This layer is also the starting point for water management on the site, where rainwater is collected and flows to one of several treatment plants around the radial grid. The middle level is the place of dwelling and circulation. As the need for space grows, beams are added to create an inhabitable layer: the beams act as a pedestrian and cycling circulation system, but also the infrastructure for dwelling and automated transit. Finally, the ground plane becomes a laboratory for bioremediation of both the soil and water systems. A combination of active and passive treatment systems for both the waste water from the site and the mine drainage are coupled with a connected system of boardwalks to allow inhabitants and visitors to experience both the industrial inheritance of the site and the renewed hope for its future.

Notes

1   Tri-State Lead and Zinc District," Oklahoma Historical Society, http://digital.library.ok-state.edu/encyclopedia/entries/T/TR014.html.

2   "Tar Creek – Ottawa County, Oklahoma," United States Environmental Protection Agency, http://www.epa.gov/region6/6sf/oklahoma/tar_creek/index.htm#infob.

3   Ibid.

Matters of Fabulation

François Roche in Conversation with Etienne Turpin

On the Construction of Realities in the Anthropocene

As the principal of New-Territories, R&Sie(n), and [elf/bʌt/c], François Roche is based mainly in Bangkok, sometimes in Paris, and during the Fall, in New York, for a research studio at the Graduate School of Architecture, Preservation and Planning, Columbia University. Through these different structures, his architectural works and protocols seek to articulate both real and fictional geographic situations and the narrative structures that can transform them. He was born in Paris in 1961, and first trained as a mathematician, later graduating from the School of Architecture of Versailles in 1987. In 1989, with French architects Stephanie Lavaux and Jean Navarro, he founded R&Sie(n) architecture studio, which developed a range of work experimenting with technological mutations, territorial transformations, and distorted appropriations of nature. His work with New-Territories, R&Sie(n), and [elf/bʌt/c] has been exhibited widely at institutions and galleries around the world, and he has held visiting professorships at a number of universities, including, most recently, the Bartlett School in London, TU Vienna, ESARQ (Barcelona), ESA (Paris), the University of Pennsylvania in Philadelphia, Angewandte (Vienna), and USC-Los Angeles, in addition to Columbia University's GSAPP every Fall since 2006. In May 2013, I met François in Bangkok's controversial Pata Zoo—an aging, rooftop animal prison overlooking the city's Bang Phlat District from the sixth and seventh floors of the Pata Department Store—where he was considering the possibility of a new design commission within the space that would re-locate human visitors more conspicuously within the confines of the zoo's enclosure. What follows is an edited transcript of our conversation.

Etienne Turpin   We are trying to consider perspectives on architecture from outside of the dominant concept of nature (as opposed to culture) in relation to the Anthropocene.

François Roche   How is the Anthropocene thesis related to the concept of Gaïa?

ET   The argument is basically that the aggregate effect of human beings on the planet has reached a geological proportion. We believe this challenges many architects' concepts of nature.

FR But we are not completely in control of what is happening. Humans are agents; sometimes humans are slave agents, sometimes swarm agents, or even intelligent agents. This is also the concept of Gaïa.

ET The Anthropocene thesis undermines any meaningful epistemological distinction between human beings and nature, or culture and nature. Bruno Latour has recently brought the concept of Gaïa into a dialogue, through his own thinking on political theology, with the Anthropocene thesis as well. Isabelle Stengers has also used the concept of Gaïa to challenge the Anthropocene thesis.[1] The projects that you have done, and the particular alchemical position you take through your work, as well as the evocation of biotopes in some of your design projects, all suggest a certain characterization of nature.

FR It started very naively, simply by taking a "weak position" in the 1980s. We wanted to develop a weak position as an attempt to avoid dominating the situation. We began with a kind of *contextualism*—I know that the idea of context has been very badly used by architects for the past 20 years—but a contextualism in terms of the biotope. The biotope is pre-existing, before we modify it, using the material substances of the biotope to be the vectors of their own transformation, the agents of their own transformation. So we start with psychasthenia, if you know Roger Caillois's approach to psychasthenia, where the biotope can create its own ornamentation, becoming a flower, or a building, through an extra-vitalism that directly extracts potential from its situation. But we reached a certain ambiguity, or kind of trouble, which, in the last 10 years, made us start to question how the position we were using *not* to dominate the situation was becoming a position of domination—not in terms of aesthetics, but intellectually.

ET It was a kind of back-door domination?

FR Weakness, as a position, became its own intellectual position and a statement of its own. This statement of weakness quickly became a vector of pretentiousness—of pretending you are over the situation because you consider the situation as an exogenous system. So, we were thinking about whether the same weakness could become endogenous. As an architect, how do you become a part of the system? Not only as an architect, but as a human, as a body, as flesh, as a species, as a breathing mammal? Are you able to take a position from inside, when you are in a position of servitude to the system you are trying to transform? That is, to lose the visibility of what you are doing and to accept a degree of uncertainty. That is why we talk a lot about uncertainty, a concept developed by Cedric Price in the 1970s, in order to accept a degree of missing knowledge, of driving horses without being able to tame them. This requires negotiation, the negotiation through an embassy between nature and yourself.

It is very interesting, the project of Ant Farm from the late 1960s, about the Dolphin Embassy. Everyone knows this project now, but even 10 years ago it was not so easy to talk about it in architecture. The possibility of making an embassy so that every-body, every thing on every side, has the right to negotiate a zone where all relations between the behaviours are plausible. Human and nature, human and dolphin, etc. So we tried to define this kind of thing, to integrate the human as an *animality*, as a degree, or as a vector of the *Part maudite*, as in Georges Bataille.[2] We are working on architecture as a Bataille-machine: psychology, physiology, history, temperament. We want to consider a premedical system, before Hippocrates, where temperament describes the body as a negotiation between the temperament of the black bile, the blood, the phlegm, etc. The body is an emotional fluidity and therefore an emotional machine. This is not so far away from Deleuze and Guattari's desiring-machine, or Antonin Artaud's body-without-organs, a provocative argument that the body is not merely a composition of organic machinery, but a constant transference of flux.

So, if we can integrate the desiring-machine, the body-without-organs, the animal body, can we understand behaviour as *acephalous*—a fundamentally headless process? Can we use the biochemistry, neurobiology, and nanotechnology of today to understand the atavism of the reptilian part of the brain that is making Pavlovian reactions—the will to survive—predicted by the DNA and the transmission of DNA, but which, at the same time, cannot be so easily categorized. We are trying to pose the question of architecture not in terms of function, but in terms of psycho-physio *phobias* or *philias*. That is, as emotional reactions constituting case studies that lead to a taxonomy and produce morphologies that can extract form from emotional flux. To elicit a program that we cannot predict through knowledge, or the normal tooling of an architect. The last 10 years was about that.

ET To go back a little bit, I am curious if you think the idea of the "weak position" became dominant within your own practice or within the broader field of architecture?

FR The so-called "weak position" became décor. It became the décor of taking care of nature; it became just a green façade. It was then only a stereotype, the merchandizing of architecture as a simulation of weakness and cooperation. But nature is monstrous!

ET You responded with the slime building?

FR Exactly, because to use nature as décor, to simplify ecology in this way, is a kind of domination through domestication. It produced a kind of Disney Land World Fair of architecture justified by pseudo-ecological values. I am very worried by that. I think we have to keep intact the intrinsic conflict of nature, especially of our own nature. But for architecture, nature is typically conceived of as a peaceful thing occasionally afflicted by catastrophes. This is a problem, because to negotiate with nature is to negotiate with brutal forces. So you have to approach it delicately, with courage, but without denying or erasing the danger.

ET To leave a place for it to appear?

FR For something to appear between repulsion and curiosity. You are curious about what is scaring you! Now nature is just a world garden, a domesticated garden. But nature always produces its own revenge. I am a surfer, and in the last five years shark attacks have also increased by a multiple of five around the world. Is this the revenge of Gaïa? This psycho-parallel universe says Gaïa is the mistress of the world and that we humans are only a part of a global equilibrium, even while we keep thinking we will just enjoy our supremacy. In fact, even when we are destroying something, it is for the benefit of Gaïa—we are never outside of this circuit. The supreme forces of the Earth, of the planet, are not divinities, but the forces of a global equilibrium in which we are just vectors, just citizens, but not controllers.

It is interesting that at the same time as ecology is developing, we are seeing the self-completion of the human though the destruction of the planet but also, through a recognition that we are destroying the planet, we realize the scale of destruction humans are capable of. We recognize the potential danger of domination, but the planet is capable of destroying us as well. So, while we desperately need to reorganize the social contract, we also need to renegotiate it with nature.

ET This is the argument of Michel Serres.

FR Certainly, *Le Contrat Naturel* is about that.[3] There is a simultaneity! We can't take care of the cats if we can't take care of the neighbourhood! If you look at the first political ecology, from the Germans in WWII, it was organized by the Nazi General Hermann Göring. He was, at the same time, directing the Final Solution. Modern ecology comes out of this incredible distinction between the suffering of the people and protecting the domestic animal. This is similar to South Africa, under the apartheid regime, where the animal reserves were incredibly sophisticated.

ET Eugenics has its counterpart in the preservation of nature.

FR Yes, and in this way people taking care of nature are very suspicious to me!

ET How do you see architecture, especially in the last ten years, in terms of its response to planetary, ecological collapse?

FR The discipline is now a refugee unto itself, just an ivory tower. But I think a lot about this concern, for instance, how the polar bear is becoming a hermaphrodite to increase its potential for reproduction because of global climate change. There are examples in the fish as well. Nature responds to change by changing its sexuality, its morphology, its physiology, its behaviour. So, architecture is not about selling green products as new merchandise that can save Willy or save the world! It is about modifying our own comportment between us and others. That is a pretty strange complexity for architects to confront today. Architects want to follow the mainstream production of global merchandise without questioning the new reductionism that says we must consume to protect the planet. This is a total antagonism; in fact, it is an absurdity—over-consuming with a green attitude! And all without questioning our proximity or relationship to others, to other species, to the environment. Architecture as green consumption is just green-washing, and we know that architecture is completely involved in this green-washing of global merchandise. Is there a way to have a voice, to say, "Perhaps we are wrong. Perhaps there are other possibilities"? There is the mainstream image of architecture, which is as univocal as a slab of concrete. Architecture then becomes a global lamentation with a univocal voice, without any care for singularities, other practices, or other ways of conducting our practice in the world.

It is terrible how the last 10 years were dedicated to the success story of the last architect making the tower in Dubai. It is funny, but look at it now—the field is entirely impoverished! The field of architecture is crashing everywhere, not just in the US, and architects are becoming even more a part of the slavery system of capitalism. Why? I don't want to answer why, but we have to question why it is so disastrous to be an architect in the world right now!

ET   But do you see yourself as an architect?

FR   I am like you! I am like the monkey in *The Jungle Book*, when the monkey says, "I am like you, I want to be like you, I want to be like you." I want to be like you, I want to be an architect, but it doesn't mean I am an architect. Just like you, I don't know what that means exactly.

ET   Does it have to mean making building-sized advertisements for merchandise?

FR   Louis Althusser described pretty well the difference between the heroic period, the classic period, and the communication period we are in now. In the heroic period, the architect was both denouncing and producing. Perhaps we know too well King Vidor's *The Fountainhead*, based on Ayn Rand's book about Frank Lloyd Wright. We know it well, of course, but beyond the stereotype, there was a debate between producing and denouncing. In the illusion of modernity, in the denunciation of the system and its failures, as we see in Carlo Scarpa and others, there is a denouncement and a possibility to produce through denouncement. The heroic period was schizophrenic. It is interesting if we conserve—not in terms of preservation—but if we travel a little bit with this kind of schizophrenic potential. You can say "Fuck you," and "I love you." If you always say "I love you," you forget how to negotiate with an occasional "Fuck you!" So, you have to negotiate, you always have to make room to negotiate.

The attitude of the smart architect today: working every day of the week, all the time, never considering societies other than their own, never trying to denounce the new economic imperialism or the situation of the system; finally, step by step, this disqualifies architecture, its potential for narration, and its potential for acting. Architects are no longer acting in society; they act within their field with incredible knowledge about new tools and with a remarkably self-referential expertise, but no one wants this knowledge outside of the field of architecture. So, we are like monkeys in a cage who develop an incredibly sophisticated language, but no one can understand the language outside the cage. The question of how to renegotiate the porosity of the cage, of re-infiltrating the cage—in both directions—this is exactly what we are trying to practice now. I am pretty optimistic. I don't want to be optimistic, but, *on arrive à toucher le fond de la piscine* [we've reached the bottom of the swimming pool]! So, there is nothing more to do except come up for air. It is a global condition that I wrote about in *Log* and there is no need to repeat it.[4] But we cannot separate research and politics. Artists are usually a lot better at becoming engaged in the debates about their own society and, at the same time, in the debates regarding the singularity of their own productions. Both have a possibility of articulating knowledge transactions and transhistorical processes, challenging what is outside of the field and what is inside, and thus negotiating the boundaries. A boundary is an osmotic membrane. When the membrane becomes entirely determined by advertising, it is no longer porous. The field of architecture declared that its own knowledge was self-sufficient, became self-confident, and stopped caring what happened outside the field. And, now we have such a deficit of attention for what is outside the discipline.

We arrive at the last Venice Biennale (2012), with some stupid, social impressions—a report on a vertical slum in Caracas that imagined, by simply reporting on the slum, it would engage society in a new debate. But we are not reporters; we are acting and transforming, and we are taking care of transformations as well. Sometimes we have to break the system, and other times we need to encourage it. But, we are not reporters; we are not sociologists reporting on miserable zones of the planet to create a sympathetic consciousness about the horrors of the world. For me, this is terribly vulgar. It was the most vulgar Biennale so far—architects simulating a good conscience!

ET But can you admit that informality is an important question for architecture in the Anthropocene?

FR I think informality is more interesting as a process in the construction of the city. We could question informality in terms of design, but slums, like the slums here in Bangkok, they don't need architects! They don't need you, they don't need me. They have incredible organization, social organization, which is not top down, but about the delegation of micro-power in a constant movement, from the bottom up. You don't have time now, but I could show you how useless architects are for the slums, but you know that already from Jakarta. We still have architects trying to force it, like a degree of justification, as if people need them to validate a process or a set of skills. This is a total vulgarity.

ET So is this position at all related to your work in film? Did you decide to move to a different kind of production altogether, for example, with *Hybrid Muscle*?[5]

FR We started with film quite a long time ago now; the first was with Philippe Parreno.

ET I have been very interested in the work of Hans Vaihinger, a German philosopher who wrote *The Philosophy of 'As If.'* In this book, Vaihinger discusses the power of fiction from a philosophical perspective, admitting the need for speculative realities, upon which both fiction and science rely.

FR Before, it might have been possible to consider science as hardware, as a kind of petrified knowledge—of course, this was unrealistic thinking—but we know now science is marked by permanent speculation. From Ptolemy to Kepler, among many others, there is a cosmic movement, and science was carrying with it a concept of the world, or a concept of the organization of the world, through this movement. And each time a choice was made to explain something, it was also political. Science is politics. Science means you want to see what your synchronicity is able to understand, able to accept, or able to justify. So, there is an incredible, perpetual incest between the concept of the universe or the concept of the world, and the will to knowledge coming from the sciences. We can try to use science to prove something, or use politics to prove something, but there is a permanent flux, and both micro- and macro-scale concerns continue.

Architects tend to have a very impressionistic understanding of science because they consider it a tautology that contains all knowledge; on the contrary, we know this is not the case. When I came to architecture from physics, there was a concern with abstractions. But, in science we know abstractions, as axioms, rely on the explanation of a reality that cannot be validated in nature or experience. This is the duplicity of knowledge. We talk about this because fiction is akin to alchemy, when the science of the Middle Ages invented its own grammar for a knowledge which is not directly operative, but operates on itself, and by doing so, according to its own logic, becomes a thesis on knowledge without direct practice, but with illusionary practices for the mutation of substances. Alchemy has an incredible alphabet and a deepness to its internal logic in order to prove that which cannot be proven real about that which doesn't exist. At the same time, we might consider the fiction of architecture as a kind of pataphysics, as in the writing of Alfred Jarry.

ET Architecture as the solution to an imaginary problem?

FR To mix narration, illusion, science, and sensation, you must insinuate yourself in the crack between the true and the false, between madness and rigor, and then you can inhabit the forbidden, as described by Michel Foucault, as another discourse. The pataphysical field is snaking; it is not a group of objects, but objects that are subjects at the same time, subjects that lead our mind somewhere that secures one zone by dislocating another. Pataphysics is a metaphor in the ety-mological sense—a vehicle of transportation. You are in a vehicle that allows you to go somewhere, and to return with a report of something you saw or touched, which modifies the perception of reality in another zone. There is another parallel with André Breton and Salvador Dalí, who used the paranoiac-critical method to question perception through mental states, physiology, optical perspectives, per-versions, etc., in order to understand the "je" as a form of negotiation, not in terms of the individual, but in terms of the species. Me—"je"—as a term of negotiation with others.

ET Is that negotiation of perspective not the work of architecture? Not that archi-tecture is the only way to negotiate perspective...

FR We have lost what it means to be an architect; we have lost this notion. It does not mean constructing a building. Many people construct buildings, but are they necessarily architects? No! So why are we architects? To define a political-aesthetic condition of construction where we produce something in order to destabilize the habits of a situation. I don't think there is anything else for us, because if we take the job of an architect, it is not for the beauty of the building alone, or for the arrogance of the discourse, or to become the master of ceremonies which so many young egos want to become today, but to question the condition of production and the context of practice.

For example, we are trying to do a building now, a contemporary art museum, and we are trying to work within a fragment of forest in central Bangkok. We are working to calculate all the positions of the main branching of the trees and their trunks to make a building without cutting anything—a building with a "shy crown." In the forest, trees do not touch each other; they have a shy crown because their leaves will not touch each other. Trees respect distances. In the forest, this is the crack in between the tree canopies, which you can't always see. They respect a zone where they do not touch. We are developing this museum project through an idea of timidity, developed through mathematics, where we resist touching nature. Antipathy has become, for this project, a design strategy.

We are immediately questioning what an object is. An object, in the contemporary situation, has to negotiate a relationship with other species. We respect the trees not because we want to save the planet, but because we want to understand how these relationships, correspondences, antagonisms, or conflicts produce both pa-thology and geometry. That is, how these relations form an architecture.

ET What about the relationship of your work to Gilles Deleuze? There is a certain crude appropriation of philosophy in architecture, but I am interested in how you relate philosophy to your practice, which seems especially committed to theoretical inquiry.

FR We take time. It is the only agent in our present condition that can develop a degree of blurry knowledge. Time for becoming unsatisfying, time for dis-identification. I think you cannot so clearly identify what we are doing in the studio. In the end, yes, it is an object, diluted by a certain narration and through its own process of objectification. But this is also not so clear.

Really, it is about taking time. For the museum I just mentioned, we asked for three months to develop a draft design, but they wanted it in two weeks. This means that we always try to slow down, we are very slow. We slow down production so that we never answer a problem of design with concepts. I am very afraid of concepts, and Deleuze said it perfectly—the only people who should work with concepts are the philosophers, nobody else! Of course, the public relations people making advertisements are not making concepts either—they are just selling production within the field of merchandise.

But, to take time is an economic problem. This is why I am in Bangkok: because the only way to take time is to minimize the daily cost of the studio, which was far too high in Paris. The last few years in Paris, I was not able to take time on projects, and I lost a lot of projects and clients trying to slow down. I could convince the client to take time, but I can't convince the bank to take time! That's the problem! The banks in Europe became worse and worse, and I ideologically bankrupted my studio in Paris by saying no to the French banks. I lost a lot of profit and gained a lot of debt. Now, in Bangkok, we are in a position where we can reconfigure the economy of production and the economy of thinking.

But, honestly, I was really astonished when I went to Japan as a young architect. I won a prize to go study in Japan and I decided to spend half of my time in a Buddhist temple, in the winter, to understand the pain of being a Buddhist—it is not so comfortable to be a Buddhist in the middle of winter—and also to meet the architect Kazuo Shinohara. Shinohara is maybe a surprising influence on me. He takes ten years to make a project. The main issue in architecture today is architects trying to brand themselves all over the world. But look at the number of projects of Mies van der Rohe and the other heroic architects—not so many. They considered a work of architecture as a way of creating themselves, not as industrial reproduction. I think this is interesting—of course, perhaps I am totally romantic—but I think the field of architecture has to be multiple. It is now purely dedicated to an industrial vision, and the replication of an industrial vision; although, to be clear, I am not saying that this should not exist. Just as in nineteenth-century Europe, there were treatises to make a temple, to make a church, etc., and architects were to follow the treatises to make proper, standard, public buildings. It is the same condition right now. It might appear as if production is not standardized because of the fancy décor of contemporary buildings, but the practice is highly standardized through its relationship to capital. And now they are using an impoverished image of nature as the outline for the treatises of today.

Okay, let me say that I think it is interesting to help some other practices. Other practices are also tolerable. There are many possibilities. You can make something very arrogant for the flagship store of some new merchandise, or you can make something very timid. But, timid does not mean without ambition! It can be very ambitious...think, for example, of Ingmar Bergman, Robert Bresson, or Dreyer's *La Passion de Jeanne d'Arc*—it is totally weak, but incredibly provocative.

So the weak, the timid, is not without ambition. We believe too much in the self-confident, self-promotion of the architect, and it is the only kind of character promoted in architecture, the architect as businessman; whether feminine or masculine, it is the same.

So, I believe that a small practice, with modest production using antagonisms to question the contemporary mode of production, is still valuable today. But, young architects are not prepared for that. They are prepared only to succeed, in a very standardized way, and when they don't succeed, when they don't get the value that they expected from their degrees, they become incredibly bitter. You used to become bitter in your 50s, or your 40s, but now we have bitter architects in their early 30s! That is the field!

ET Within the higher education industry, the role of the profession is to help sell an image of success that encourages student debt and maximizes industry profit. If the profession helps sell the image, the discipline serves this industry.

FR Yes, exactly. It is connected to a kind of propaganda which was started by *Wallpaper* in London, and *Blueprint*, which confused the character of the architect with her own production. This is how branding became a kind of valuable self-promotion for young architects. This is why R&Sie(n) had an avatar, to avoid becoming a branding portrait, but it is not so useful now, perhaps.

But, I would like to say again that art practices negotiate much better than architecture the kind of multiple possibilities of production, as well as accepting an exposure to vulgarity. Architects are simulating, as best they can, that everything is fine. They must maintain an attitude of hygienic thinking, a hygienic relation to a world they repeatedly tell us is fine. This is architecture as a brand of permanent optimism. But when we erase deception, nostalgia, the forbidden—all of these things that are very important for understanding human pathology and emotion—we have erased everything which could be a danger. We try to contain the whole world. The last ten years of architecture have only been about efficiency and expertise—it has been terrible! This erases everything that could elicit a degree of subjectivity in the architect. But architecture wants to say, instead: we are building, we are constructing, we are making the future. How stupid is this? Everyone knows we are not doing that, and we all know architecture is trapped. Except, you know, it's great for capitalism, which tells us: great, work for the future, work every day, and we don't need to pay you because you are working for the future! We know perfectly well that the replication of the present as the production of the future is a catastrophe.

ET So you are going to reintroduce the subjective dimension of the architect by going to find the Minotaur in Crete?

FR I think we have to find the Minotaur. We have to renegotiate metaphor, nostalgia, forbidden words, deception, weakness, and delusion in order to renegotiate a relationship to the world that has been condemned. We need to bring the vocabulary of the world back into architecture, which has tried to minimize the ways that ideas can be expressed and limit the emotional flux of expression as much as possible.

For now, R&Sie(n) is sleeping. After 25 years, we are taking a break from the masochism of architecture. Of course, I am swimming in this masochism as well—I think it is my biotope—but it is still a very interesting concept about negotiating, through the contract, one's dependence and one's servitude. You accept a degree of servitude on the condition that it is contractual, as in Deleuze's book about Leopold von Sacher-Masoch.

As New-Territories, we are now going to Crete. Within the Schengen Zone, Crete is in a very strange situation.[6] The Schengen Zone is a very peculiar barrier that tries to protect the people on the inside by jailing them. This is both increasing the temptation to get inside, but also creating a sensation of security and importance that is a barrier to understanding the condition of the world. The planet, its energy, and its refugees must be excluded from the zone, but the need to fight economic imperialism still remains. I was thinking that a project could be more sophisticated in Crete. They have a background as a philosophical and cultural foundation of Europe, and they now have a fantastic conflict arising on the Mediterranean scene. There is potential in antagonism and negotiation.

So, we are doing a project with students to construct the platform for one fictional Greek citizen revolting against the barrier of the Schengen Zone, redefining a second zone within his own house as a kind of Robinson Crusoe figure. Within the second barrier is a kind of autonomous zone. We want to consider this intellectually and physically, and in relation to the "inter-zone" of William Burroughs. It could be inside or outside, as a Klein bottle.

We are working in an area where people speak German, basically a vacation camp for German tourists. Why do they go there? To relax, to siesta, to use the soft economy to quiet themselves. But why is the Greek economy so much trouble? Because they are not producing enough! Germans demand the Greeks to be more like them, sacrifice like them, while they expect to go on vacation to a quiet camp where everyone is smiling, relaxed, and not working!

We are in the absurd situation where in order to have a quality of life, an authentic life, a relaxed life, you have to pay! It is only possible as a vacation camp; you cannot try to live like that. In Europe today, you have to pay for it—freedom cannot be free!

Notes

1   See Bruno Latour, *Facing Gaia: Six Lectures on the Political Theology of Nature*, 2013 Gifford Lectures on Natural Religion, http://www.bruno-latour.fr/node/486; and, Isabelle Stengers, in this volume.

2   Georges Bataille, *The Accursed Share*, Vol. 1, translated by Robert Hurley (New York: Zone Books, 1991).

3   Michel Serres, *The Natural Contract* (Ann Arbor: University of Michigan Press, 1995).

4   François Roche, ed., *Log* 25, 'reclaim resis(lience)stance' (Spring/ Summer 2012).

5   R&Sie, "Hybrid Muscle" (2003) in "Boys from Mars," by Philippe Parreno (2003).

6   "The Schengen Area is a group of 26 European countries that have abolished passport and immigration controls at their common borders. It functions as a single country for international travel purposes, with a common visa policy. The Area is named after the village of Schengen in Luxembourg where the Schengen Agreement, which led to the Area›s creation, was signed. Joining Schengen entails eliminating internal border controls with the other Schengen members, while simultaneously strengthening external border controls with non-Schengen states." Source: http://en.wikipedia.org/wiki/Schengen_Area.

The Geological Imperative

by Paulo Tavares

On the Political Ecology of the Amazonia's Deep History

"The Fierce People": Images from the ethnographic film *The Ax Fight*, which documents a conflict within a Yanomami community witnessed during field-work research carried by North-American ethnologist Napoleon Chagnon. Realized in collaboration with Timothy Ash, 1975.   Fig. 01

Beginning in the late 1960s, a series of reports produced by various media and non-governmental agencies around the world began to expose an international public to the critical situation confronting the indigenous peoples of Amazonia, whose territories, and cultural and physical survival, were under severe threat due to the aggressive developmental programs being implemented in the region. Out of this lineage of activist reports came *The Geological Imperative: Anthropology and Development in the Amazon Basin of South America*, a 90-page compilation of four articles written by the North American anthropologists Shelton H. Davis and Robert O. Mathews and published in 1976. "An exercise in political anthropology," as the authors described it, the document presented an up-to-date cartography of the depth of mining and oil-drilling activities in the former "isolated" areas of the Amazonia. Since the early 1970s, such operations had been aggressively expanding, particularly in Ecuador, Peru and Brazil, in a process that the authors associated with a condition of generalized violence and human rights violations inflicted on the indigenous communities inhabiting these lands. By offering a critical map of the contemporary context within which ethnological fieldwork was taking place in Amazonia, a situation that was representative of several other ethnographic fronts in the Third World, *The Geological Imperative* made a case for political engagement through anthropological practice. They contended that ethnographers should consider this specific historical conjecture and position research alongside the development program that was being deployed in the Amazon, which, at that time, was largely carried out through partnerships established between powerful multinational corporations, international financial institutions, and the militarized states that ruled much of Latin America. The proposed exercise in political anthropology did not, therefore, refer to the traditional concerns of ethnology regarding the internal symbolic order and social hierarchy that shape "primitive societies," which the authors claimed was the dominant concern among North American anthropologists working in Amazonia. Rather, political anthropology was called on to address the role of the discipline of anthropology itself, insofar as it was inevitably immersed within, and most often complicit with, external arrangements of power responsible for, according to Davis and Mathews, the process of "ethnocide" of South American Indians.[1]

The *Geological Imperative* was published in the context of the contentious etho-political debates that unfolded in professional circles of North American anthropology in the 1960s and 1970s following revelations that the US Army was applying ethnographic research in the design of counter-insurgency strategies in Latin America and Southeast Asia. During WWII, with the official support and sponsorship of the American Anthropological Association, anthropologists had openly employed their expertise to help with the Allied campaign. Defined in reaction to the Nazi's "scientific" theories of racial superiority, this war-time politicization of anthropology was accompanied by the growing militarization of ethnographic research and led to the establishment of both intellectual links and institutional networks that, in the subsequent Cold War era, would be less overtly yet more incisively applied in the service of communism-containment strategies deployed by the United States in Central and South America, Africa and Asia. Thanks to the work of the anthropologist David Price, and to the rich archive of disclosed state-documents that he collected, it is now evident how the discipline of anthropology became instrumental for US intelligence agencies in the post-war period. Ethnographic expertise was especially useful to the CIA and the Pentagon when shaping counter-insurgency campaigns. Less directly associated with warfare, but equally committed to the anti-communist ideology that informed US foreign policy, anthropology also played an important role within scientific research and development programs coordinated by private foundations such as Ford, Carnegie, and Rockefeller, often in close alliance with the political economic interests of the US.[2]

In the case of Amazonia, during the Second World War, ethnographers working under the auspices of the Office of Coordinator of Inter-American Affairs were responsible for the production of maps that sought to identify potential Indian labour and locate strategic natural resources, chiefly rubber.[3] Julian Steward, a North American anthropologist whose reinvigorated vision of environmental determinism was responsible for the "cultural ecology" sub-field of anthropology, contended that *The Handbook of the South American Indian*, a massive, influential ethnologic catalogue he edited in the 1940s, was also a form of collaborating in the war effort. As the director of the Institute of Social Anthropology founded in 1943 by the US State Department, Steward oversaw anthropologists conducting research throughout Latin America. He was also responsible for coordinating the compilation of large sets of data that, as David Price notes, formed an important contribution to an emergent knowledge-apparatus on "under-development, poverty and traditional culture" that would come to occupy a central place within US foreign policy.[4] Filtered through the sort of ideas promoted by economist-turned-national-security-adviser Walt Whitman Rostow and his 1960 publication *The Stages of Economic Growth: A Non-Communist Manifesto*, this literature was fundamental to the elaboration of modernization theories and development programs that the United States deployed in Latin America with the aim of containing popular support for the socialist and communist Left.[5] While the use of ethnographic intelligence as a tool for control is arguably constitutive of the science of anthropology itself and intrinsic to its colonial origins,[6] knowledge about the "culture of others" regained geo-political importance as the US either indirectly or directly attempted to expand military and political economic influence over the resource-rich, largely indigenous, frontiers of the Third World.

This was the context from which *The Geological Imperative* emerged and in relation to which its authors contended anthropological practice should situate itself—the Cold War. With the coup in Argentina in March 1976, the United Stated added another entry to an extensive list of collaborations with military regimes that were responsible for deposing democratically elected governments throughout Latin America—Guatemala in 1954, Brazil in 1964, Bolivia in 1971, Uruguay and Chile in 1973, among others—all of which imposed murderous programs of political repression supported by successive US administrations. Overlapping interests between state and capital defined the basic framework for US interventions in Central and South America during the Cold War, as compromises with authoritarian regimes were measured both in relation to the objective of containing the Left, as well as the advantages those governments provided for the penetration of US corporate capital into regional markets.[7] For their part, the military juntas that governed Latin

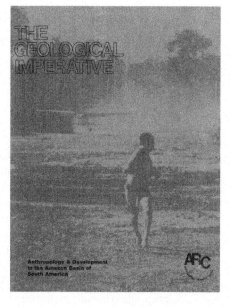

The Geological Imperative: Cover of the report on Amazonia published by anthropologists Davis Shelton and Robert Matthews in 1976.

Fig. 02

America tended towards a form of "modernizing capitalism," which combined authoritarian control in planning and legislation with radical economic liberalism. The impressive GDP-growth rates achieved with this model in the early 1970s were driven by patterns of capital accumulation structurally dependant on international financial loans, corporate investment, and large-scale exploitation of natural resources for export. By the mid-1970s, when *The Geological Imperative* was published, countries like Brazil and Peru were trying to expand their extractive-sector economies. In parallel, the prospects of an international energy crisis triggered by the Middle East oil-embargo and the subsequent escalation in prices of raw-materials had unleashed a global rush among multinational corporations to secure supply-sources of strategic minerals and fossil fuels. The combination of these factors led to unprecedented efforts to intervene in the subsoil of Amazonia and open it to international markets.

Fig. 03   *Operation Amazonia:* The overlap between natural and political territories.

Similar to reports produced by various US-based documentation centres such as INDIGENA, the North American Congress on Latin America (NACLA), and the Brazilian Information Bulletin (BIB), *The Geological Imperative* was part of a wider network that served to monitor and publicize information about the participation of the US government, international corporations, and the World Bank and IMF in the policies and projects being implemented by military regimes in Latin America. At a moment when political dissidence and freedom of speech were severely curtailed across most of the continent, these publications functioned to document the human-rights record of military governments and attempted to create public pressure against the international networks that supported them. Equally significant, *The Geological Imperative* also engaged in the internal debate concerning the role that Amazonian ethnology was playing in the process. From mid-1960s on, in parallel to the escalation of the United States politics of interventionism in the Southern Cone and the expansion of resource-extraction activities in the Amazon Basin, Davis and Mathews noted the increasing influence of theories of socio-evolutionism on the work of North American anthropologists. They argued that the images produced and transmitted by researchers associated with this lineage were helping legitimize the processes of expropriation of indigenous territories. Exemplary socio-evolutionists included the playwright-cum-anthropologist Robert Ardrey, whose widely read 1966 book *The Territorial Imperative* provided Davis and Mathews with a critically appropriated title for their report. In the case of Amazonia, they listed the 1968 best-seller *The Fierce People*, an ethnographic account of Yanomami communities living at the border between Brazil and Venezuela by anthropologist Napoleon Chagnon. These texts promoted the notion that human societies evolve according to a naturalist path of linear progress, which Davis and Mathews criticized for reproducing the colonial logic of power that was responsible for generating Darwinist theories of social evolution in the nineteenth-century.

Given the expansion of resource-frontiers into the lands of indigenous peoples, Davis and Mathews argued that imaginaries such as those produced by Chagnon became even more problematic. Through a series articles published in magazines such as *Time* and *National Geographic*, as well as a series of films and television programs, Chagnon disseminated an image of the Yanomami as an extremely violent society, whose isolation from the outside world had preserved inherent traits of human aggressiveness, supposedly demonstrative of their proximity to the "state-of-nature" in the process of socio-biological evolution. In the hands of the modernizing governments of Brazil and Venezuela, this imaginary served to reinforce the racist perceptions driving the "civilizing" discourse that accompanied the occupation of indigenous lands. In the context of the counter-insurgent ideological apparatus nurtured by the US, such images effectively functioned as Cold War propaganda. "It is hardly surprising," Davis and Mathews noted, "that Professor Chagnon's early theories of Yanomamo 'brinkmanship' were first espoused at the highpoint of the United States military involvement in Vietnam."[8] Like earlier ethnographic images that served to grant moral legitimacy to the slaughter of indigenous peoples and the colonization of their territories, the visions generated by Chagnon and Ardrey were accomplices in masking the social and environmental violence of Cold War's "geological colonialism" as it expanded across the Third World. Rather than imposed by natural determinism, the imperative, Davis and Mathews concluded, was decisively ethical and political: "In contrast to those who would describe this phenomenon as a natural occurrence, i.e. as one of the inevitable results of social progress and economic growth, we see the 'geological imperative' as a unique historical phenomenon related to specific distribution of wealth and power which presently exists in the world."[9]

Operation Amazonia

Beyond its historical analogy with earlier forms of colonialism, the concept of the "geological imperative" described a whole new geo-political space being shaped through the Global Cold War. Moreover, the concept also pointed to the radical reconfiguration of the natural terrain of Amazonia that took place during this period. Until the 1960s, initiatives to colonize the Amazon Basin—first by imperial powers and later by the independent nation-states that emerged in South America in the early nineteenth-century—had typically abided by the spatial arrangements dictated by the logic of territorial surface. Although there had already been some exploration of mineral and oil deposits, the subsoil had been of much less importance than both the extraction of surficial products such as timber and rubber, and the use of land for agricultural and livestock production. In the post-war decades, however, Amazonia was visualized and interpreted in its "ecological depth": a complex environment composed of various geological and biophysical factors offering unlimited economic potential. Novel ways of identifying, charting, and accessing formerly unknown or unreachable resources created possibilities for intervention in the region at an unprecedented scale. This objective was pursued with different degrees of intensity, but largely similar spatial patterns, under the ubiquitous developmental ideology adopted by the states of the continental basin. For the governments of South America, the colonization of Amazonia played at least two crucial roles. First, taming the vastness of the tropical forest became symbolically important in the context of nationalist and modernizing discourses. "The incorporation of the jungle into the national economy," wrote the Peruvian president and architect Fernando Belaúnde Terry in 1965, "is the great battle yet to be waged in the conquest of Peru."[10] On the other hand, the region's sheer natural wealth was considered a fundamental source for the primitive accumulation of capital that would propel these countries out of underdevelopment. Further, the understanding that Amazonia was a "continental void" to be conquered and developed was not restricted to the nationalist elites and militarized technocracy of South America, but formed part of a general perception also shared by policy makers and planners working for bi-lateral and international agencies helping to foster development in the Third World.

An extreme example of this perspective was a project promoted in the late 1960s by the Hudson Institute to build a massive dam across the Amazon River that would result in the formation of a "Mediterranean sea" at the interior of the basin. The dam was intended to function as a giant energy reservoir for South America and the US as well as a means to produce millions of migrants to populate the region.[11] Another remarkable example was a study produced in 1971 by the Food and Agricultural Organization of the United Nations suggesting that, in order to absorb the impacts of the exponential global demographic increase, Amazonia should be converted into vast agricultural fields of grain production.[12] Inside the belligerent rush for raw materials that characterized the Cold War, the Amazon Basin was conceived as a vast, primordial reserve of natural resources, which, once properly mastered with modern technologies, would serve to guarantee the development of regional economies, help to meet growing rates of world consumption, and secure steady flows of energy, strategic minerals, and fossil fuels to feed the expansion of the global military-industrial complex. Observed from a contemporary perspective, it may be difficult to imagine that such views formed the dominant development sensibility. Nevertheless, and despite the intrinsic ecologically destructive potential embodied in these views, what was consolidated in the 1960s and 1970s was a proper environmental understanding of Amazonia. Less associated with counter-cultural activism and more with neo-Malthusian manifestations of the ecological discourse that emerged at the time, Amazonia was gradually apprehended as a deep geo-physical terrain upon which a series of novel cartographic imaginaries, governmental discourses, and grand planning strategies would be projected and deployed, and which in turn would lead to dramatic changes in both its natural and social landscapes.

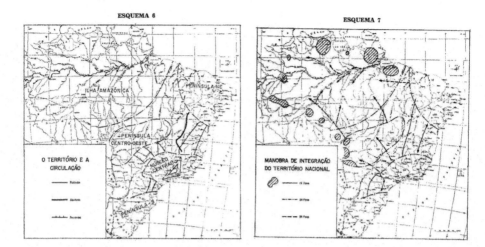

ESQUEMA 6

ESQUEMA 7

The geopolitics of integration: Gal. Golbery do Couto e Silva's influential territorial interpretation of the National Security Doctrine.   Fig. 04

The first map show the Brazilian territory divided into four regions: the "central nucleus" connected with three "peninsulas" located at the south, center-west and northeast. Floating at the margins, the "Amazonian Island". The second map describes the "maneuver for the integration of the national territory."

The clearest expression of this transformation was Operation Amazonia, a large-scale program of development launched by the military government of Brazil, two years after the 1964 coup, which sought to convert the entire region into a massive frontier of resource-extraction, agriculture and livestock production through the implementation of a series of projects of continental proportions. The first move in this operation was the establishment of a territorial jurisdiction named "Legal Amazonia," which covered the whole portion of the basin within Brazilian sovereign borders—more than five million square kilometres, 59 percent of the territory of Brazil, and practically 60 percent of the natural area of Amazonia—and the placement of this vast zone under direct control of the federal government. This juridical-political regime was, in fact, not completely new. Similar forms for governing the Brazilian Amazon had already been used since the colonial period. In the mid-eighteenth century, for example, when Portuguese administrators vowed to modernize governmental practices, they instituted the "Companhia Geral de Comércio do Grão-Pará e Maranhão," a sort of Amazonian version of the East India Company, which, like the Superintendence of Development of Amazonia (SUDAM), the agency created by the military in 1966 to deal exclusively with Legal Amazonia, functioned as a centralized administrative body directly subordinated to the executive departments of the State. Parallels between colonial and modern governmental rationales are not fortuitous, especially when they testify to the unabated perception that Amazonia was characterized by a state of chronic territorial isolation and demographic emptiness, detached from the social and political life of Brazil, a situation which, in the eyes of colonial and post-colonial governments, made the region prone to foreign invasion and economic stagnation, and which therefore called for an orchestrated and forceful strategy of occupation—i.e., a politics of modern colonization.

ESTAMPA 3
Folha SB.22-Z-B – (imagem de radar, escala 1:250.000) – *Anticlinal escavado do Rio Lontra*. Folha de Xambioá. Observa-se ao centro, um braquianticlinal arrasado por pediplanação. As estruturas salientadas pela erosão formam "hog back". À direita, a borda da Bacia Sedimentar do Paui–Maranhão. À esquerda, margem do Rio Araguaia. Os terrenos rebaixados pertencem ao Pediplano Pleistocênico. O Rio Lontra está superimposto aos "hog back".

ESTAMPA 4
Folha SB.22-V-B – (imagem de radar, escala 1:250.000) – *Pediplano Pleistocênico no Médio Xingu*. Folha de Rio Chiché. Notam-se "inselbergs" numa superfície de aplainamento bem conservada, datada de Pleistoceno. Deposições holocênicas formam algumas ilhas, diques marginais e bancos de areia, constituindo uma planície fluvial inundável. Os topos aplainados à direita, são testemunhos Pliocênico.

Fig. 05   *Imaging Amazonia*: SLAR remote sensing image of the south-central regions of the basin.

In the book *Geopolítica do Brasil*, a territorial interpretation of Brazilian history that exerted great influence on the armed forces during the military dictatorship, General Golbery do Couto e Silva, perhaps the most important intellectual of the regime, described Amazonia as a giant island floating at the margins of the national polity, "mostly unexplored, devitalized by the lack of people and creative energy, and which we must incorporate into the nation, integrating it into the national community and valuing its great physical expression which today still is almost completely passive."[13] Although this perspective actualized older colonial ideologies, there are obvious radical differences that are important to demarcate. The drive to "occupy and integrate" Amazonia after the military coup was informed by the combination of the Cold War National Security Doctrine, the global hegemony that the concept of development assumed in the post-war period, and the unchallenged belief in the powers of modern planning cultivated by geographers, urbanists, economists, and all sorts of technicians and bureaucrats. Until the 1960s, the spatial organization of Amazonia remained largely defined by territorial patterns inherited from the "Atlantic Trade," more closely connected to the river and sea than the continent. Migrant communities, towns, and cities were concentrated along major waterways and served mainly as transit points for commercial exchange. The hinterlands, where indigenous communities sought refuge, remained relatively safe beyond colonial projects and mostly unmapped. Operation Amazonia initiated a campaign that would generate a different image and completely alter the territorial logic of the Amazon watershed. By projecting a nearly symmetrical relation between an artificial political space and the natural boundaries of the basin, the operation could conceptualize and deploy planning strategies that encompassed Amazonia as a bio-geographic unit; that is, it enabled design interventions at the point where the "ecological scale" intersected with the "legal scale" of Amazonia.

Deep Cartography

This overlap between political and natural space was forged through a peculiar combination that included the introduction of new governmental and economic frameworks (as exemplified by the creation of SUDAM and various others institutional and legal mechanisms dedicated exclusively to stimulating capital investment into the region), together with unparalleled efforts to map the geophysical and biophysical aspects of the basin. The military's perception that Amazonia was a homogenous green void in need of occupation and modernization was also a reflection of the lack of precise cartographic information. Starting in 1970, the large-scale mapping survey conducted by NASA-trained researchers at the National Institute of Spatial Research of Brazil named *Radar Amazonia*—or RADAM—was as one of the most remarkable initiatives that contributed to the process of re-shaping the ways by which Amazonia was visualized and interpreted. Coordinated by the Brazilian National Department of Mineral Production, with the financial and technical support of US-AID, the project aimed at identifying mineral resources in the 44,000 km² area along the Trans-Amazonian Highway, a major transport artery cutting east-west across the entire basin. In the following years, RADAM was gradually expanded to cover all of Legal Amazonia, and later the entire Brazilian territory. Simultaneously, the project also grew in scope to incorporate detailed geographical, geological, and soils mapping; surveys of agricultural and forest resources; hydrology and fishing charts; and the identification of actual and potential land-uses. By the mid-1970s, as one of the geologists involved in the project put it, "the imaging of the whole nation was concluded."[14]

Before RADAM, the mapping of Amazonia had been undertaken primarily by on-the-ground surveys conducted by various military, scientific, or missionary incursions and was therefore fairly limited by the trajectories of major water channels that offered accessible routes into the harsh geography of the hinterlands. Notable examples of this cartographic archive include the early-twentieth-century charts produced by the Brazilian Army during expeditions to lay the ground for telegraphic cabling, and the detailed maps signed by North American geographer Alexander Hamilton Rice, who pioneered the use of aerial photography to map the rainforest. More recent examples are related to large state-sponsored exploratory campaigns, as in the case of the highly publicized incursions towards the Xingu River initiated in 1943 by the *Fundação Brazil Central* [Central Brazil Foundation], an agency created with the exclusive objective of opening up routes into southern Amazonia. In all these enterprises, the act of mapping and effective territorial control coalesced into a single practice. As such, they reproduced a long tradition in the science of cartography, whose historical evolution is often indistinguishable from the global history of colonization. Cartographic expeditions in Amazonia were responsible for creating outposts and airfields that later would serve as nodes for frontier-expansion, while at the same time they helped identify soil types, fauna, flora, and other natural resources. Moreover, those exploratory missions became important forms of gathering ethnographic information about the indigenous populations they encountered. The attendant images they produced described a fragmented mosaic of regional cartographies with little geological depth. Amazonia was, from this vantage point, viewed as a sea-like space formed by extensive macro-bio-geographical surfaces, penetrated by an intricate hydrological network of rivers and marshlands. Insofar as it was designed concomitantly to and in support of the process of "occupation and integration" launched with Operation Amazonia, RADAM helped to actualize a similar logic, but at the same time projected it on completely new terms. Because of the modern technology that was employed, a whole new picture of the natural terrain emerged, one which corresponded to the militarized forms that the process of development/colonization of the Amazon Basin assumed in the Cold War context.

By the early 1970s, following the rapid evolution of remote sensing systems designed for military reconnaissance, a series of visual technologies—multispectral aerial photography, airborne radars, and satellite scanners—became common tools for the identification and location of natural resources. RADAM's cartographic inventory was expanded with the aid of these new Earth-sensing technologies. Most important among them was radar-imaging made possible by Side-Looking Airborne Radar [SLAR], a technology used extensively for patrolling missions at the fringes of the Iron Curtain and for battlefield surveillance and reconnaissance in Vietnam. The design of RADAM was based on a similar system pioneered in the observation-and-attack aircraft OV-10 Mohawk developed by the US Army during the Vietnam War, without the weapons. While most optical devices are severely limited both by climatic conditions and surface cover, SLAR is capable of penetrating the moist atmosphere and dense foliage of tropical forests, providing high-quality, real-time images of the terrain beneath.[15] Radar-imaging technology thus allowed for the rapid mapping of large areas of Amazonia despite the persistent cloudiness and rainfall intensity that had obstructed previous attempts to collect data. In parallel to the remote sensing efforts, the RADAM project also included scientific expeditions to collect soil-samples and ground-proofing of vegetation patterns and geological formations. With the support of the Brazilian Air Force, more than six-hundred forests clearings were opened up to receive research crews arriving with small aircraft. In total, this field-work covered more than three thousand points distributed throughout the basin at an average of more than one point per 1200 km^2.[16] Samples from the ground were entered into a large database of soil profiles, which, together with the cartographic analysis derived from aerial reconnaissance, were then compiled into a bulky catalogue series that provided detailed taxonomical descriptions of the biological and geophysical features of the whole territory of Legal Amazonia.

This new image of the Amazon then served as the guide for the bellicose program of economic and territorial integration put forward during the 1970s and 1980s. After Operation Amazonia was launched, successive military governments vowed to accelerate the process through the introduction of various basin-wide planning schemes. Each time, these macro-strategies assumed different titles: in 1970, *The*

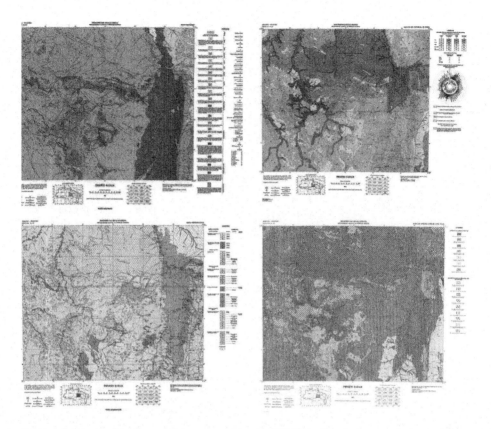

Deep terrain: Samples of the cartographic inventory produced by RADAM on the region between the Xingu and Araguaia Rivers, southern tributaries of the Amazon. Respectively, the maps describe geology, land potential, phytogeography, and agricultural suitability.

Fig. 06 – Fig. 09

Plan for National Integration; in 1974, PoloAmazonia; each scheme perpetuated the same spatial rationale, combining the imperatives of development, the aggressiveness of extractive capitalism, and the geopolitical concerns of the National Security Doctrine. Sustained by these three powerful ideological pillars, the Brazilian military dictatorship lasted more than twenty years. On the ground, the projects unleashed a radical process of "territorial design" based on a continental network of highways overlaid with telecommunication channels and energy cables that linked strategically located "development-poles." The poles themselves were selected according to the economic potential of the surface and the subsoil as identified by RADAM, and were conceived as modernizing enclaves that would be equipped with infrastructure, such as dams, airports, and seaports, to advance the capacity needed to enable large-scale resource extraction. The road matrix was planned as the primary means through which agricultural and cattle frontiers could expand towards the interior, while simultaneously providing routes for the massive migration of labour force. A project of this magnitude could only be implemented by a centralized and authoritarian state-apparatus, which guaranteed its enforcement through bypassing democratic debate and minimizing dissidence. Operation Amazonia, in its multiple forms and manifestations, was as much the result of the generalized state of repression that characterized this period in Brazil as well as a means deployed by the generals to achieve political containment. The discourses of modernization, security, and nationalism that supported this planning strategy played a decisive role in legitimizing the violent political order by which the military ruled, and the radical process of territorial re-organization that they imposed.

The White Peace

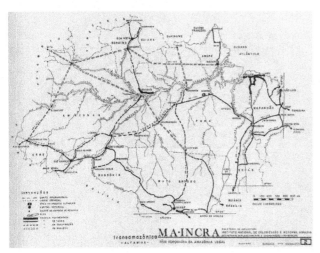

Fig. 10   *Territorial design:* The continental urban-matrix as planned in the Plan for National Integration, 1970.

Published at the moment when this process was at its greatest intensity, *The Geological Imperative* traced a counter-cartography of the this new terrain, identifying perpetrators and collaborators, describing the forces and mechanisms that were supporting the military's blueprint for Amazonia onto the ground, and calling attention to the intrinsic ecological and social violence of its design. As noted above, Davis and Matthews were not isolated voices. Their report was part of a larger body of literature that began to circulate after the launch of Operation Amazonia. One of the earliest and most famous manifestations was the report *Genocide: From Fire and Sword to Arsenic and Bullets, Civilization Has Sent Six Million Indians to Extinction,* written by journalist Norman Lewis and published by *The Sunday Times* in February, 1969. It gained notoriety by being one of the first reports to direct attention to what was happening in Amazonia at a moment when the human-rights situation of indigenous peoples was already extremely acute. Lewis went to Brazil to report on the findings of an Inquiry Commission established in 1967 by the Brazilian Ministry of Interior, which was investigating allegations of crimes and corruption among officials of the SPI, the *Serviço de Proteção aos Índios* [Service for the Protection of the Indians], a state-agency responsible for implementing and governing policies directed toward indigenous communities and overseeing their welfare. Following his visit, Lewis listed a series of atrocities documented in *Genocide,* the twenty-volume, 7000-page report that was released by the commission in 1968, ranging from the massive usurpation of indigenous lands, to

Earthworks: Images of the *Trans-Amazonian Highway* being carved out in the middle of the jungle became one of the most powerful symbols of the nationalist ideology of the military regime.

Fig. 11

bacteriological warfare and the bombing of villages, to the abduction of children, torture, and massacres. As evidences of these crimes started to circulate globally, during the first United Nations International Conference on Human Rights, held in Teheran in 1968, the Brazilian government was accused of being complicit in the annihilation of its indigenous population, prompting more foreign observers and journalists to travel to Amazonia. Because of this attention, other, lesser-known reports also appeared around the same time as *Genocide*, including, for example, the article *Germ Warfare Against Indians is Charged in Brazil*, published by the medical attaché to the French Department of Overseas Territories at the Medical Tribune and Medical News of New York in 1969.[17] With few discrepancies, all of these reports provided a similar, haunting picture, best synthesised by Norman Lewis's precise historical analogy: "The tragedy of the Indian in the USA in the last century was being repeated," he suggested, "but it was being compressed into a shorter time."[18]

Created in 1910, the SPI was a response to the escalation of bloody inter-ethnic conflicts that were leading to the slaughter of entire tribes in southern Brazil. While migrant settlers attempted to conquer new lands in order to expand coffee plantations—at that time a highly lucrative commodity and the major product of the Brazilian economy—they were met with fierce resistance from indigenous tribes. Railroad works were interrupted and agricultural colonies that had been officially established by the government were abandoned. For many people, the death of indigenous populations was not only considered an unfortunate fatality caused by the inexorability of progress, but the very means through which the hinterlands

Fig. 12 –   *Geological taxonomy:* Sample images of the RADAM catalogue describing field-work research used for the
Fig. 15   geological classification of soil profiles in Amazonia.

would be modernized and incorporated within the national polity. As anthropologist Darcy Ribeiro wrote in his historical account about the SPI, "the extermination of the Indians was not only practiced, but defended and claimed as a remedy which was essential to the safety of those who were building a civilization in the interior of Brazil."[19] Whether directly or indirectly informed by racist social theories, these views were openly advocated in political and academic circles, as well as in the national press. The most infamous advocate, the zoologist-cum-ethnologist Hermann von Ilhering, founder and first director of the *Museu Paulista* (the History Museum of the University of São Paulo), claimed in a polemic published in the museum's 1907 magazine that because "the savages were an obstacle to the colonization of the regions of the interior where they live, there seems no other way we can call upon if not their extermination."[20]

In the early twentieth century, the urban elites of São Paulo and Rio de Janeiro, who were geographically detached from the lawless frontier zones but whose desire to emulate a Parisian cosmopolitan lifestyle was totally dependant on the financial benefits generated by the coffee economy, were facing a modern dilemma: in the name of progress and nation-building, the colonization of the hinterlands was an unquestionable imperative; however, news of the slaughter of Indians, which started to appear more frequently in the press, was also increasingly condemned as excessively violent, contradictory to the humanistic values they were keen to cultivate. For intellectuals like von Ilhering and his peers in academia and Congress,

Brazilian society was to be forged on the model of the frontier ideologies that shaped the history of the United States, thus assuming the war against "hostile tribes" as a full-fledged state-policy.[21] In opposition to this expansionist view, a growing group of scientists, philanthropists, politicians, and military officers began to advocate for government policies based on the non-violent pacification and protection of indigenous communities.

The SPI was ultimately the product of lobbying efforts carried out by the latter group. Informed by the humanistic social evolutionism of Augusto Comte's positivist philosophy, they argued that indigenous populations should be granted enough space to develop at their own pace and gradually adapt to the paradigms of modern civilization. It was therefore necessary for the State to assume legal protection over the Indians and to create an institution that would operate as a mediator between the fragile modes of life of the "primitives" and the violent forces of the expansionist frontier. The SPI was responsible for establishing peaceful contact with isolated tribes, securing lands for their survival and administering pedagogical programs that would slowly prepare those populations to be assimilated into national society. The origin of this humanitarian practice is located in the work Marshal Cândido Mariano da Silva Rondon, a younger officer of indigenous descent, who, while in command of military expeditions was dispatched to build telegraphic lines towards the interior of Brazil, developed a series of innovative techniques to contact Indian tribes without resorting to armed force. The founder and first director of the SPI, Rondon's famous motto was: "Die, if necessary; kill, never." In the decades following its creation, the SPI established over one hundred outposts across the Brazilian territory. Initially serving as logistical centres where dispersed indigenous groups could be attracted to in order to be pacified, these encampments latter developed into agricultural and cattle farming colonies commanded by SPI officials, who were then responsible for introducing modern labour techniques to the Indians, providing medical care, and teaching them the habits of civilization and the sentiments of nationalism. The foundation of SPI marked a turning point in the relations between the Brazilian State and its indigenous population because it was the first time that indigenous cultural and territorial integrity were granted some sort of legal and institutional protection. Yet, the humanitarian governmentality that the agency instituted was hugely contradictory, to say the least. Although advocating secularism and legitimized by positivism, the SPI-model shared similarities with forms of political tutelage and territorial control employed by Jesuit missionaries on behalf of the colonial administration since the sixteenth century. The "protectionist intervention," as Darcy Ribeiro has called it, which was promoted by the ideologues of SPI to stop the slaughter of indigenous tribes, offered a fine solution to the paradoxes imposed by the "question of the Indian" in relation to the process of territorial expansion of the Brazilian modern nation-state: simultaneously pacifist and expansionist, ideologically opposed to the extermination of indigenous populations, while at the same time serving as one of the most efficient mechanisms for opening up their lands for colonization.[22]

By the mid-1950s, when Brazil started building the modernist capital Brasília in the middle of its territory—a powerful demonstration of the program to conquer the hinterlands that accelerated exponentially in the following decades—there were alarming signals that the pacifist program launched by the SPI had been severely damaged. In a landmark report published in 1957, Darcy Ribeiro demonstrated through detailed statistics that most of the 230 tribes known in 1900 were on the verge of total disintegration, and that in the areas of expansion of cattle raising, agricultural, and mineral-extraction activities, more than 80 tribes had completely disappeared. In less than 60 years, the indigenous population of Brazil had dropped from one million to two hundred thousand, and the communities that had survived the process of contact were living in wretched conditions, facing poverty, malnutrition, disease, and depopulation.[23] Apart from a handful of experiences—the earlier heroic years of Marshal Rondon; the remarkable ethnological documentation gathered by the Studies Section founded in 1942 (in which Ribeiro worked between 1947 and 1957); and the creation of the Xingu Indigenous Park in 1961—the history of SPI was less a success than one a series of failures. Under the powerful influence of landowners and mining corporations, successive governments never really granted the financial and political support that was necessary to accomplish its ambitious protectionist mission and, with notable exceptions, the urban headquarters and frontier outposts of SPI were increasingly occupied by professional bureaucrats who showed little commitment to its original ethos. The agency found itself repeatedly threatened with extinction, accused of corruption and riddled with complaints of inefficiency. After the coup of 1964, when frontier expansion assumed the authoritarian face of the dictatorship, this situation worsened considerably.[24] As with the majority of governmental institutions, the command of the SPI was assumed by a military officer, Major Luis Vinhas Neves, who turned out to be one of the main perpetrators accused in the crimes documented by the Inquiry Commission. Amidst mounting national and international public pressure, in December 1967, a few months before the commission's report was released, Minister of Interior Gal. Albuquerque Lima dissolved the SPI and a new institution was established, the FUNAI, the National Indian Foundation.

FUNAI was the response of the Generals to allegations that the Brazilian military regime was complicit in a genocidal campaign against indigenous populations. There were many promises of reforms that came along with the creation of the new agency. Its statute incorporated a series of progressive elements, officially endorsing the principles prescribed by the United Nations and the International Labour Organization regarding the rights of ethnic minorities.[25] In parallel, the government issued a set of decrees to demarcate five large indigenous reserves across the country, and Albuquerque Lima welcomed foreign fact-gathering expeditions to assess the situation, including a medical mission of the International Committee of the Red Cross to Amazonia in 1970 and another conducted by the London-based NGO Survival International in 1971.[26] The optimism generated by those measures was nevertheless short-lived. The establishment of the SPI Inquiry Commission and the subsequent creation of FUNAI came at a particular moment

Genocide: The first page of Norman Lewis report published in the *Sunday Times* in 1969.

Fig. 16

in the history of the Brazilian military dictatorship which reflected the worldwide political expectations of the late 1960s. While protests spread through the streets of Paris and thousands marched against the Vietnam War in Washington and in London, the urban squares of Rio de Janeiro were also filled with massive student demonstrations. In 1968, militant workers staged the first major strikes since the 1964 military coup, progressive members of the Catholic Church started to publicly criticize the regime, and denouncements of torture of political prisoners were openly voiced in Congress. From different corners, multiple manifestations of dissent emerged, generating a volatile situation that prompted a swift crackdown by hard-line military commanders. In December of 1968, President Gal. Artur da Costa e Silva issued the infamous Institutional Act No. 5, a state-of-emergency law that gave overwhelming powers to the "Supreme Command of the Revolution" over every aspect of civilian life. From that point onwards, a much more pervasive surveillance apparatus came into effect and Brazil descended into the most repressive period of the dictatorship.[27] This radical change in the political atmosphere also had severe consequences for the indigenous populations of the country.

While the promised territorial reserves remained on paper, the philosophy of FUNAI was re-oriented towards the tenets of the National Security Doctrine. On the ground, the working agenda that the agency had to fulfil became totally subordinated to the program of "territorial design" that was deployed in Amazonia after the launch of the Plan for National Integration in 1970. Commanded by Gal. Bandeira Melo, a former intelligence officer who presided the institution between 1970 and 1974, FUNAI established a contract with SUDAM committing to the rapid

Fig. 17 *The Protectionist Intervention:* Still frames of the film archive of the SPI. Visual records of SPI activities served both as state-propaganda as well as important ethnographic documentation.

pacification of the "hostile tribes" that inhabited the regions where the continental roads were being carved out, thus inaugurating a whole new phase in a long history of colonization that arguably surpassed any previous efforts.[28] It was clear that the reforms promoted by the military regime had generated little change, and if so, only for the worse. The comparison between SPI and FUNAI was even more pertinent in the context of the recently opened frontier-zones of Amazonia, with a substantial difference: in order to keep pace with the rapid advancement of development schemes, the campaign of pacification in the region became increasingly militarized. This situation was aggravated in December 1973, when dictator Gal. Garrastazu Médice sanctioned Law 6001, also known as the Indian Statute.[29] As with the document that established FUNAI, the text of this law was permeated with modern, liberal rhetoric claiming to further expand indigenous rights. However, it ruled that "interventions" into indigenous lands could be enacted in order "to realize public works" or "to exploit the wealth of the subsoil" if they were "of interest for national security and development," and in that manner converted the violent process of territorial expropriation that was taking place in Amazonia into a legitimate, official state-policy.

Much faster than before, the interventionist policies put forward by the military regime were leading to outright extermination of entire tribes, but because Brazilian society was under widespread media censorship and political repression, it was even more difficult to report on the situation than in previous years.

Yet again, attempts to mobilize international public attention started to emerge. A few days after the approval of the Indian Statute, a group of bishops and Catholic missionaries published a historical document titled *Y-Juca Pirama,* an expression in Tupi language meaning "he who must die." Through a detailed compilation of facts and declarations that appeared in the Brazilian press, this report offered evidence for the allegations that FUNAI was operating with "unprofessed support" of the economic interests of multinational corporations and big landowners, further claiming that, nonetheless, the responsibility for the ongoing process of extinction of indigenous peoples in Brazil should not be attributed exclusively to the agency. Its main causes lay much deeper, the authors contended, for the practices and policies of FUNAI were in fact the result of a larger "global scheme."[30] By the term "global scheme," they referred to what was then known as the "Brazilian Model," a designation used by economists to describe the articulation between state incentives, international aid, and private capital that formed the triangular base for the development program being implemented by the military regime. The violent scenario that the combination of those actors and forces unleashed in Amazonia was also denounced in another important document of this period, *The Politics of Genocide against the Indians of Brazil,* which began circulating in September 1974 at an academic symposium in Mexico City. For the Brazilian anthropologists who wrote this report, whose names were not revealed because they feared repression, the post-FUNAI politics of pacification launched by the military amounted to acts of genocide as defined in international law, and therefore they called on the United Nations to conduct a fully fledged criminal investigation into the practices of the Brazilian State.[31] It was in this context that *The Geological Imperative* was published two years later. While pointing to the participation of multinational corporations and international financial institutions in the "global scheme" that sustained the dictatorship, Davis and Matthews sought to assert their share of responsibility for what the Brazilian anthropologists claimed to be a genocidal campaign, but which they described with a slightly different concept—ethnocide.

"Genocide assassinates people in their bodies," wrote the French anthropologist Pierre Clastres, "ethnocide kills them in their souls."[32] Although closely related and to a large extent inseparable, these concepts were created to give name to different forms of violence, each originating in relation to a specific historical context. Coined by jurist Raphael Lemkin in 1944 to describe the systematic extermination of the European Jews by the Nazi regime, genocide was made an international crime in 1948 after the Nuremberg Trials.[33] In Lemkin's original definition, genocide referred to an overall strategy intended to destroy in whole or in part a national, racial, religious or ethnic group; that is, the concept was invented to nominate a form of violence that was directed towards a collective *qua* collective. As the scholar Dirk Moses points out in a thorough analysis of the unpublished research notes left by Lemkin, his early attempts to define genocide included both physical and cultural annihilation, violence against the body and the soul. "Physical and biological genocide are always preceded by cultural genocide," Lemkin wrote, "or by an attack on the symbols of the group or by violent interference with religious or cultural activities."[34] The jurist considered "cultural genocide" an essential aspect of the crime he was trying to name, but due to a series of political compromises and diverging interests of different nation-states, and despite the fact that some drafts of the 1948 UN Genocide Convention did included the term, cultural genocide was erased from the codes of international law. This historical outcome, Moses argues, "advantaged states which sought to assimilate their indigenous populations and other minorities after World War II."[35]

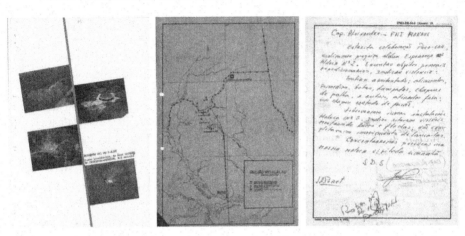

Fig. 18   *The white peace:* sample pages of a report disclosed from the archives of FUNAI describing a mission conducted in northwestern Amazonia to "pacify" the Waimiri-Atroari.

By the early 1970s, while new resource frontiers were expanding throughout the "isolated" territories of the Third World, militant ethnologists started to employ the concept of ethnocide to describe the dimension of cultural violence that had been left outside the legal definition of genocide. Not necessarily involving physical annihilation but equally committed to the destruction of otherness, ethnocide was the word invented to name what the Brazilian military called "integration." It was the anthropologist Robert Jaulin who contributed most to defining the term, particularly in the book *The White Peace: Introduction to Ethnocide* (1970). While conducting field-work among the Bari people on the border between Colombia and Venezuela, Jaulin witnessed the campaign of assimilation to which the they were being forced to succumb, similar to the situation in Brazil, carried out by armed forces and civilizing missionaries in order to open up land for multinational oil companies. "Integration is the right to life granted to the other with the condition that they become who we are," he concluded, "but the contradiction of this system is precisely that the other, detached from himself, dies."[36] Whereas genocide expresses the total negation of the other with the aim of physical destruction, ethnocide is a form of violence that transforms that negativity into a positive, humanitarian intent. As Pierre Clastres wrote, "the spirit of ethnocide is the ethics of humanism," a perverse ethos which has been historically mobilized, and is still, on behalf of establishing the "white peace."[37]

Ecocide

"After the end of World War II, and as a result of the Nuremberg Trials, we justly condemned the wilful destruction of an entire people and its culture, calling this crime against humanity genocide. It seems to me that the wilful and permanent destruction of environment in which a people can live in a manner of their own choosing ought similarly to the considered as a crime against humanity, to be designated by the term *ecocide*."[38] North-American botanist Arthur W. Galston, a pioneer inventor of defoliants and one of their harshest critics, made this statement during a panel titled "Technology and American Power: The Changing Nature of War," at a conference organized in Washington in 1970 to debate the war crimes that were being committed by the US Army in Vietnam.[39] Words come into being to nominate existing phenomena that have not yet been given a proper description, enabling us to draw new understandings of the past and the present, and perhaps to project different futures. As with genocide and ethnocide, the concept of ecocide was invented to describe a form of violence which, although not completely new, achieved unprecedented intensity during the scorched-earth campaign that the US military forces deployed against the forests of Indochina. Certainly, the mobilization of nature as a weapon of war is as old as the history of human conflict itself. But what the conflict in Vietnam made visible was a heretofore unseen destruction of entire ecologies in a short period of time, painfully demonstrating the potential implications of the "environmental violence" intrinsic to the techno-scientific apparatus being developed in support of the Cold War, whether applied in military or civilian industries. Hence, Galston concluded his statement with the following words: "I believe that most highly developed nations have already committed auto-ecocide over large parts of their own countries. At the present time, the United States stands alone as possibly having committed ecocide against another country, Vietnam, through its massive use of chemical defoliants and herbicides. The United Nations would appear to be an appropriate body for the formulation of a proposal against ecocide."[40] Amidst the burgeoning debate about the degradation of the global environment by civilian offshoots of the war industry, throughout the 1970s the concept of ecocide was widely debated by legal scholars, many of whom advocated that the UN should indeed follow Galston's proposal and incorporate acts of "deliberate environmental destruction" into the list of crimes against peace.[41] Since then, discussions on whether or not to include ecocide into the frameworks of international law have continued, but no resolutions have been implemented to date.[42]

The novel methods and the unprecedented brutality of the violence unleashed since WWII forced the creation of new concepts and defied established ethical and legal codes. In the context of Amazonia, this new lexicon of destruction coalesced into a single spatial strategy. Whether or not the Brazilian military regime was complicit in acts of genocide against its indigenous populations is a highly controversial question which is only now being properly investigated after the much delayed truth commission of Brazil—the CNV, *Comissão Nacional da Verdade*—was finally established in early 2011. Recent disclosures of military state-archives, as well as the appearance of previously unheard testimonies, are unveiling new evidence of the human-rights violations committed by state agents during the dictatorship. It has been argued, for example, that during the construction of the BR-174 highway in northwest Amazonia, an estimated two thousand Waimiri-Atroari Indians were killed, a figure two times greater than the (contested) current official accounts of the number of murdered and disappeared persons by the military regime in Brazil.[43] What is beyond doubt is that the militarization of the politics of pacification attending Operation Amazonia was based on the logic of ethnocide, that its implementation on the ground led to the physical destruction of hundreds if not thousands of Indians and, no less important, that this process was accompanied by widespread ecological destruction.

Before Operation Amazonia, most of the land in Amazonia lacked proper legislation and was defined as *terras devolutas*, a form of property inherited from the colonial period which, although belonging to the state, has no defined public use, thus remaining common but available for private appropriation. As roads opened up these unlegislated areas for colonization, massive deforestation followed. The production of pasturelands turned out to be one of the most effective means used by speculators to claim and secure land titles, engendering a mechanism of "enclosure-by-destruction" that resulted in a vicious cycle of ecological and social violence that continues today. Uprooted by the expansion of soya plantations in the South and sugar-cane latifundia in the Northeast, hundreds of thousands of landless peasants migrated to the frontier zones of Amazonia to settle near the highways, only to be expelled by powerful landowners. Lacking adequate technical and financial support from the government to produce in the harsh climatic and edaphic conditions of the rainforest, large contingents opted to move to urban centres. Around the sites where large-scale extractive industries were installed and dams were constructed, old and new towns grew uncontrollably, turning Amazonia in one of the fastest growing urban frontiers in the world. Despite the grand planning strategies of the generals, cities sprawled without the necessary infrastructure and facilities to accommodate demographic increase. As Mike Davis sharply observed, in Amazonia "urbanization" and "favelization" became practically synonymous.[44]

In the mid-1980s, when Brazil was entering into a process of gradual "transition to democracy" and the ecological crisis had become an issue of broader public concern, Amazonia was turned into a powerful symbolic space of the defence of the global environment. While the decades-long development ideology was fractured by the new paradigm of "sustainability," the remote sensing technologies introduced by RADAM were now being used to try to make sense of the scale of environmental destruction caused by the planning schemes implemented during the dictatorship. The urgent quest to monitor and preserve ecosystems became one of the most important debates inside the new forums of environmental politics, both because of the threat of biodiversity loss and because climate change was emerging as a contentious problem. Tropical forests perform a crucial function in global climate

Environmental violence: before (1975) and after (2001) satellite images showing patterns of deforestation at   Fig. 19
one of the "development poles" at southwestern Amazonia (image analysis by UNEP). Patterns of environmental degradation in Amazonia followed the blueprint elaborated by the militaries.

regulation, removing large amounts of CO_2 from the atmosphere and locking it up in a dynamic cycle of vegetation growth and decay. Amazonia is a giant reservoir of carbon, containing roughly one-tenth of the global total.[45] When burned, it is also a powerful source of greenhouse gases emissions. In 1990, two years before the first UN Earth Summit was convened in Rio de Janeiro and months after a presidential election was held after more than twenty years of military dictatorship, the Space Research Institute of Brazil published the first detailed quantification of the scale of deforestation in Legal Amazonia. Through an analysis of LANDSAT imagery, researchers demonstrated that between 1970 and 1989 nearly 400,000 square kilometres of the original forest cover of the Brazilian Amazon had been cleared, at an average rate of 22,000 kilometres per year, equaling an area the size Portugal and Italy combined.[46] Patterns of environmental degradation in Amazonia followed the blueprint elaborated by the military and its planners, moving deeper into the jungle through the new highways and expanding in centrifugal movements from the sites where so-called development polls were installed. Often portrayed as a chaotic process resulting from lack of governmental control, the "ecocide" that spread over the Brazilian Amazon was in fact produced by design. Conceptualized and implemented at the conjunction between the natural and legal Amazonia, these spatial strategies implied forms of state intervention at the scale of basin-wide ecological dynamics, thus making the boundaries between environmental and political forces practically indistinguishable. As such, insofar as Amazonia plays an important function within the larger Earth-system, it also necessarily contained the potential of unleashing ecological consequences of global scope.

The Archaeology of Violence

Although the proposed date marking the passage from the Holocene to the Anthropocene was set to coincide with the industrial revolution in Europe, an event to which we must add the parallel movement of massive colonial enclosures and the consequential changes in land-use patterns that swept throughout the Third World as the non-European peasantry was forcibly integrated into the global market,[47] the Cold War arguably stands out as a radical and decisive turning point in the historical records of stratigraphy. At the scale of Earth's deep time, the late twentieth century is comparatively just a tiny, insignificant fragment. But if measured in degrees of intensity, these short but extremely violent decades may be seen as a moment of exponential geochronological acceleration. Potentialized by the singular combination of the arms-race and resource-rush that characterized the Cold War, modern technology and science reached previously unknown domains in their Promethean attempt to master planetary ecological dynamics, trying to domesticate remote desert and forest lands, conquering polar ice caps and ocean floors, altering atmospheric layers and intervening into previously unchartered layers of the Earth's crust. The capacity of anthropogenic-induced environmental modifications increased significantly as the alliance between techno-science, modern industry and militarism pushed innovations beyond the limits of the imaginable. Informed by the doctrines of development and security, and the theories of modernization and unlimited economic growth, scientists, technicians, planners, and strategists advocated for grand schemes that sought to manipulate bio-geo-physical dynamics at a planetary scale, from diverging the currents of the open seas to chemically altering vast tracts of soils, purposefully inducing weather modifications or creating an artificial Mediterranean at the middle of the Amazon Basin.[48] These geo-engineering designs were encouraged and legitimized by the geopolitics of Cold War's bi-polar world order, and to a large extent our current perception of the nature of the globe is the product of epistemic models that were forged under this dialectic of enmity. Within this bellicose ideology, the ultimate casualty was the Earth itself. "We so-called developed nations are no longer fighting among ourselves," philosopher Michel Serres wrote in 1990, in the aftermath of the conflict, "together we are all turning against the world. Literally a world war."[49]

The global Cold War was fought at an environmental scale. At the same time, it was a period during which states-of-exception and political violence turned into the normalized form of governing, chiefly at the margins of the Third World, where coup-enforced military regimes were responsible for widespread killings and disappearances of innocent civilians. Most often, violence directed towards human collectives and ecological destruction were condensed as two-sides of the same rationale. Hence the paradigmatic importance of the attacks deployed by the US Army against the forests of Indochina, which were strategically conceived in terms of ecological metaphors such as "draining the water to kill the fish" or "scorched-earth." Insofar as the crucial question posed by the Anthropocene thesis refers precisely to the impossibility of maintaining the divisions between natural

Geoglyphs, an urban forest: recent archeological evidences uncovered on deforested areas in Amazonia led to a radical change in the perception of the nature of the forest. Large tracts of Amazonia are today considered "human-made."

Fig. 20

and social forces that inform Western philosophy and politics, one of the crucial questions that we must ask is how the histories of power have influenced, and have been influenced by, the natural history of the Earth. The re-shaping of the nature of Amazonia that took place during the military dictatorship in Brazil was the product of entanglements between political and environmental violence, the fundamental engines of by which the "geological imperative" could be enforced on the ground. The collateral effects that ensued can be felt in the alterations of the global climatic dynamics that we experience today, transformations that are as much natural as social-political. The Anthropocene, indeed, is the product of military *coups d'état.*

***

In 1999, while flying over the south-western edges of the Amazonia, one of the regions that had been most severely affected by the colonization schemes implemented during the 1970s and 1980s, the Brazilian palaeontologist Alceu Ranzi noticed traces of various geometric earthworks of large dimensions scattered throughout the deforested areas of large cattle-ranches. The *Amazonian geoglyphs*, as these structures became known, turned out to be one of the most significant archaeological discoveries of recent times in Amazonia, for they are completely reconfiguring the ways by which we understand both the nature and history of the rainforest. Before Operation Amazonia, they were hidden underneath the vegetation cover. As the forest was cleared out and this region turned into a vast savannah landscape, the earthworks became increasingly visible. Because of the enormous size of the excavations, and also because they are filled with recent sedimentation, it is hard to distinguish the geoglyphs when looking from the ground. Observed from the sky, however, it is possible to identify their dimensions and territorial patterns of distribution. Using remote sensing technologies, archaeologists have located more than 210 geometric earthworks distributed over an area covering 250 km^2 in western Amazonia. They are shaped in perfect circles or rectangles of 90 to 300 metres in diameter and sculpted by ditches of approximately eleven meters wide and roughly one to three meters deep, which are surrounded by earthen walls up to one meter high. Some of these giant structures are linked by walled roads, and most of them are located near headwaters, strategically placed at elevated plateaus above major river valleys from where it is possible to visually embrace the surroundings in a panoramic perspective. Archaeologists are still debating the function of these structures, some suggesting that they were ceremonial enclosures or defensive fortifications, others arguing that the ditches could have been used as resource management systems, for example, to store water or cultivate aquatic fauna for human consumption. Radiocarbon analysis of soil samples date to the year 1238, coinciding with the period of rapid urbanization of the medieval towns in Europe. Geo-archaeological data of this sort demonstrate that only as 300 years before the arrival of the Europeans colonizers, substantial populations inhabited this region of Amazonia. The archaeologists who led this research contend that many more similar structures are buried beneath the forests that remain standing, and estimate that only ten per cent of the total of possible existent geoglyphs have been identified. These impressive architectural forms are interpreted as evidence of the ancient presence of "complex societies" that for centuries modified an environment that until now we thought to be pristine. The consequent conclusion is that Amazonia's deep history is not natural, but human.[50]

Until the 1970s, the relations between nature and society in Amazonia were framed by scientific descriptions dominated by socio-evolutionist theories, which portrayed the region as a hostile environment populated by dispersed and demographically reduced tribes, constrained by harsh environmental determinants and therefore unable to overcome a primitive stage of social-political organization

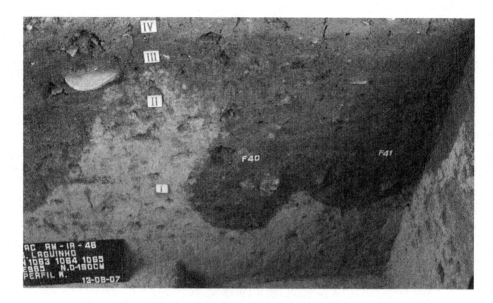

Terra-preta: Black-earth soils, anthropogenic in origin, supply some of the most significant evidence that the nature of Amazonia was gradually shaped by human interference. As archaeologist Michael Heckenberger argues, "Much of the landscape was not only anthropogenic in origin but intentionally constructed and managed." Today, we cannot assume that any part of Amazonia is pristine "without a detailed examination of the ground." Fig. 21

and develop larger polities. During the following decades, and increasingly so in the last ten years, a series of archaeological findings such as the geoglyphs, or the identification of many sites containing *terra preta*—anthropogenic black-soils that are rich in carbon compounds and highly fertile—or the incredible urban clusters mapped out by archaeologist Michael J. Heckenberger at the Upper Xingu River Basin are radically transforming this image of Amazonia.[51] In a seminal article published in 1989, anthropologist William Balée estimated that large portions of upland forests were human-made, concluding that "instead of using the 'natural' environment to explain cultural infrastructures in the Amazon, probably the reverse should be more apt."[52] The usual ethnological and ecological perception of Amazonia is largely derived from the eighteenth century, forged at a moment when the majority of the area's population had already been wiped out by the violence of colonial conquest. An important fact supporting these views was the lack of physical indexes showing traces of urbanization. Heckenberger's recent archaeological excavations provide evidence that in the Upper Xingu region there existed highly populous societies, spatially organized in regional networks of fortified villages, forming a pattern that he calls "galactic urbanism." Because of the sophisticated resource management system developed by these societies in relation to the ecological dynamics of tropical forests, he compares the Xinguano's "regional planning" and modes of settlement and land-use with Ebenezer Howard's model of the Garden City. "Much of the landscape was not only anthropogenic in origin but intentionally constructed and managed," Heckenberger explains, further claiming that today we cannot assume that any part of Amazonia is pristine "without a detailed examination of the ground."[53]

Up to now, Amazonia has been the quintessential representation of what Western civilization calls "nature." New archaeological findings and studies are showing that, in fact, this image is the product of colonial violence. The Amazon Basin was conceived as ahistorical because of the multiple genocides and ethnocides that ravaged the region, and it was this conception of pristine and virgin nature, and the social-evolutionist imaginary that supported it, that legitimated the developmental schemes designed by the Brazilian military regime. Just as patterns of deforestation registered in Amazonia provide evidence of the social and environmental violence of the politics of integration implemented by the military during the Cold War, the earthworks unveiled by this process of ecological destruction provide evidence of a moment in which the political violence of colonialism was immediately related to radical social-environmental transformations. Their histories are separated by hundreds of years, yet they are also entangled by a historical continuum that collapses two different time-scales—the ancient and the recent temporality of Amazonia, the archaeological and the historical, coloniality and modernity—which converge into a novel natural-political territory that challenges pre-conceived notions of both nature and politics. The violence of the Cold War allowed us see the deep history of Amazonia, exposing the traces of an unknown deep past. While we look back and learn from it, we may therefore conclude that human collectives have been shaping the natural history of the Earth long before the "Anthropocenic turn," albeit in radically different directions. Amazonia's deep geochronology enables us to frame the Cold-War's ecocides and genocides as an important chapter of the historical process by which geo-power—through violence, destruction, and death—came to produce a completely new natural terrain. And this is perhaps the crucial paradox that the Anthropocene has brought to light: different regimes of power will produce different natures, for nature is not natural; it is the product of cultivation, and more frequently, of conflict.

Notes

1   Shelton H. Davis and Robert O. Mathews, *The Geological Imperative: Anthropology and Development in the Amazon Basin of South America* (Cambridge, Mass.: Anthropology Resource Centre, 1976), 4.

2   As, for example, in the case of the study conducted in 1964 by the army-sponsored Special Operations Research Office (SORO) on the use of "witchcraft, sorcery, and magic" by rebel militias in the Congo. See David Price, *Anthropological Intelligence: The Deployment and Neglect of American Anthropology in the Second World War* (Durham: Duke University Press, 2008), and "How the CIA and the Pentagon Harnessed Anthropological Research during the Second World War and Cold War with Little Critical Notice," *Journal of Anthropological Research* 67, no. 3 (2011): 333–356. Price argues that the alignment between anthropology and warfare established in the 1940s was "normalized" and to a large extent silenced by the secrecy apparatus that surrounded military-scientific research programs during the Cold War.

3 See Gerard Colby and Charlotte Dennett, *Thy Will Be Done: The Conquest of the Amazon* (New York: HarperCollins, 1995).

4 On Julian Steward's commitment to wartime ethnography, see Price, *Anthropological Intelligence*, 113. On the influence of his work on Amazonian ethnology, see Eduardo Viveiros de Castro, "Images of Nature and Society in Amazonian Ethnology," *Annual Review of Anthropology* 25 (1996): 79–200.

5 On the role played by anthropologists in the application of modernization-development programs that formed part of US "low-intensity" counter-insurgency policies during the Cold War, and the relation between Walt W. Rostow's ideas and the work of anthropologists, see David Price, "Subtle Means and Enticing Carrots: The Impact of Funding on American Cold War Anthropology," *Critique of Anthropology* 23, no. 4 (2003): 373–401.

6 For example, in the case of the United States, ethnographic intelligence has been used by the US Army since the American Indian Wars.

7 Guatemala, Brazil, and Chile are notable examples of "corporate-military" coups. On the history of US interventionism in Latin America during the Cold War, see Greg Grandin, *Empire's Workshop: Latin America, the United States and the Rise of the New Imperialism* (New York: Holt, 2006), and David Slater, *Geopolitics and the Post-Colonial: Rethinking North-South Relations* (London: Blackwell, 2004). The origins of US imperialism over the hemisphere can be traced back to the nineteenth-century Monroe Doctrine. Between 1889 and 1934, David Slater counted more than thirty US military interventions in Latin America.

8 Davis and Mathews, *The Geological Imperative*, 9. What Napoleon Chagnon left outside his portrait of the Yanomami as a pre-contact society whose mode of life was determined by natural laws was in fact the very historical context within which his research was being carried out. The patterns of violence that Chagnon witnessed among the Yanomami and diffused through his films and texts were exacerbated, if not caused by, the rapid expansion of mining frontiers into their lands, as well as, by the presence of Chagnon himself and objects such as axes and machetes that he introduced into the villages in exchange for ethnographic information. Chagnon also allegedly collaborated in bio-genetic research sponsored by the US State Department conducted with the Yanomami. His work is now counted as one of the most infamous episodes of ethical misconduct in the history of modern anthropology. For a detailed account on Chagnon's practice, see Patrick Tierney, *Darkness in El Dorado: How Scientists and Journalists Devastated the Amazon* (New York: W. W. Norton & Company, 2002). Marshal Sahlins wrote an important review of this book: "Jungle Fever," *Washington Post Book World*, 10 December 2000, http://anthroniche.com/darkness_documents/0246.htm. Chagnon was recently appointed to the US National Academy of Sciences, prompting Sahlins to resign in protest.

9 Davis and Mathews, *The Geological Imperative*, 3.

10 Fernando Belaúnde Terry, *Peru's Own Conquest* (Lima: American Studies Press, 1965).

11 Darino Castro Rebelo, *Transamazônica: integração em marcha* (Brasília: Ministério dos Transportes, 1973).

12 Walter H. Pawley, *In the Year 2070: Thinking Now about the Next Century Has Become Imperative*, Ceres: FAO Review 4 (July–August 1971): 22–27. The article is a condensation of Pawley's book *How Can There Be Secured Food for All—In This and the Next Century?* (FAO, 1971).

13 Golbery do Couto e Silva, *Geopolítica do Brasil* (Rio de Janeiro: Livraria J. Olympio, 1967), 40.

14 Claudio R. Sonnenburg, *Overview of Brazilian Remote Sensing Activities, Report to the NASA Center for Aerospace Information (CASI)* (NASAA/INPE, August 1978).

15 J. K. Petersen, *Handbook of Surveillance Technologies* (CRC Press, 2012).

16 Sonnenburg, *Overview of Brazilian Remote Sensing Activities*, 16.

17 Several articles appeared in the international press, such as "Killing of Brazilian Indians for their Lands Charged to Officials," *New York Times*, 21 March 1968, and "Brazil Gets Inquiries on Alleged Indian Slayings," *Los Angeles Times*, 29 March 1968. Translations of Norman Lewis's reportage were published in the French newspaper *L'Express*, "Le Massacre systematic des indiens," April 1969, and in the German weekly news magazine *Der Spiegel*, "Sie werden alle ausgerottet," November 1969. For a more detailed account, see Shelton H. Davis, *Victims of the Miracle* (New York: Cambridge University Press, 1977).

18 Norman Lewis, *Genocide: From Fire and Sword to Arsenic and Bullets, Civilization Has Set Six Million Indians to Extinction, The Sunday Times*, 23 February 1969, 34–48.

19 Darcy Ribeiro, "A Intervenção protecionista", in *Os índios e a civilização* (São Paulo: Companhia das Letras, 1996), 148.

20 Herman von Ihering, "A antropologia no Estado de São Paulo," *Revista do Museu Paulista* 7 (1907): 215. See also Ribeiro, "A Intervenção protecionista."

21 Hermann von Ihering, "A Questão dos Índios no Brasil," *Revista do Museu Paulista* 8 (1911): 112–40.

22 Antonio Carlos de Souza Lima, *Sobre indigenismo, autoritarismo, e nacionalidade: considerações sobre a constituição do discurso e da prática da proteção fraternal no Brasil* (Rio de Janeiro: PhD Thesis, Museu Nacional, 1987).

23 Darcy Ribeiro, "As Etapas da Integração", in *Os índios e a civilização* (São Paulo: Companhia das Letras, 1996): 254–293. Originally published as *Culturas e Línguas Indígenas do Brasil*, Educação e Ciêcias Sociais (Rio de Janeiro, 1957): 1–102. A shorter version of this article appeared as part of a report published by UNESCO in 1957, "Cultures en vie de disparition," *Bulletin International des Sciences Sociales* 9, no. 3 (1957), and was later translated in H. Hopper, *Indians of Brazil in the Twentieth Century*, (Washington, DC: Institute for Cross-Cultural Research, 1967).

24 See Ribeiro, "As Etapas da Integração," and specially Carlos de Souza Lima, *Sobre indigenismo, autoritarismo, e nacionalidade*.

25 As stated in the first article of the statute of FUNAI, these progressive measures included: "respect to tribal institutions"; the "guarantee to the permanent possession of the lands inhabited by Indians and the exclusive use of natural resources and all existing utilities therein"; and the commitment to guard against "the spontaneous acculturation of the Indian so its socioeconomic evolution proceeds safe from sudden change." See the Legislative Decree 62.196, 31 January 1968, available at: http://www6.senado.gov.br/legislacao/ListaTextoIntegral.action?id=175883&norma=193337.

26 International Committee of the Red Cross, *Report of the ICRC Medical Mission to the Brazilian Amazon Region* (Geneva, 1970); Robin Hanbury-Tenison, *A Report of a Visit to the Indians of Brazil* (The Primitive Peoples Fund & Survival International, London, 1971). See also the report *Supysáua: A Documentary Report on the Conditions of Indian Peoples of Brazil* (INDIGENA and American Friends of Brazil, 1974).

27 Thomas E. Skidmore, *The Politics of Military Rule in Brazil, 1964-1985* (New York: Oxford University Press, 1988).

28 See Carlos Fausto, *Inimigos fiéis: história, guerra e xamanismo na Amazônia* (São Paulo: Edusp, 2001), 89–93.

29 Law No. 6001, 19 December 1973, available at http://www.funai.gov.br/quem/legislacao/estatuto_indio.html.

30 Pedro Casaldáliga et al., *Y-Juca Pirama, o índio: aquele que deve morrer*, (1973), 15.

31 *A política do genocídio contra os índios do Brasil* (Porto: AEPPA, Associação de Ex-presos Políticos Antifascistas, March 1974).

32 Pierre Clastres, *Arqueologia da violência* (São Paulo: Cosac & Naify, 1974), 83.

33 Raphael Lemkin, *Axis Rule in Occupied Europe: Laws of Occupation, Analysis of Government, Proposals of Redress* (Washington DC: Carnegie Endowment for International Peace,

1944). Genocide was established as crime in international law by the Convention on the Prevention and Punishment of the Crime of Genocide adopted by the General Assembly of the United Nations in 1948.

34 A. Dirk Moses, "Raphael Limkin, Culture, and the Concept of Genocide," in *The Oxford Handbook of Genocide Studies*, ed. Donald Bloxham and A. Dirk Moses (Oxford: Oxford University Press, 2010), 34.

35 Moses, "Raphael Limkin, Culture, and the Concept of Genocide," 38.

36 Robert Jaulin, *La Paz blanca: introducción al etnocidio* (Buenos Aires: Editorial Tiempo Contemporaneo, 1973), 13. Originally published as *La paix blanche* (Paris: Editions du Seuil, 1970).

37 Clastres, *Arqueologia da violência*, 84.

38 Arthur Galison, as quoted in Erwin Knoll and Judith Nies McFadden, *War Crimes and the American Conscience*, (New York: Holt, Rinehart and Winston, 1970), 71.

39 Knoll and Judith Nies, *War Crimes and the American Conscience*, 68.

40 Ibid.

41 See, for example, the proposal for an "Ecocide Convention" made by legal scholar Richard Falk in 1973. See Falk, "Environmental Warfare and Ecocide: Facts, Appraisal, and Proposals," *Bulletin of Peace Proposals* 1 (1973).

42 William A. Schabas, *Genocide in International Law* (Cambridge: Cambridge University Press, 2000), 464–468..

43 See the first report published by the Truth Commission of the State of Amazonas, *The Genocide of the Waimiri-Atroari People* (Manaus, 2012). On the controversial number of political assassinations and forcibly disappeared, see the article published at the daily newspaper *Folha de São Paulo*, Lucas Ferraz, "Lista oficial de mortos pela ditadura pode ser ampliada" ["Official List of Killed by the Dictatorship Can Be Enlarged"], 1 August 2012, http://www1.folha.uol.com.br/poder/1129485-lista-oficial-de-mortos-pela-dit-adura-pode-ser-ampliada.shtml.

44 Make Davis, *Planet of Slums* (London: Verso, 2006), 17.

45 Nikolas Kozloff, *No Rain in the Amazon: How South America's Climate Change Affects the Entire Planet,* (New York: Palgrave Macmillan, 2010), 2–4.

46 Philip M Fearnside, Antonio Tebaldi Tardin and Luiz Gylvan Meira Filho, *Deforestation Rate in Brazilian Amazonia* (Manaus: INPE, 1990).

47 See Mike Davis, *Late Victorian Holocausts* (London: Verso, 2001).

48 For an important initiative to frame the history of the Cold War in relation to environmental histories, see J. R. McNeill and Corinna R. Unger (eds.), *Environmental Histories of the Cold War* (New York: Cambridge University Press, 2010).

49 Michel Serres, *The Natural Contract* , trans. Elizabeth MacArthur and William Paulson (Ann Arbor: University of Michigan Press, 1995), 32.

50 Martti Pärssinen, Denise Schaan and Alceu Ranzi, "Pre-Columbian Geometric Earthworks in the Upper Purus: A Complex Society in Western Amazonia," *Antiquity* 83 (2009): 1084–1095; and Denise Schaan, Martti Pärssinen, Alceu Ranzi and Jacó César Piccoli, "Geoglifos da Amazônia ocidental: evidência de complexidade social entre povos da terra firme," *Revista de Arqueologia* 20 (2007): 67–82.

51 For a critical overview of the history of archeology in Amazonia, see Pärssinen, Schaan and Ranzi, "Geoglifos da Amazônia occidental"; and Michael J. Herckenberger, *The Ecology of Power* (New York: Routledge, 2005).

52 William Balée, "The Culture of Amazonian Forests," *Advances in Economic Botany* 7 (1989): 1–21.

53 Herckenberger, *The Ecology of* Power, 23.

Contributors

Nabil Ahmed is a contemporary visual artist, writer, and curator. His works have been presented internationally, including at The 2012 Taipei Biennale, Haus der Kulturen der Welt in Berlin, The Centre for Possible Studies Serpentine Gallery, Resonance FM, CCA Glasgow, Nottingham Contemporary, no.w.here, South Asian Visual Arts Centre (SAVAC) in Toronto, and the Royal Geographic Society. He has written for *Third Text* and *Media Field Journal*. He is co-founder of Call & Response, a sound art collective and curatorial project based in London. He is currently a Ph.D. candidate in Research Architecture at Goldsmiths University of London where he also teaches. He lives and works in London.

Meghan Archer currently works as a designer at Payette Associates in Boston. She was educated at Taubman College of Architecture and Urban Planning, University of Michigan, where she graduated with a Masters in Architecture in 2012 with high distinction. Her interests lie in design that operates on multiple scales and engages the public realm, from infrastructure, to installation art. Meghan has served on architectural design reviews at several colleges, and has lead youth programs on architecture in the Boston metro area.

Adam Bobbette is a researcher, writer and designer based in Hong Kong with training in landscape architecture, philosophy, and cultural studies. He currently teaches at the University of Hong Kong. He has published widely and his work has been included in exhibitions at the Canadian Centre for Architecture, Graham Foundation, Architectural Association, Storefront for Art and Architecture, and Eyebeam, among others. Currently, his research focuses on international comparative histories and theories of civic infrastructures and the urban ecologies of contingency, care, and danger. He is working on a monograph about the history of air in Indonesia. He is a co-founder and editor of the journal *Scapegoat: Architecture | Landscape | Political Economy*.

Emily Cheng lives in Toronto, Canada, where she designs architecture, objects, and graphics. www.emcheng.com

Heather Davis is a researcher, writer, and community-based artist from Montreal. She is currently a FQRSC postdoctoral fellow in the Department of Women's Studies at Duke University, where she is working on a project which traces the ethology of plastic as a materialization of the philosophic division of the subject and object. She completed her Ph.D. in the joint program in Communication at Concordia University in 2011 on the political potential of community-based art. In 2010, she was a visiting scholar with the Hemispheric Institute of Performance and Politics at NYU and the Department of Women's and Gender Studies at Rutgers University. She explores and participates in expanded art practices that bring together researchers, activists, and community members to enact social change. She is the co-founder of

Ouvert/Open, an art and activist collective which seeks to re-envision public space and circulation in Montreal and is an active member of Kabane 77, a radical art, film and education collective. She has written about the intersection of art, politics, and community engagement for *Fibreculture, Public, Politics and Culture, Canadian Women's Studies Journal, The Encyclopedia of Social Movement Media, No More Potlucks, Scapegoat* and *Reviews in Cultural Theory*.

Sara Dean is an architectural and graphic designer in the Detroit area, and the designer of *Architecture in the Anthropocene*. Her work examines the implications of digital methodologies on design and activism practices. She has a Master of Architecture and a Master of Science in Design Research from the University of Michigan. Some of her work can be found at www.linch-pin.org

Seth Denizen is a designer and researcher trained in landscape architecture and evolutionary biology. Since completing research on the sexual behavior of small Trinidadian fish, his work has focused on the aesthetics of scientific representation, madness and public parks, the political ecology of desertification, and most recently the design of taxonomies for the mapping and historical analysis of urban soil. He currently lives in Hong Kong, where he teaches in the Division of Landscape Architecture at Hong Kong University.

Mark Dorrian holds the Forbes Chair in Architecture at the University of Edinburgh and is Co-Director of the art, architecture and urbanism atelier Metis. His books include (with Adrian Hawker) *Metis: Urban Cartographies* (2002), (with Gillian Rose) *Deterritorialisations: Revisioning Landscapes and Politics* (2003), (with Jane Rendell, Jonathan Hill and Murray Fraser) *Critical Architecture* (2007), *Warszawa: Projects for the Post-Socialist City* (2009), and (with Frédéric Pousin) *Vues aériennes: Seize études pour une histoire culturelle* (2012). Recent essays include 'Clouds of Architecture', *Radical Philosophy* 144 (2007), 'The Way the World Sees London' in A. Vidler, ed, *Architecture Between Spectacle and Use* (2008), 'Transcoded Indexicality', *Log* 12 (2008), 'The Aerial Image: Vertigo, Transparency and Miniaturization', *parallax* 15(4) (2009), 'Falling Upon Warsaw: the Shadow of Stalin's Palace of Culture', *The Journal of Architecture* 15 (1) (2010), 'On Google Earth', *New Geographies*, 4 - Scales of the Earth (2011), and 'Adventure on the Vertical', *Cabinet* 44 (2011/12). He is member of the advisory board of the Institute for Advanced Studies in the Humanities at the University of Edinburgh, where he is organizing a research theme on 'Atmospheres and Atmospherics.' www.iash.ed.ac.uk/themes.atmospheres.html

Elizabeth Grosz is Jean Fox O'Barr Women's Studies Professor in Trinity College of Arts and Sciences at Duke University. She is the author of *Chaos, Territory, Art. Deleuze and the Framing of the Earth* (Columbia University Press, 2008) and has written widely on French Philosophy.

Lisa Hirmer is an artist, writer, and designer based in Guelph, Canada. Her work can be divided between two main practices, though the thematic overlap is significant:

she is an emerging photographer and writer producing work that reflects her background in architecture and is primarily concerned with examining material traces found in complex landscapes, especially those that act as evidence of unseen forces. She is also a co-founder and principal of DodoLab, an experimental arts-based practice that has been producing innovative public research and socially engaged projects since 2009. DodoLab's work is focused on investigating, engaging and responding to the public's relationship with contemporary issues. Hirmer has a Master of Architecture from the University of Waterloo.

Jane Hutton is a landscape architect and Assistant Professor in Landscape Architecture at the Harvard Graduate School of Design. She is director of the GSD Materials Collection in the Frances Loeb Design Library, and her research focuses on the expanded relations of construction materials used in landscape architecture. In 2010, she curated *Erratics: A Genealogy of Rock Landscape*, an exhibition that looked at the cultural and scientific antecedents to contemporary design's interest in geology.

Eleanor Kaufman is professor of Comparative Literature, English, and French and Francophone Studies at the University of California, Los Angeles. She is the author of *The Delirium of Praise: Bataille, Blanchot, Deleuze, Foucault, Klossowski* (Johns Hopkins, 2001), *Deleuze, the Dark Precursor: Dialectic, Structure, Being* (Johns Hopkins, 2012), and *At Odds with Badiou: Politics, Dialectics, and Religion from Sartre and Deleuze to Lacan and Agamben* (forthcoming, Columbia University Press); and co-editor of *Deleuze and Guattari: New Mappings in Politics, Philosophy, and Culture* (Minnesota, 1998).

Amy Catania Kulper is an assistant professor of architecture at the University of Michigan Taubman College of Architecture and Urban Planning, where she teaches theory and design. For the 2010-2011 academic year she was the Steelcase Research Professor at the University of Michigan's Humanities Institute, working on a book manuscript entitled I*mmanent Natures: The Laboratory as a Paradigm for Architecture's Experimental Practices*. She is a three-time recipient of the Donna M. Salzer Award for teaching excellence. Kulper is the Design Editor of the *Journal of Architectural Education* (JAE). Her publications appear as chapters in *Experiments: Architecture Between Sciences and the Arts* edited by Ákos Morávansky and Albert Kirchengast; and *Intimate Metropolis: Urban Subjects in the Modern City* edited by Diana Periton and Vittoria di Palma. Her articles appear in the *Journal of Architecture, Candide: Journal of Architectural Knowledge*, and *Field: Journal for Architecture*. Kulper holds masters' degrees from both the University of Pennsylvania and Cambridge and a Ph.D. in the history and philosophy of architecture from Cambridge University. She is currently co-editing a special issue of the *Journal of Architecture* on the subject of 'City Air.'

Clint Langevin and **Amy Norris** co-founded the research and design studio Captains of Industry after completing professional degrees in architecture at the

University of Toronto in 2011. The studio investigates the problems and potentials of our industrial heritage. Their work has been exhibited internationally at the 2012 International Architecture Biennale Rotterdam and Arup's Phase 2 Gallery in London, and featured in publications such as *OnSite Review* 29: Geology, *Volume* #31: Guilty Landscapes, and the forthcoming *BRACKET* [at extremes]. Their most recent work includes an installation at Toronto's Harbourfront Centre as part of the exhibition titled *Rapid Response - Architecture Prepares for Disaster*, where they explored the relationship between human activity and natural ecosystems, and our own complicity in the occurrence of natural disasters. www.captainsofindustry.ca

Michael CC Lin is a Toronto-based designer working in the field of Architecture & Design. Having graduated from University of Toronto with a Master of Architecture, and from the University of Waterloo with a Bachelor of Architectural Studies, Michael is embarking on a long journey in a medium that engages and challenges him continuously in new and exciting ways. His Master of Architecture Thesis, *AnthroPark*, is a labour of love borne from Michael's passion for stories, films, art, and philosophy over the course of his studies. *AnthroPark* won the Kuwabara-Jackman Architecture Thesis Gold Medal (2012), was featured in *Scapegoat* journal (2012), and was exhibited in *Here Be Monsters* (2012), as well as inspiring various commissions. Working with Omar Aljebouri under the alias *ccomma design*, the duo has exhibited work such as *Cabinet of Curiosities: Toronto Expedition 001* (2011-2012), testing the theme of identity and the city. www.anthropark.com

Territorial Agency is established by **John Palmesino** and **Ann-Sofi Rönnskog**. Territorial Agency is an independent organisation that promotes and works for integrated sustainable territorial transformations. Its works combine analysis, contemporary architecture and urbanism, advocacy and action. Projects include the *Anthropocene Observatory, Museum of Infrastructural Unconscious, North, Unfinishable Markermeer, Kiruna, Taiwan Project, The Coast of Europe*. They convene Diploma unit 4 at AA Architectural Association School of Architecture, London and have initiated the AA Think Tank. They are research fellows at the Centre for Research Architecture, Goldsmiths, University of London, where John also convenes the MA studio seminar and researches for his PhD. He has been Research Advisor at the Jan van Eyck Academie, Maastricht, and previously led the research activities of ETH Zurich/Studio Basel – Contemporary City Institute, and he is a founding member of Multiplicity. Ann-Sofi has been a researcher at ETH Zurich/ Studio Basel – Contemporary City Institute. She is a research fellow at AHO Oslo School of Architecture.

Chester Rennie works as a designer at Public Work, a Toronto-based design studio engaged in building the contemporary city.

François Roche is the principal of New-Territories (R&Sie(n) / [eIf/bʌt/c]). He is based mainly in Bangkok, [eIf/bʌt/c], sometimes in Paris, R&Sie(n), and during the Fall in New York, with his studio of research at GSAPP, Columbia University.

Through these different structures, his architectural works and protocols seek to articulate the real and/or fictional, the geographic situations, and narrative structures that can transform them. His architectural designs and processes have been show at, among other places, Columbia University (New York, 1999-2000), UCLA (Los Angeles, 1999-2000), ICA (London, 2001), Mori Art Museum (Tokyo, 2004), Centre Pompidou (Paris, 2003), MAM / Musée d'Art Moderne (Paris, 2005, 2006), the Tate Modern (London 2006) and Orléans/ArchiLab (1999, 2001, 2003). Work by R&Sie(n), New-Territories were selected for exhibition at the French pavilion at the Venice Architecture Biennales of 1990, 1996, 2000 and 2002 (they rejected the invitation that year), and for the international section in 2000, 2004, and 2008, and, in 2010, for both the International and Austrian Pavilion; in 2012, for Dark Side Curating, Slovenian Pavilion, and Writing Architecture. Among the teaching positions held by Roche over the last decade are guest professor at the Bartlett School in London in 2000, the Vienna TU in 2001, the Barcelona ESARQ in 2003-04, the Paris ESA in 2005, the University of Pennsylvania in Philadelphia in 2006, the Angewangde in Vienna in 2008, the USC-Los Angeles in 2009-10-11 and currently Columbia, GSAPP every Fall since 2006. In 2012, François Roche was the guest editor of *Log* #25, NY Critical Revue, for the issue released in July 2012 *reclaim resis(lience)stance*. www.new-territories.com

Isabelle Stengers (b. 1949) teaches philosophy at the Université Libre de Bruxelles, in Brussels, Belgium. She began her career in collaboration with Nobel Prize Laureate Ilya Prigogine, co-authoring *La Nouvelle Alliance*, which presents physics as a passionate adventure rather than as the triumph of objective knowledge. She has gradually extended her approach, resisting a model of scientific objectivity that silences the diverging multiplicity of scientific practices. Instead, she emphasizes the need for these practices to cultivate the risks of relevance, developing the concept of an active ecology that embeds scientific practices in democratic and politically demanding environments. She is the author of numerous books, many of which have been translated into English, including *Order out of Chaos* with Ilya Prigogine, *A Critique of Psychoanalytical Reason* with Léon Chertok, *A History of Chemistry* with Bernadette Bensaude-Vincent, *Power and Invention: Situating Science*, *The Invention of Modern Science*, *Capitalist Sorcery: Breaking the Spell* with Philippe Pignarre, *Cosmopolitics I and II*, and *Thinking with Whitehead*.

Paulo Tavares is a Brazilian architect and urbanist based in Quito/London. He is currently developing a project on the violence of planning and the politics of ecology in Amazonia at the PhD Programme of the Centre for Research Architecture, Goldsmiths, UK. Tavares teaches architecture at the Universidad Católica de Ecuador - Facultad de Arquitectura, Diseño y Arte, Quito, and previously held teaching posts at the Centre for Research Architecture - Goldsmiths, and at the Visual Lab of the MA in Contemporary Art Theory, also at Goldsmiths, UK. Writings appeared in many publications worldwide and his work has been exhibited in various venues including CCA: Centre for Contemporary Arts - Glasgow, Haus der Kulturen der Welt - Berlin, Portikus - Frankfurt and the Taipei Biennial 2012.

Etienne Turpin is the director of anexact office, a design research practice committed to multidisciplinary urban activism, artistic and curatorial experimentation, and applied philosophical inquiry. Etienne is also a Vice Chancellor's Postdoctoral Research Fellow with the SMART Infrastructure Facility, Faculty of Engineering & Information Sciences, and an Associate Fellow with the Institute for Social Transformation Research, Faculty of Law, Humanities, and The Arts, University of Wollongong, Australia. With the support of this joint appointment, Etienne is living and working in Jakarta, Indonesia, where his research helps produce strategies for community resistance and resilience among informal settlements of the urban poor facing the combined violence of climate change and rapid development. www.anexact.org

Eyal Weizman is an architect, Professor of Spatial & Visual Cultures, and director of the Centre for Research Architecture at Goldsmiths, University of London. Since 2011, he also directs the European Research Council (ERC) funded project - Forensic Architecture - on the place of architecture in International Humanitarian Law. Since 2007, he is a founding member of the architectural collective DAAR in Beit Sahour/ Palestine. Weizman has been a Professor of Architecture at the Academy of Fine Arts in Vienna and has also taught at the Bartlett (UCL) in London, at the Städelschule in Frankfurt, at the Berlage Institute in Rotterdam, and is a Professeur invité at the École des hautes études en sciences sociales (EHESS) in Paris. He lectured, curated, and organised conferences in many institutions worldwide. His books include *Mengele's Skull* (with Thomas Keenan at Sternberg Press 2012), *Forensic Architecture* (dOCUMENTA13 notebook, 2012), *The Least of all Possible Evils* (Nottetempo 2009, Verso 2011), *Hollow Land* (Verso, 2007), the co-edited *A Civilian Occupation* (Verso, 2003), the series *Territories 1, 2 and 3, Yellow Rhythms* and many articles in journals, magazines, and edited books. He has realized a number of architectural and design commissions including the Ashdod Museum of Arts, set design for Electra (with Rafi Segal), the installation Page in Berlin (with Zvi Hecker and Mich Ullman), and a permanent pavilion for Gwangju, South Korea, amongst other projects. Weizman is a regular contributor and an editorial board member for several journals and magazines including *Grey Room, Humanity, Inflexions, Political Concepts*, and *Cabinet* where he is an editor at large, and has also edited a special issue on Forensics (Issue 43, 2011). He has worked with a variety of NGOs worldwide and was member of B'Tselem (the largest Israeli human rights organization) board of directors. He is currently on the advisory boards of the Institute of Contemporary Arts (ICA) in London, the Human Rights Project at Bard in NY, as a jury member for architecture at the Akademie Schloss Solitude and of other academic and cultural institutions. Weizman is the recipient of the James Stirling Memorial Lecture Prize for 2006-2007, a co-recipient of the 2010 Prince Claus Prize for Architecture (with Sandy Hilal and Alessandro Petti for DAAR), and was invited to deliver many key note addresses and memorial lectures for Nelson Mandela (Bob Hawkes Prime Ministerial Centre, Adelaide), Edward Said (University of Warwick), Rusty Bernstein (University of The Witwatersrand), Paul Hirst (Birkbeck College), the Edward H. Benenson Lectures (Duke), and the Mansour Armaly (MESA), amongst others. He studied architecture at the Architectural Association in London and completed his Ph.D. at the London Consortium/Birkbeck College.

Jane Wolff is associate professor and former director of the landscape architecture programme at the Daniels Faculty of Architecture, Landscape, and Design, University of Toronto. She was educated as a documentary filmmaker and landscape architect at Harvard University. Ms. Wolff's research interests deal with the hybrid landscapes formed by interactions between natural process and cultural intervention. The author of *Delta Primer: a field guide to the California Delta*, she is a partner in the *Gutter to Gulf* initiative, which provides information about urban infrastructure and ecology in New Orleans through its website, www.guttertogulf. com. Her current projects include an exhibit at the Exploratorium of San Francisco on the cultural landscape of San Francisco Bay and initial studies for an atlas of Toronto's landscape as infrastructure. In addition to her academic work, she also serves as a member of the Design Review Board of Waterfront Toronto and on the board of the Landscape Architecture Foundation. Ms. Wolff's work has been supported by two Fulbright scholarships and by research grants from the Harvard Graduate School of Design, the Graham Foundation, the Great Valley Center, the LEF Foundation, the Ohio State University, the University of Toronto, the Exploratorium and the Seed Fund of San Francisco. In 2006, she was Beatrix Farrand distinguished visiting professor at the University of California, Berkeley.

Guy Zimmerman is a playwright and director, and has served as the artistic director of Padua Playwrights in Los Angeles since 2001. Under his direction, Padua has staged over 35 productions of new plays, moving several to venues in New York City, Atlanta and abroad, and garnering a host of LA Weekly, Ovation, Garland, and Los Angeles Drama Critics Circle awards and nominations. As a playwright, his critically acclaimed work includes the plays *La Clarita*, *The Inside Job*, *Vagrant*, and *The Black Glass*, which opened at the Ballhaus OST in Berlin in February 2013. He is also the Supervising Editor of Padua Press, which has published six anthologies of new work by such nationally prominent playwrights as Maria Irene Fornes, Murray Mednick, John Steppling and John O'Keefe. His essays about film, theatre, art, and politics have appeared in *Theater Forum*, *LA Weekly*, *LA Theater Magazine*, *the LA Citizen*, and *Times Quotidian*, where he serves as Associate Editor. Zimmerman received a BA in History from the University of Pennsylvania; he is currently completing a doctorate in Drama and Theatre at UC Irvine.

Permissions

AnthroPark, design project by Michael C.C. Lin
Copyright retained by the author/designer.

Radical Meteorology, design project by Nabil Ahmed
Copyright retained by the author/designer.

Three Holes: In the Geological Present, essay by Seth Denizen
Fig. 01. *En construcción* (*Under Construction*), directed by José Luis Guerín (2001). Courtesy of Ovideo TV.
Fig. 02. Hiroshi Sugimoto, *Ordovician Period Photo* (1994). Photo 81 x 71 cm. © Hiroshi Sugimoto, courtesy Pace Gallery.
Fig. 03. Hiroshi Sugimo, *Earliest Human Relatives* (1994). Photo 81 x 71 cm. © Hiroshi Sugimoto, courtesy Pace Gallery.
Fig. 05. J. C. Farman, B. G. Gardiner and J. D. Shanklin, "Large Losses of Total Ozone in Antarctica Reveal Seasonal ClO_x/NO_x Interaction," *Nature* 315 (May 1985): 207–210.
Fig. 07. From F. A. Fallou, *Pedologie oder Allgemeine und besondere Bodenkunde* (Dresden: Schöenfeld, 1862), in Alfred E. Hartemink, "The Depiction of Soil Profiles since the Late 1700s," *Catena* 79 (2009): 113–127.
Fig. 09. Venezia 2003, Societa Italiana di Geologia Ambientale. Scale = 1:50,000.
Fig. 10. Seth Denizen, "Adams Family Series," *Eighth Approximation: Urban Soil in the Anthropocene* (MLA Thesis: University of Virginia, 2012). Copyright retained by the author/designer.
Fig. 11. Seth Denizen, "Robert Moses Series," *Eighth Approximation: Urban Soil in the Anthropocene* (MLA Thesis: University of Virginia, 2012). Copyright retained by the author/designer.

Episodes from a History of Scalelessness: William Jerome Harrison and Geological Photography, essay by Adam Bobbette
Fig. 01. H.T. Hildage, "Mining Operations in New York City and Vicinity,T" in *Transactions of the American Institute of Mining Engineers* (New York: Institute of Mining Engineers, 1908), 392, Fig. 18.
Fig. 02. G. Bingley, *Baldersby Park, near Thirsk. Large Boulder of Carboniferous Grit*, 1891. Courtesy of the British Geological Survey. © NERC. All rights reserved.
Fig. 03. From John A., Dresser and T. C. Denis, *Geology of Quebec* (Quebec: Rédempti, 1944), Plate v.
Fig. 04. William Jerome Harrison, *Sheringham Beach. Paramoudra in Chalk*, 1886. Courtesy of the British Geological Survey. © NERC. All rights reserved.
Fig. 05. William Jerome Harrison, *Beeston Beach. Paramoudra*, 1886. Courtesy of the British Geological Survey. © NERC. All rights reserved.
Fig. 06. William Jerome Harrison, *W. of Sheringham. Pinnacle of Chalk, embedded in drift*, 1886. Courtesy of the British Geological Survey. © NERC. All rights reserved.

Inquiries and Interpretations Concerning the Observations and Findings from Atmosphere-Investigating, Landscape-Exploring, Universe-Tracking Instruments, their Experiments, Studies, Etc., design project by Emily Cheng
Copyright retained by the author/designer.

Landscapes of San Francisco Bay: Plates from Bay Lexicon, design project by Jane Wolff
Copyright retained by the author/designer.

Architecture's Lapidarium: On the Lives of Geological Specimens, essay by Amy Catania Kulper
Fig. 02. Ferdinand Cheval, *Palais Idéal* (1879-1912), Louis-Ernest Barrias, *Nature Unveiling Herself Before Science* (1899), John Collier, *Priestess of Delphi* (1891), Sir Edward Coley Burne-Jones, *Sisyphus* (c. 1870).
Fig. 05. Joseph Michael Gandy, *Architecture: Its Natural Mode* (1838).
Fig. 06. Joseph Michael Gandy, from *Architecture: Its Natural Mode* (1838).
Fig. 07. Joseph Michael Gandy, *A Selection of Parts of Buildings, Public and Private, Erected from the Designs*

of John Soane (1818).

Fig. 09. Giovanni Battista Piranesi, *Foundations of the Theater of Marcellus*, from *Antichità Romane* (1756). From the Collection of the Toledo-Lucas County Public Library.

Fig. 10. Piranesi, "Mausoleum of Cecilia Matella," from *Antichità Romane* (1756). From the Collection of the Toledo-Lucas County Public Library.

Fig. 11. Athanasius Kircher, *The Eruption of Mount Etna, 1637,* from *Mundus Subterraneus* (1664).

Fig. 12. Basil Valentine, The Twelve Keys (1678), Ernst Rutherford in his Laboratory. Ernst Rutherford and Hans Geiger, Physics Laboratory. Manchester University, England. Marsden, Lady Joyce: Assorted photographs and negatives from the papers of Sir Ernest Marsden. Ref: PA Coll-0091-1-011.Alexander Turnbull Library, Wellington, New Zealand.

Fig. 13. Athanasius Kircher, detail from *Pictorial Stones with Human Faces* (1664).

Erratic Imaginaries: Thinking Landscape as Evidence, essay by Jane Hutton

Fig. 01. Kidston Lake Rocking Stone, Kidstone Lake, Nova Scotia. Gardner Collection of Photographs, Harvard College Library.

Fig. 02. Pierre des Marmettes, from Jean De Charpentier, *Essai Sur Les Glaciers et Sur le Terrain Erratique du Bassin du Rhone* (Lausanne: Imprimerie et Librairie de Marc Ducloux, 1841).

Fig. 03. Postcard, Pierre des Marmettes, (1905) R. Heyraudt, Publisher, St. Maurice, collection of Vincent Franzen.

Fig. 04. Postcard, Rollstone Boulder, Fitchburg, Massachusetts Peter Cristofono collection.

Fig. 05. Babson Boulders Map. Courtesy of Jane Hutton.

Fig. 06. Babson Boulder, Courage, Dogtown, Massachusetts. Courtesy of Jane Hutton.

Fig. 07. Medicine or Prayer Rock, Ipswich, South Dakota Photo courtesy of J. Stephen Conn.

Fig. 08. Postcard, Massasoit Statue, Portico over Plymouth Rock, The Mayflower. 1930-45. The Tichnor Borthers Collection, Boston Public Library.

Fig. 09. National Day of Mourning plaque, Plymouth, Massachusetts Photo courtesy of Gerald Azenaro.

Swimming in It, design project by Chester Rennie

Copyright retained by the author/designer.

Fortune Head Geologies, photo essay by Lisa Hirmer

Copyright retained by the author/designer.

Utopia on Ice: The Climate as Commodity Form, essay by Mark Dorrian

This essay is reprinted, with some modifications, with the permission of *Cabinet* magazine; it first appeared in Issue 47 - Logistics, pp. 25-32.

Fig. 01. Promotional image from the indefinitely postponed Sunny Mountain Ski Dome project, Dubai.

Fig. 02. Image from Buckminster Fuller and Shoji Sadao's "Cloud Nine" project, ca. 1960. Courtesy of the Estate of Buckminster Fuller.

Fig. 03. Rainmakers Irving Langmuir, Vincent Schaefer, and Bernard Vonnegut at work on cloud seeding in a GE Laboratory. 1947.

Fig. 04. Promotional Poster for Dubailand.

Fig. 05. Airborne Laputa preparing to menace the citizens of Balnibarbi. From a 1930 edition of Gulliver's Travels [Whistler Laputa]. ©Artist Rights Society (ARS), New York/ DACS, London.

Amplitude Modulation, design project by Meghan Archer

Copyright retained by the author/designer.

In the Furnace of Disorientation: Tragic Drama and the Liturgical Force of Metal, essay by Guy Zimmerman

Fig. 01. A. Ramage and P. Craddock, *King Croesus Gold,* Archaeological Exploration of Sardis Monograph 11 (Cambridge, Mass.: 2000), Fig. 4.28. ©Archaeological Exploration of Sardis/Harvard University.

Fig. 02. Archaeoloical Research at Aphrodisias in Caria, 1994. R.R.R. Smith, Chrisopher Ratte, *American Journal of Archeology*, 100, no. 1 (January 1996), Fig. 23. Courtesy of Archaeological Institute of America/

American Journal of Archaeology.

Fig. 03. A. Ramage and P. Craddock, *King Croesus Gold* Archaeological, Exploration of Sardis Monograph 11 (Cambridge, Mass.: 2000), Fig. 10. 1. ©Archaeological Exploration of Sardis/Harvard University.

Fig. 04. Archaeoloical Research at Aphrodisias in Caria, 1994. R. R. R. Smith, Christopher Ratte, *America Journal of Archeology*, Vol. 100, No. 1 (Jan., 1996), Fig. 23. Courtesy of Archaeological Institute of America/ American Journal of Archaeology.

Fig. 05. G. M. A. Hanfmann, *Sardis from Prehistoric to Roman Times* (Cambridge Mass., 1983), fig. 55 (reconstruction). ©Archaeological Exploration of Sardis/Harvard University.

Tar Creek Supergrid, design project by Amy Norris and Clinton Langevin
Copyright retained by the author/designer.

The Geological Imperative: Notes on the Political-Ecology of Amazonia's Deep History, essay by Paulo Tavares

Fig. 01. Still from the *The Ax Fight,* 1975. Courtesy of Documentary Educational Resources, Inc.

Fig. 02. Cover of the report on Amazonia published by Davis Shelton and Robert Matthews, 1976.

Fig. 03. *Operation Amazonia:* the overlapping between natural and political territories. Map by Paolo Tavares.

Fig. 04. Gal. Golbery do Couto e Silva's influential territorial interpretation of the National Security Doctrine.

Fig. 05. SLAR remote sensing image of the south-central regions of the basin.

Figs. 06 – 09. Samples of the cartographic inventory produced by RADAM. Courtesy of IBGE - Brazilian Geographic Institute.

Fig. 10. Continental urban-matrix as planned in the Plan for National Integration, 1970. Courtesy of INCRA – National Institute for Colonization and Agrarian Reform.

Fig. 11. Transamazônica Highway. Manchete Magazine, 1973.

Figs. 12 – 15. Sample images of the RADAM catalogue describing field-work research. Courtesy of IBGE - Brazilian Geographic Institute.

Fig. 16. First page of Norman Lewis reportage published in the Sunday Times in 1969.

Fig. 17. Still frames of the film archive of the SPI. Courtesy of the Museu do Índio, Brasil.

Fig. 18. The white peace: sample pages of a report disclosed from the archives of FUNAI.

Fig. 20. Geoglyphs, an urban forest. Courtesy of Diego Gurgel.

Fig. 21. *Terra-preta*: black-earth soils, anthropogenic in origin.